Malloy
Plastic Part Design for Injection Molding

SPE Books from Hanser Publishers

Robert A. Malloy

Plastic Part Design for Injection Molding

An Introduction

With 427 Illustrations

Hanser Publishers, Munich Vienna New York

Hanser/Gardner Publications, Inc., Cincinnati

The Author:
Prof. Robert A. Malloy, Department of Plastics Engineering, University of Massachusetts, Lowell, MA 01854, USA

Distributed in the USA and in Canada by
Hanser/Gardner Publications, Inc.
6600 Clough Pike, Cincinnati, Ohio 45244-4090, USA
Fax: +1 (513) 527-8950

Distributed in all other countries by
Carl Hanser Verlag
Postfach 86 04 20, 81631 München, Germany
Fax: +49 (89) 98 48 09

The use of general descriptive names, trademarks, etc., in this publication, even if the former are not especially identified, is not to be taken as a sign that such names, as understood by the Trade Marks and Merchandise Marks Act, may accordingly be used freely by anyone.

While the advice and information in this book are believed to be true and accurate at the date of going to press, neither the author nor the editors nor the publisher can accept any legal responsibility for any errors or omissions that may be made. The publisher makes no warranty, express or implied, with respect to the material contained herein.

Library of Congress Cataloging-in-Publication Data
Malloy, Robert A.
   Plastic part design for injection molding : an introduction /
Robert A. Malloy
      p.   cm.
   Includes index.
   ISBN 1-56990-129-5
   1. Injection molding plastics.   2. Machine parts.
3. Engineering design.   I. Title.
TP1150.M35   1994
668.4'12--dc20   94-4213

Die Deutsche Bibliothek - CIP-Einheitsaufnahme
Malloy, Robert A.:
Plastic part design for injection molding : an introduction /
Robert A. Malloy. - Munich ; Vienna ; New York : Hanser,
1994
   ISBN 3-446-15956-8 (München ...)
   ISBN 1-56990-129-5 (New York ...)

© Carl Hanser Verlag, Munich Vienna New York, 1994
Camera-ready copy prepared by the author.
Printed and bound in Germany by Schoder Druck GmbH & Co. KG, Gersthofen

This book is dedicated to the memory of
S J, Eileen, and Ahn-Ahn Chen

Forward

The Society of Plastics Engineers is pleased to sponsor and endorse "Plastics Part Design for Injection Molding" by Dr. Robert A. Malloy. Dr. Malloy's work at the University of Massachusetts Lowell and his long-time contributions to the SPE Injection Molding Division make him eminently qualified to write with authority on this timely topic. His writing style and knowledge of the subject matter have resulted in an enjoyable presentation suitable for practicing engineers as well as senior and graduate students.

SPE, through its Technical Volumes Committee, has long sponsored books on various aspects of plastics and polymers. Its involvement has ranged from identification of needed volumes to recruitment of authors. An ever-present ingredient, however, is review of the final manuscript to insure accuracy of the technical content.

This technical competence pervades all SPE activities, not only in publication of books but also in other areas such as technical conferences and educational programs. In addition, the Society publishes four periodicals - *Plastics Engineering, Polymer Engineering and Science, Journal of Vinyl Technology and Polymer Composites* - as well as conference proceedings and other selected publications, all of which are subject to the same rigorous technical review procedure.

The resource of some 25,000 practicing engineers has made SPE the largest organization of its type in plastics worldwide. Further information is available from the Society at 14 Fairfield Drive, Brookfield Center, Connecticut 06805.

Executive Director   Eugene De Michele
Society of Plastics Engineers

Preface

The injection molding process is the most widely used manufacturing process for the production of plastic parts. The process is so versatile, that it can be used for the production of small electronic and medical parts, or for the production of very large automotive or building construction components. The growth in the injection molding industry continues due in large part to advances in both plastic material and injection molding process technologies.

Unfortunately, designing injection molded plastic parts can be an extremely difficult task due to the complexities of both the part geometry and the molding process. It is also very difficult for even experienced designers to work with new plastic material grades that may process and perform in a different manner than those materials used previously. It is in fact very difficult to design a plastic part that is functional, manufacturable, and esthetically pleasing. The part design process involves a series of tradeoffs or compromises so that each of these important demands can be met. Ideally, injection molded plastic parts are developed using the *Concurrent Engineering* practices discussed in this book.

The need for a book describing the various aspects of the plastic part design process was recognized by the author when searching for suitable design course texts. The author's integrated approach to plastic part design and plastic materials selection is described in the book, which includes hundreds of original figures that are used to illustrate specific points. The book goes into great detail on the subject of *Design for Manufacturability*, specifically how the various phases of the injection molding process can impact a part design. Common problems, such as weld lines, warpage, or ejection difficulties are discussed, as are potential solutions. In addition, the fundamentals of plastic material performance and structural design are covered, along with the subject of plastic part prototyping. The last section of the book reviews the various assembly methods that can be used for injection molded plastic parts.

The book should serve as a well illustrated reference and introductory design guide for the plastic part designer. It is hoped that the book provides an overview of the many different considerations that must be taken into account when designing a plastic part that will be manufactured by the injection molding process.

The author would like to thank the many friends, students, colleagues and companies whose names appear in the reference sections of this book. It is their work that has served as the basis for this text. Special thanks go to Garrett Gardener for all his valuable comments and corrections. The author would also like to thank the employees of Carl Hanser Verlag, especially Dr. E. Immergut for his continued encouragement and patience throughout the course of this project, and Martha Kurzl for her assistance in the production stages of the project. However, above all, the author would like to thank his family; his wife Ellen, and his children for the many sacrifices they made during the preparation of this manuscript.

Londonderry, New Hampshire   Robert Malloy
Spring 1994

Contents

1 Introduction

Undoubtedly, the single most important characteristic of plastic materials, as a general family, is their versatility. Most plastics are synthetic materials built up from monomeric building blocks to produce high molecular weight polymers. These high molecular weight polymers are classified as being either thermoplastic or thermosetting, depending on the specific material chemistry [1-6].

1.1   Thermoplastic Materials

Most of the plastic materials that are used in the injection molding process are described as thermoplastics. Thermoplastics are linear or branched polymeric materials that "soften" when heated, and "resolidify" when cooled. Thermoplastic materials are available in a variety of types and grades having properties that range from rigid to elastomeric. In theory, the processing of thermoplastic materials involves only physical changes (e.g. phase changes), therefore the materials should be readily recycled. Thermoplastic materials are recyclable; however, it is very likely that at least some small degree of chemical change (e.g. oxidation, thermal degradation) will take place during processing, and the second generation material properties may not be equivalent to those of the virgin polymer.

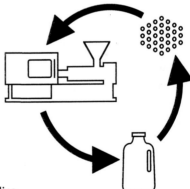

Figure 1.1. Concept of thermoplastic recycling.

There are several different ways to classify thermoplastic materials. One classification is based on polymer chain conformation or morphology. Based on this concept, thermoplastic materials are described as being either amorphous, semi-crystalline, liquid crystalline.

Amorphous Thermoplastics: Amorphous polymers consist of polymer molecules with no particular conformation as shown in Figure 1.2 (i.e. random configuration). When amorphous polymers are heated (such as in the plasticating cylinder of a molding machine), the intertwined chains become more mobile/active, and disentanglement and chain slippage occur, resulting in a gradual softening and ultimately flow. As the level of molecular activity increases, the material becomes more fluid, since the attractive forces between the polymer molecules (i.e. intermolecular attractions) decrease as the average distance between the polymer chains increases. After the molten, amorphous polymer is shaped or formed (i.e. during mold filling), the polymer is cooled, and regains its rigidity as the molecular mobility is reduced. Polymers such as polystyrene, polycarbonate and polymetyl methacrylate are examples of amorphous thermoplastics.

Semi-Crystalline Thermoplastics: Some polymer molecules have enough regularity and flexibility built into their chemical structure that they can form ordered (rather than random) molecular arrangements. These ordered regions are crystals that form as the thermoplastic cools from the molten state. Upon reheating, the crystals remain intact until the polymer reaches its crystalline melting temperature (or temperature range) where melting occurs. In the melt or molten state, these materials have an amorphous or random molecular configuration. It should be noted that crystalline thermoplastics are more appropriately described as "semi-crystalline", since these polymers contain both amorphous and crystalline regions as shown in Figure 1.2.

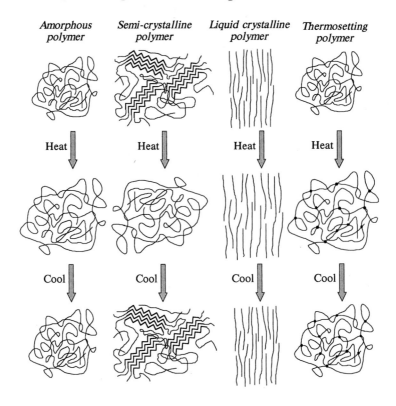

Figure 1.2. Plastic materials are categorized as being either amorphous, semi-crystalline, liquid crystalline or thermosetting [2].

The "degree of crystallinity" (i.e. the relative percentage of crystalline vs. amorphous areas in the material) is influenced by both the chemical structure of the polymer and by the manufacturing / processing conditions; particularly the rate at which the molten polymer cools. Processing variables that reduce the rate of cooling will generally increase the degree of crystallinity. Polymers such as polyethylene, polypropylene, and the polyamides (nylons) are examples of semi-crystalline polymers.

Liquid Crystalline Thermoplastics: Like semi-crystalline thermoplastics, liquid crystalline thermoplastics (LCPs) have ordered domain-type chain arrangements in the solid state. However, unlike conventional semi-crystalline polymers, liquid crystalline polymers also exhibit ordered (rather than random) molecular arrangements in the melt state. These unique materials are characterized by their stiff, rod like molecules that form the parallel arrays or domains. LCPs offer a number of processing and performance advantages including low melt viscosity, low mold shrinkage, chemical resistance, stiffness, creep resistance and overall dimensional stability [2].

1.2   Thermosetting Plastic Materials

Thermosetting polymers (or thermosets) are polymers that chemically react during processing to form a cross-linked polymer chain network as shown in Figure 1.2. The chemical reaction is irreversible. Unlike thermoplastics, thermosets are not directly recyclable. Because there is a chemical reaction involved in thermoset molding, a number of additional reaction related process variables enter into processing. Thermoset materials (as a group) can be difficult to work with and require special molding equipment / practices, however, the materials do offer some outstanding properties. The cross-linked chain network characteristic of thermosetting polymers leads to properties such as excellent creep resistance, dimensional stability and chemical resistance. However, the difficulties encountered when processing thermosetting polymers, along with their lack of recyclability, limits their use in most applications. Examples of thermosetting polymers include phenolics, epoxies, unsaturated polyesters, and a variety of elastomeric materials.

1.3   Structure-Property Relationships

The properties of a plastic material formulation can literally be "tailored" to meet the requirements of almost any specific end-use application. The properties of different plastic material formulations (or grades) will vary due to (i) differences in its chemical composition and (ii) differences in the additives incorporated into the material formulation. The chemical compositions of the different plastic materials can vary in many ways including:

- Structure of the repeat unit
- Homopolymer or copolymer
- Average molecular weight
- Molecular weight distribution
- Linear vs. branched vs. crosslinked

A change in any one of these chemical characteristics will have an influence on the plastic materials behavior and properties. Polycarbonate is a very different material than polystyrene because the repeat unit that makes up the chain is different. The repeat units that make up a polymer molecule are analogous to the "links" that make up a chain as shown in Figure 1.3. The properties of polymers having different repeat units will be different, in much the same way that the strength of a chain will differ when different types of links are used.

Polymer	*Structure*	*Chain Analogy*
Polypropylene homopolymer	$\begin{matrix} H & H \\ | & | \\ +C - C+ \\ | & | \\ H & CH_3 \end{matrix}$	
Linear polyethylene homopolymer	$\begin{matrix} H & H \\ | & | \\ +C - C+ \\ | & | \\ H & H \end{matrix}$	
Ethylene/ propylene copolymer	$\begin{matrix} H & H & H & H \\ | & | & | & | \\ +C - C + C - C+ \\ | & | & | & | \\ H & H & H & CH_3 \end{matrix}$	

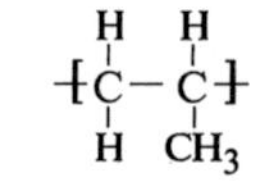

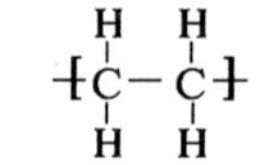

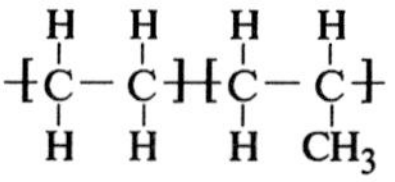

Figure 1.3. The repeat unit(s) that make up the polymer chain have a large influence the properties and processability of the material.

Many plastic materials are described as copolymers because they have chain structures that are built from more than one type of monomer unit. A material such as poly(styrene-acrylonitrile), SAN, exhibits different properties than polystyrene because it is a copolymer. The properties of the SAN will vary according to its exact copolymer composition and molecular weight characteristics. There are in fact an infinite number of possibilities with respect to chemical composition, and a wide variety of end-use properties can be achieved in this way.

Both the type of chain link(s) and the length of the polymer molecules will have an impact on the end-use performance and the processing related properties of a polymer. Plastic material manufacturers can fine tune the properties and processing behavior of a particular material type by altering the polymerization process to produce a polymer having a specific average molecular weight, and a specific molecular weight distribution.

The average molecular weight of a polymer is typically expressed as either the number average molecular weight, M_n (the total weight of material divided by the number of molecules), or the weight average molecular weight, M_w (places greater emphasis on the higher molecular weight fractions and therefore relates to properties that depend on the larger molecules) [1]. The number and weight average molecular weights of a polymer can be determined using equations 1.1 and 1.2 respectively where M_i is the molecular weight each incremental fraction, and N_i is the number of molecules in each fraction.

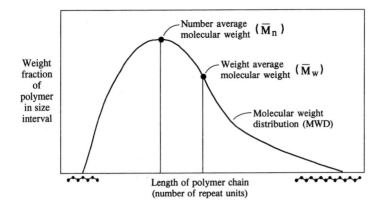

Figure 1.4. Both the average molecular weight and the molecular weight distribution will have an influence on the processability and end use properties of a polymer.

The breadth of the molecular weight distribution curve for a particular polymer is typically characterized using the polydispersity index (PDI). The polydispersity index of a polymer is determined using equation 1.3.

$$M_n = \Sigma \, (N_i \cdot M_i) / \Sigma \, N_i \qquad (1.1)$$

$$M_w = \Sigma \, (N_i \cdot M_i^2) / \Sigma \, (N_i \cdot M_i) \qquad (1.2)$$

$$PDI = M_w / M_n \qquad (1.3)$$

Table 1.1. Effect of Molecular Weight on the Properties of Polyethylene

Number of $-(CH_2\text{-}CH_2)-$ units (links)	Molecular weight (g/mol)	Softening temperature (°C)	Characteristic of material at 25°C		
1	30	-169 *	Gas		
6	170	-12 *	Liquid		
35	1,000	37	Grease		
140	4,000	93	Wax		Polymer
250	7,000	98	Hard wax		
430	12,000	104	Hard resin		
750	21,000	110	Hard resin	Plastic	
1,350	38,000	112	Hard resin	material	

* melting point

The average molecular size and size distribution will have a very significant influence on the processability and end-use properties of a polymer (e.g. mechanical properties, thermal properties, chemical resistance, etc.). Changes in the molecular weight for a particular polymer type will alter molecular entanglement, total intermolecular attraction, and end group effects. Consider the case of the series of polyethylenes (with the same repeat unit structure) listed in Table 1.1 [1]. The polyethylenes in Table 1.1 have different average molecular weights, and therefore different properties. Very low molecular weight polyethylenes are grease - or wax-like materials that are in theory injection moldable, however, do not have the property requirements for durable goods. Once the average molecular weight of the polyethylene reaches a certain point, the properties are useful enough that the material is categorized as a "plastic material". There is no well defined average molecular weight value where the material changes abruptly from a wax to a plastic material. There is simply a gradual increase in performance with an increase in average molecular weight. This concept can also be demonstrated using the graphical format given in Figure 1.5.

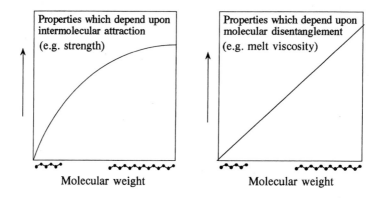

Figure 1.5. Both the end use properties and processability of a polymer depend upon the material's molecular weight characteristics. Polymers having a high average molecular weight tend to offer improved performance, but are more difficult to process due to higher melt viscosity.

Figure 1.5 shows that properties such as mechanical strength are dependent upon average molecular weight up to a point, after which an increase in molecular weight will not lead to a significant increase in strength. One could use the analogy of the "weak link" in a chain. It is also extremely important to note that there is effectively a continuous increase in melt viscosity with increasing average molecular weight. The use of very high molecular weight polymers, which have improved mechanical or performance properties, can lead to very significant processing problems. As an example, consider ultra-high molecular weight polyethylene. The material has a number of outstanding properties including chemical and abrasion resistance, however, it is nearly impossible to process via conventional melt processing techniques. Thermoplastics with higher average molecular weights tend to be more difficult to injection mold (process) because there melt viscosities are higher than lower molecular weight grades.

The importance of balancing "processability" and "properties" can be summarized using Table 1.2 [6]. Table 1.2 lists selected mechanical and flow properties of two grades of polycarbonate (i.e. two unfilled polycarbonates having different average molecular weights). The polycarbonate grade with the 4.0 grams/10 minutes melt flow rate value (see section 3.8) has a higher average molecular weight value than the polycarbonate with the 15 grams/10 minutes melt flow rate. The higher molecular weight polycarbonate does indeed have somewhat better mechanical properties. For example, the higher molecular weight material offers a 2.3% improvement in tensile yield strength, a 3.0% increase in tensile yield elongation, and an 11% increase in Izod impact strength compared to the lower molecular weight polycarbonate. However, note that the maximum spiral flow length (a measure of processability described in section 2.2.2) for the more viscous, higher molecular weight grade of polycarbonate is 35% lower. The point here is that the property improvements associated with the higher molecular weight polymer *must* be balanced against the significant loss in processability (in terms of factors such as pressure losses, achievable surface finish, residual orientation and reduced flow lengths).

Table 1.2. Effect of Molecular Weight on the Properties and Flow Behavior of Polycarbonate

MFR (g/10 min)	σ_y (MPa)		ε_y (%)		E_T (MPa)		Izod impact strength (J/m)		Spiral flow length (m)	
4	61.4		6.7		2280		928		0.495	
		-2.3%		-3.0%		0.0%		-11%		+35%
15	60.0		6.5		2280		827		0.668	

Spiral flow at equivalent conditions (T_m = 316°C, constant cavity thickness......)
σ_y = Tensile strength at yield E_T = Initial tensile modulus
ε_y = Tensile elongation at yield   MFR = Melt flow rate

1.4   Additives for Plastic Materials

There are few instances where a designer will have the leverage or lead time to work with materials suppliers on the development of an entirely new polymer (having a "new" chemical composition or molecular weight) for a particular product application. In most cases designers must select a material to meet his/her needs from one of the thousands of material grades that are commercially available. Almost all of these commercially available plastic material grades are modified to some degree using additives. In effect, a designer selects a polymeric system rather than a simple homogeneous polymeric material.

Additives are commonly used to enhance certain specific properties (e.g. UV stability, stiffness, color etc.) that the base polymer is lacking. Additives include processing stabilizers, antioxidants, UV stabilizers, internal or external lubricants, colorants / pigments, plasticizers, fillers or reinforcements, flame retardants, other polymers, or any number of other organic / inorganic additives used alone or in combination. However, it should be noted that like medication, additives do have side effects which are sometimes important, particularly when the additives are used at high concentrations. For example, the addition of glass fibers to a material will typically improve properties such as modulus, strength and thermal conductivity, however, the reinforced materials are typically more difficult to process when considering problems such as equipment / mold abrasion, achievable part surface finish, weld (knit) line quality, and fiber orientation. The side effects of additives such as antioxidants or antiaging additives that are used at very low concentrations (typically parts per million) are generally less of a concern, however, even a small concentration of these additives can affect properties such as color or taste.

In any case, it is important for designers to recognize the fact that commercial plastic material grades do contain additives, and the effect of these additives on all aspects of performance (including processability) should be considered. While it is unlikely that designers will work with material suppliers on the creation of an entirely new chemical composition, it is not uncommon for designers to work with material suppliers (especially compounding houses) on the development of new material formulations using a new additive package. This is commonly done in situations where there is no commercial grade of material available for a particular end-use application (or no material available at the right price). An example of a new material developed using additives could simply be a custom colored thermoplastic grade. These material lots are commonly supplied as precompounded custom color lots, or as custom compounded color master batches that are blended with "standard" (natural) resin grades during production.

1.5   General Characteristics of Plastic Materials

Product designers have the option to choose from a variety of different materials when selecting the material(s) of construction for a particular product. Depending on the application, plastics compete with materials such as woods, sheet metals, cast or forged metals, ceramics or glass. In many cases, plastics offer distinct advantages over the other materials in terms of performance, cost, or performance / cost ratio. However, in most cases, the competing materials all offer inherent benefits, and of course some limitations. The designer must attempt to correlate the end-use performance requirements of the product with the property profiles of the individual materials in an attempt to obtain the best material for the application. While there are literally thousands of commercial grades of plastic materials to choose from, there are certain generalities that can be stated with respect to the relative advantages and limitations of plastics in comparison with other more conventional materials [7-11].

Versatility: As stated earlier, the single most important characteristic of plastic materials, as a general family, is their versatility. Plastics are generally synthetic materials built up from monomeric building blocks that are joined together to produce high molecular weight polymers. The properties of a plastic material can literally be "tailored" to meet the requirements of a specific end-use application. These tailor made properties can be obtained by either (i) altering the basic chemical composition (using different monomers, co-monomers, polymerization conditions etc) or (ii) using different additives that are melt blended with the polymer to enhance specific properties that are lacking in the base polymer.

Relatively Easy to Mold into Complex Shapes: The injection molding process can be used to produce thermoplastic or thermosetting plastic parts of very complex geometry. These parts can be mass produced and require little or no secondary finishing. For example, it is common practice to incorporate assembly features such as holes, bosses, snap beams etc. directly into the molded part. These integral design features greatly simplify, or possibly eliminate, the need for secondary assembly operations. The part geometries that are achievable using the injection molding process are becoming even more complex as advanced injection molding technologies, such as fusible core molding, continue to evolve.

Low Specific Gravity: Neat plastic materials have specific gravities that range from approximately 0.8 to 1.8. These values are much lower than those for steel, which has a specific gravity of more than seven. Plastic materials also have good strength / weight or stiffness / weight ratios. This is an advantage in terms of performance, since it is possible to make lightweight, easy to handle products that are durable and long lasting. The low specific gravity is a distinct advantage in the automotive industry, where product weight savings are essential. Plastic foams, such as injection molded structural foams, have even lower specific gravities (typically 15-25% density reduction), however, thicker part walls are often required for these foamed polymers. Reinforced plastic material grades, most commonly filled with inorganic fillers or reinforcements having specific gravities greater than 2.0, have specific gravities that are influenced by the filler concentration and specific gravity (i.e. the composite material specific gravity will essentially follow the rule of mixtures).

Ironically, the low specific gravity has limited the use of plastic materials in many applications, since many consumers associate "strength" or "toughness" with weight. Material manufacturers have actually developed grades that are loaded with high specific gravity fillers. The fillers are purposely added to the polymer in order to increase the specific gravity of the formulation, thereby allowing the production of "heavy" molded parts that have the look and feel of a ceramic material.

Sometimes Transparent: Some amorphous thermoplastics, such as polystyrene, polymethyl methacrylate or polycarbonate, are available as transparent material grades. Materials such as polycarbonate offer light transmission that is similar to glass, along with toughness, low specific gravity and good manufacturability. However, unlike glass, transparent plastic grades tend to "yellow" or "cloud" over time, particularly when the plastic material is exposed to ultraviolet radiation for extended periods of time. In addition, the scratch resistance of plastics is often limited. Transparent plastic parts slated for outdoor applications are sometimes coated with a combination UV screener/hard coating to extend their service life.

Most semi-crystalline materials are translucent or opaque. Translucent semi-crystalline polymers, such as polypropylene, offer a relatively high degree of light transmission, particularly in thinner wall moldings. Clarified or nucleated grades of polypropylene (that reduce the physical light scattering effects of the crystals) offer improved light transmission capabilities. Semi-crystalline materials are commonly used for products, such as medical syringes, where a limited degree of light transmission is required.

Coloring Throughout: Coloring additives such as pigments or dyes are commonly melt blended directly into the polymer formulation. The colored materials can be purchased from the supplier or compounder as pre-colored pellets, or colorants can be added to a natural resin at the molding machine (as liquids, powders, or most commonly in the form of a masterbatch additive). Internal coloring offers a number of distinct advantages over the alternative, painting. The use of colorants obviously eliminates the cost of secondary operations associated with painting and potential cleaner or solvent hazards. Problems such as paint chipping are also eliminated since the color is integral. In addition, damage due to abrasion or scratching is much less obvious when the color is distributed throughout the thickness of the part.

However, it can be difficult, if not impossible (depending on the standards) to obtain a class-A finish on the molded part using internal colorants. Color matching can also be a problem, since factors such as residence time, shear history, and heat history (therefore regrind level) can cause color shifts due to the effects on the color of both the colorant and the base plastic material (for an overall net color change). Fading can also be a problem over the long term, depending on the conditions of ultraviolet exposure and the thermal or ultraviolet stability of the colorant and polymer. Painting is a secondary operation that is sometimes required (i.e. in cases where very high gloss, defect free, precisely color matched surfaces are required). Many plastic materials can also be plated or metallized.

Relatively Low Energy Requirements for Processing: The process of thermoplastic injection molding begins with the injection of molten polymer into a relatively cool mold cavity. Once in the cavity, the polymer cools by conduction, and eventually becomes rigid enough that it can be ejected from the tool. After ejection, the part cools to room temperature. The energy requirements for processing are determined by the molding machinery efficiencies (e.g. electric machines are more energy efficient than hydraulic machines), and by the plastic material's processing requirements. Processing conditions such as drying temperature, "melt" temperature, and mold temperature contribute to the overall energy requirements. For example, the energy, Q, required to bring a polymer from room temperature, T_o, the the processing (melt) temperature, T_m, is given by:

$$Q = m \cdot Cp \cdot [T_m - T_o] \tag{1.4}$$

where m is the mass of the polymer, and Cp is the specific heat of the polymer at constant pressure. The energy required to bring the polymer to its processing temperature is the result of both electrical conduction (from the heated barrel), and viscous dissipation / internal friction (associated with plastication and injection). Compared to other materials (such as metals), polymers generally have significantly lower processing temperature values (i.e. lower T_m) and lower specific gravities/part weights (i.e. low m). The specific heat values for polymers are generally higher than for other competitive materials, however, the overall energy requirements for polymer processing (considering all three terms in equation 1.4) are significantly lower than for metals, glasses, or ceramics. While low processing temperatures are beneficial from an energy consumption viewpoint, it should be noted here that the high temperature capabilities of most polymers is of course limited for the same reason.

Chemical Resistance: Most plastic materials offer good resistance to corrosion caused by the presence of moisture, salts, weak acids and bases. However, most thermoplastics are soluble or will swell in the presence of specific organic solvents (i.e. those with a similar solubility parameter) especially at elevated temperatures. In general, thermosetting, liquid crystalline, and semi-crystalline offer improved chemical resistance over amorphous polymers. The chemical resistance of a polymer must be carefully matched with the application for which it is intended. For example, in automotive applications, resistance to organic chemicals such as fuels, and a variety of other automotive fluids must be given careful consideration.

Different chemicals will affect a plastic material in different ways. For example, the chemicals can react with the polymer. An example of a chemical reaction would be the hydrolysis that can occur when a polyester is heated in the presence of water. Water can also have a plasticizing effect (a physical softening effect) for hygroscopic polymers such as polyamides. In other cases, organic chemicals can solvate the polymer. This problem is commonly encountered when amorphous thermoplastics are exposed to an organic chemical, such as a hydrocarbon solvent. Chemicals, particularly organic chemicals, can also cause environmental stress cracking and crazing (ESCC). The phenomenon of environmental stress cracking and crazing can be summarized as follows. In an unstressed state, a plastic material may appear to be unaffected by the presence of a certain chemical. However, when the same polymer is subject to a stress (even a low stress) *and* the same chemical, crazing or cracking (and eventual catastrophic failure) can occur. The stresses can be due to external loads, or can be residual (locked-in) molding stresses. It is therefore critical that injection molded products are designed and molded properly, minimizing their internal stress level, and the potential for environmental stress cracking and crazing in applications where chemical contact is anticipated.

Mechanical Performance: Plastic materials are available with mechanical properties that range from elastomeric to rigid and stiff. However, even very rigid materials have modulus values that are an order of magnitude lower than steel. When stiffness is a product requirement, designers must obtain the stiffness using geometric features such as ribs and edge stiffeners. Plastic materials can also be very impact resistant or tough, and are useful in a variety of high abuse / high impact applications. The mechanical properties of plastics are commonly modified using additives that range from toughening agents to reinforcing fibers. In some cases, particularly for fiber reinforced polymer grades, the mechanical performance can be anisotropic due to molecular or fiber orientation effects.

Unlike metals, a plastic's mechanical properties can be very sensitive to even small changes in temperature, rate of loading, and in some cases, relative humidity (an important factor for hygroscopic polymers). Designers must consider the mechanical performance of a plastic material over the range of temperatures, times, and relative humidities associated with the application. For example, plastic materials can become very brittle at low temperatures. At higher temperatures, plastic materials can exhibit excessive creep deformation. However, if a designer does consider the extremes of temperature, a suitable material for the application can usually be identified, and a part designed accordingly.

Good Electrical Insulation: Many plastic materials offer outstanding electrical insulating properties, and as a result find widespread use in electrical insulating applications such as switches and electronic enclosures. This is an advantage in these applications, however, in other applications, some degree of conductivity is required. For example, computer enclosures must provide a level of electromagnetic interference (EMI) shielding. In these applications, additives such as conductive stainless steel or nickel coated fibers can be compounded into the polymer matrix to enhance electrical conductivity, or alternatively the part can be painted, plated, or metallized to provide the required conductivity.

Good Thermal Insulation: Plastic materials also offer good thermal insulation. This is important in a variety of energy conservation applications. The reduced heat transfer rates give plastic products a warm feel, even when the temperature of the plastic object is cool. On the other hand, the low thermal conductivity can be a problem in dynamic applications such as gearing (where frictional heat is generated), or in applications such as computer enclosures (where electrical sources generate heat). Forced ventilation systems (e.g. fans) are often required for applications where natural conduction and convective heat transfer to the environment cannot keep pace with heat generation. When heat dissipation is a problem, designers must pay strict attention to both the surface area to volume ratio for the part and the material's thermal properties. Filled or reinforced thermoplastic material grades (composite materials) can offer significantly improved heat . transfer capabilities.

Flammable: Almost all plastic materials will burn to some degree or decompose when subject to combustion conditions. A polymer such as polyethylene will ignite and burn readily, while a thermosetting phenolic will simply char. The flammability resistance of most plastic materials can be improved using flame retardant additive packages. Designers must be concerned with a number of issues with respect to flammability, including combustibility, dripping, and combustion by products, including the by-products of the additives.

Poor Weather Resistance: Many plastic materials have poor long term weather resistance. While most materials are unaffected by the presence of moisture at low temperature (with the exception of the plasticizing effect for hygroscopic polymers), the combined effects of ultraviolet energy (from sunlight) and oxidation can lead to a deterioration in color, transparency, and other properties over time. This is a concern for the many long term, outdoor applications such as automotive, toys, sporting goods or building construction products. Some plastic materials such as acrylics have excellent inherent weather resistance, while others such as polypropylene require additional stabilization. The long term weather resistance of any polymer can be improved significantly using ultraviolet stabilizers and antioxidants as additives. In some cases, coatings are used to overcome the problems associated with long term aging.

Relatively High Coefficient of Thermal Expansion: In general, plastic materials have relatively high coefficients of thermal expansion (CTE). This becomes a concern when plastics are used as a component of a larger product assembly containing metals, glass, ceramics or even another plastic material (having a different CTE value) due to the thermal expansion mismatch. The thermal expansion coefficients for plastic materials vary greatly from material to material. Materials such as filled or reinforced liquid crystal polymers have very low coefficients of linear thermal expansion, while a material such as an unfilled polyethylene, has a coefficient of linear thermal expansion that is an order of magnitude greater than that of steel. Designers must incorporate provisions to compensate for this thermal expansion mismatch into their product designs. The coefficient of linear thermal expansion for a polymer can be reduced significantly by adding inorganic fillers and reinforcements such as glass fiber (glass has a very low CTE). However, when fiber reinforced materials are used, anisotropic thermal expansion behavior can be observed due to fiber and molecular orientation effects. It should also be noted here that hygroscopic polymers, such as acetals or nylons, can also exhibit dimensional changes with changes in relative humidity due to its effect on the level of absorbed moisture within the polymer. A hygroscopic thermoplastic will tend to swell as the level of absorbed moisture increases.

1.6   References

1.   Deanin, R., *Polymer Structure, Properties, and Applications*, Cahners Publishing, Boston, MA (1972).
2.   Technical Bulletin, *Designing with Plastics*, Hoechst Celanese, Chatham, NJ (1989).
3.   Technical Bulletin, *Engineering Materials Design Guide*, General Electric Plastics, Pittsfield, MA (1989).
4.   Moore, G. and Kline, D., *Properties and Processing of Polymers for Engineers*, Prentice-Hall, Inc., London (1984).
5.   Clements, L., "Polymer Science for Engineers", *Engineering Plastics Handbook*, American Society of Metals, International, Metals Park, OH (1988).
6.   Technical Bulletin, *Engineering Thermoplastics Basic Design Manual*, The Dow Chemical Co., Midland, MI (1988).
7.   Dym, J., *Product Design with Plastics*, Industrial Press, Inc., NY (1983).
8.   Powell, P., *Plastics for Industrial Designers*, The Plastics Institute, London (1973).
9.   MacDermott, C., *Selecting Thermoplastics for Engineering Applications*, Marcel Dekker, Inc., NY (1984).
10. Ehrenstein, G. and Erhard, G., *Designing with Plastics*, Hanser Publishers, Munich (1984).
11. Patton, W., *Plastics Technology, Theory, Design and Manufacture*, Reston Publishing Company, Reston, VA (1976).

2 Manufacturing Considerations for Injection Molded Parts

2.1 Introduction

The injection molding process is a high speed, automated process that can be used to produce plastic parts with very complex geometries. The process can produce either very small or very large parts using virtually any plastic material. It is important, however, for part designers to recognize that the design of the product will ultimately determine the "ease of molding" or the "manufacturability" of the part, as well as the tooling requirements and cost. It is also important for the part designer to recognize that the overall shape of a product and specific feature details may need to be altered in order to improve the moldability of the plastic part. In addition, the part designer must recognize that the properties of the molded plastic part will be greatly influenced by factors such as the tool design and processing conditions. In order to develop a quality part, the plastic part designer, the mold designer, the material supplier, and the process engineer must all work together in an effort to develop a part that is both moldable and fully functional. Plastic part designs are more likely to be successful if such concurrent engineering practices are followed.

The injection molding process is a complex process that involves a series of sequential process steps. The different phases of the injection molding process include; the mold filling phase, the packing phase, the holding phase, the cooling phase, and part ejection.

Mold Filling	After the mold closes, the melt flows from the injection unit of the molding machine into the relatively cool mold through the sprue the runners, the gates, and then into the cavity.
Packing	The melt is pressurized and compressed to ensure complete filling and detailed surface replication.
Holding	The melt is held in the mold under pressure to compensate for shrinkage as the part cools. Holding pressure is usually applied until the gate solidifies. Once gate solidification occurs, melt can no longer flow into (or out of) the cavity.
Cooling	The melt continues to cool and shrink with no shrinkage compensation.
Part Ejection	The mold opens and the cooled part is then stripped from the core or cavity, in most cases using a mechanical ejector system.

Each phase of the injection molding process has an influence of the design of a plastic part. In order for a plastic part to be considered moldable, it must satisfy the moldability requirements for each of these five processing phases. While there is a great deal of interaction between the various phases of the injection molding process, the discussion given below highlights the important design considerations associated with each phase of the process.

2.2   Mold Filling Considerations

2.2.1   Gating Considerations

One of the most important decisions associated with mold filling is determining the type, number, and location of the gate(s) used for the plastic part. The gate, as the name implies, is the melts' point of entry into the mold cavity. Gates can be placed at one or more locations on the part and can have various designs. Different gating designs and locations can have dramatic influences on the overall part quality. The gating scheme will influence the filling, packing and holding phases of the molding process, and will have a large impact on a part's final dimensions, as well as its performance and esthetics. The gating scheme can influence part quality in many ways including:

Mold filling pattern	Pressure distribution in the cavity
Weld or knit quality and location	Gas traps and short shots
Degree and direction of orientation	Ease of degating
Dimensional tolerances	Size and location of gate restage
Ability to control sink marks	Residual stress
Ability to control shrinkage voids	Warpage and flatness

Historically, a product designer would bring a part print or prototype part to a tool designer. The designer would generally indicate locations on the part where the gate could not be placed for esthetic reasons. At this point, the tool designer would begin the process of designing the mold. This is no longer the case. This series or over the wall approach to plastic part design has to a large extent been replaced with a more concurrent design approach. Product designers now recognize that the gating scheme can have a dramatic impact on part quality. In many cases today, it is the product designer rather than the tool designer who specifies the gating scheme for a part. However, it is generally best to bring the tool designer into the design loop at the early stages of part design, as the part geometry is taking form. In this way, the tool and part designers can work together on the critical decisions associated with gating. Consider the closed sleeve, cup type molding shown in Figure 2.1. A number of possible gating schemes are proposed.

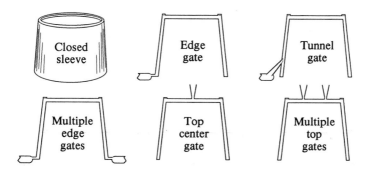

Figure 2.1. Typical gating options for a closed sleeve (cup) type molding. The gating options shown include edge gates, tunnel gates, and pin gates.

Each gating scheme has its own specific advantages and limitations. It is generally good practice for a part designer to consider as many gating options as possible, and to establish the design that offers the best balance of moldability and end use performance. For example, the single edge gated part can be produced in a simple two plate mold; however, this gating approach could lead to core deflection, gas traps, a potentially weak weld and dimensional problems. The multiple edge gating scheme would be an improvement over the single edge gate, however, weld and venting issues remain a concern, and it is likely that additional runner scrap would be generated. With closed sleeves of this type, it is generally preferable to gate into the top of the part rather than into the side. For example, the top center gate results in more balanced flow, natural venting at the parting line, and no weld lines.

Spoke gating (2 spokes)   Spoke gating (4 spokes)   Diaphragm or disk gate

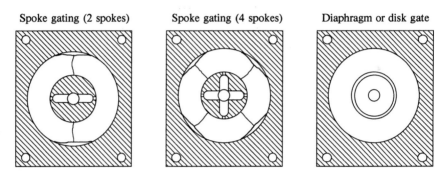

Figure 2.2. Internal spoke and disc gating options for a rim shaped molding. The disc gate ensures uniform filling and packing without weld line formation.

Gating schemes can have a large impact on the dimensions of a plastic part. The rim-like part shown in Figure 2.2 is to be produced in a single cavity tool. Possible gating schemes for the part include internal spoke gating or disc (diaphragm) gating. Plastic parts tend to shrink less in the regions near the gate due to cavity pressure gradients and compressibility effects. Therefore, the final dimensions of the molded part will be influenced by the number of gates. From a dimensional, performance, and overall part quality viewpoint, the disc gating option shown in Figure 2.2 is the best option since it results in balance flow, uniform pressure distribution, good dimensional control, and no welds. Unfortunately, this gating option will likely result in additional runner scrap, and may require an additional post molding (secondary) operation such as punching or machining to remove the gate. These conflicting concerns must be balanced when making gating related decisions.

Gating With Two and Three Plate Molds: Gate location decisions will determine the general type of mold that will be used to produce the plastic part and will influence the cost of the injection mold as well. For example, edge or sub gated parts can be produced with the standard cold runner two plate mold configuration. When top center gating or multiple top gating is to be used, the part can be produced using a three plate mold configuration. In the special case of a single cavity mold, top cental gating into a closed sleeve can also be accomplished using a two plate mold and a sprue gate as indicated in Figure 2.4.

In almost all cases, the mark left on the molding when the gate is removed is an esthetic concern. In addition, the sections of the part around the gate often show flow, blush, or splay marks, as well as the potential for discoloration. Consider the part shown in Figure 2.5. From a flow point of view, it may be easiest and best to gate a part such as a clamshell appliance housing from the top center position.

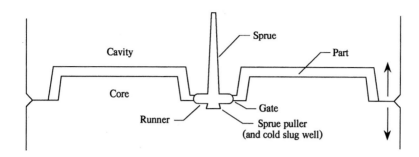

Figure 2.3. Typical cold runner, two plate (single parting line) multi-cavity mold configuration.

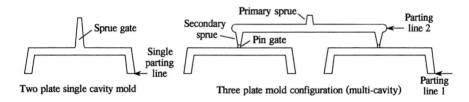

Figure 2.4. Sprue gates can be used to gate into the top of a single cavity mold (left), while three plate molds (two parting lines) provide a means of top gating for multi-cavity molds.

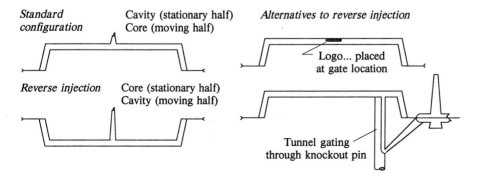

Figure 2.5. A variety of options can be used to relocate or disguise objectionable gate vestiges.

Using the "standard" cavity and core set-up (i.e. stationary cavity and moving core), the part can be gated on the top surface. Unfortunately, with this configuration, the gate vestige is a visual imperfection since it is located on the appearance surface of the molding. If on the other hand, the melt is injected through the core, rather than the cavity, the gate vestige remains hidden on the non-appearance, inside surface of the part. Unfortunately, the tooling costs associated with this "reverse injection" option can be significant, since the part must also be ejected from the stationary side of the tool. Like the sprue, ejection pin witness marks are also visual defect. Special ejection provisions must be added to activate the stationary side ejection system since the machine knockout system is located behind the moving platen of the molding machine. Fortunately there are alternatives to reverse injection however. For example, the part could be produced using the standard cavity and core configuration, if the gate vestige could be disguised using a design feature such as a logo or label. Another option would be to gate into the backside of the molding by tunnel gating into a modified ejection pin as shown in Figure 2.5.

In some cases, a designer has an option to use either a two or three plate mold configuration. Consider a deep draw part such as that shown in Figure 2.6. Using the conventional cavity and core configurations, the part can be gated at the top using a three plate mold.

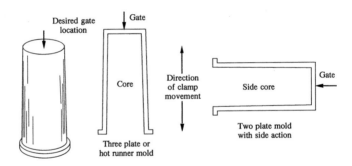

Figure 2.6. Sleeve type moldings are typically produced using three plate (or hot runner) molds, however, two plate molds with side core pull provide another option.

The part produced using this tool configuration would benefit by having a well drafted cavity and core to facilitate release during mold opening and part ejection. If design features such as circumferential ribs were added to the outside of the cylindrical part, the part might not release from the cavity. The more complex ribbed part could be produced using a split cavity or alternatively a two plate mold with a side core pull. Both of these tooling options are described as having "special actions" that are associated with part ejection. The two plate mold with the side core pull is also commonly used in deep draw applications where there is not enough "die height" to allow the deep draw part to be ejected.

Gating With Hot Runner Molds: Hot runner systems have evolved to the point where they can be used with virtually any plastic material and part geometry. These runner systems are used to produce parts as small as pen caps and as large as automotive bumpers. Hot runner systems offer the obvious advantage of eliminating runner scrap and the many problems associated with regrind use. However, hot runner systems offer other advantages such as providing a great deal of freedom with respect to the gate location and helping to improve part quality.

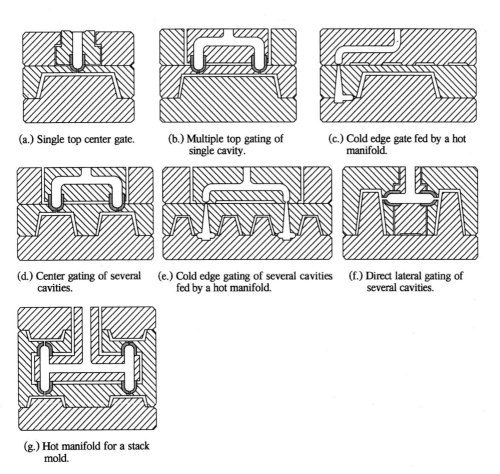

(a.) Single top center gate.

(b.) Multiple top gating of single cavity.

(c.) Cold edge gate fed by a hot manifold.

(d.) Center gating of several cavities.

(e.) Cold edge gating of several cavities fed by a hot manifold.

(f.) Direct lateral gating of several cavities.

(g.) Hot manifold for a stack mold.

Figure 2.7. A variety of gating schemes are possible with hot runner molds.

Hot runner systems can be viewed as extensions of the molding machine nozzle into the tool. When hot runner systems are used, the frozen layer effects associated with cold runner fed systems can be eliminated. Molding related orientation levels can be reduced resulting in parts with lower residual stress levels. Hot runner gates are available in a variety of configurations and shapes including the most common open circular and annular geometries. When gate vestige is a particular concern, a hot valve gating system can be used. Valve gates have a mechanically activated valve pin that shuts off the gate as the pin moves forward, providing a mechanical seal and a relatively clean vestige [1,2].

2.2.2   Mold Filling Orientation

It is important for a designer to recognize that almost all injection molded plastic parts will have some degree of "frozen-in" molecular orientation. The degree of frozen-in orientation in for finished part will be influenced by the polymer's molecular weight and relaxation characteristics, by the processing conditions used during production. Process variables that promote molecular relaxation will tend to reduce the net orientation level in a molding. The mold filling related orientation can be minimized through design and process variables that minimize the mold filling pressure requirements. The net orientation level will be the difference between the orientation level imparted by the mold filling and packing phases, and the degree of relaxation.

Residual (Frozen-in) Orientation = Orientation Level Due to Flow - Relaxation

For example, warmer tool temperatures will promote molecular relaxation (rerandomization) by keeping the melt warmer for longer periods of time. Process adjustments such as an increase in mold temperature or melt temperature can be used to minimize orientation, however, these changes will most likely increase the production cycle time. The opposing considerations must be balanced in production. It is for this reason that the degree of orientation caused by mold filling and packing deserves special attention.

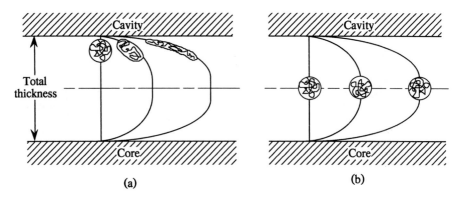

(a)   (b)

Figure 2.8. The pseudoplastic laminar velocity profile causes the polymer molecules near the wall to become oriented while those towards the center of the flow stream remain in the random coil configuration.

It has also been shown that a passive mold cavity insulation layer, with low thermal inertia, leads to higher temperatures at the cavity surface during mold filling. This keeps the temperature of the polymer near the cavity / core walls hotter, allowing the flow induced shear stresses and molecular orientation to relax after mold filling [3]. The concept is good; however, these coatings must be durable enough to withstand harsh production conditions, and should not result in an excessive cycle time increase (due to their insulating effect). Process variables such as injection rate also influence the degree of orientation at the time of fill. A fast injection rate can result in high orientation levels at the instant of fill, but much of this orientation can relax due to the higher melt temperatures associated with the fast fill, since the fast fill leads to an increase in viscous heating and a decrease in the amount of conductive cooling. As a result, there is more molecular mobility at the instant of fill and relaxation can occur.

Molecular orientation develops during the mold filling phase as the melt is injected through the nozzle, runners, gates and cavity. The polymer chains become stretched out due to the velocity gradient associated with the laminar flow behavior. The blunted shape of most polymer melt velocity profiles (pseudoplastic flow behavior) causes most of the orientation to occur towards the surface of the part, while the molecules at the core remain in a random coil configuration as indicated in Figure 2.8. This is a significant problem in injection molding since the melt adjacent to the "relatively cold" mold cavity and core wall will freeze first, leading to high interfacial shear stresses between the melt and the solid layer, and the problem of frozen-in orientation [4-7]. Orientation will continue to develop during the holding phase of the molding process as melt continues to flow into the mold cavity to compensate for volume shrinkage. This is particularly true near the gate region of the part. Packing or holding related processing variables, such as time dependent decreasing holding pressure profiling, can be used to minimize the degree of packing related orientation [6]. Orientation problems are most significant for higher molecular weight (long chain) polymer grades and fiber reinforced polymers. Unlike polymer molecules, reinforcing fibers cannot relax or rerandomize, even when favorable conditions exist.

Polymer chains tend to orient along the direction of flow. Since all of the melt that enters the cavity passes through the gate, the oriented chains tend to radiate from the gate towards the end of flow as shown in Figure 2.9.

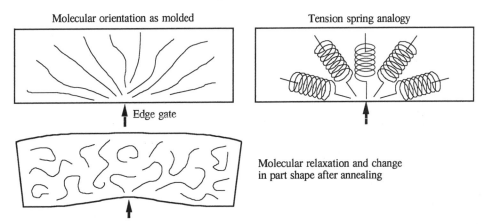

Figure 2.9. Oriented molecules tend to radiate from the gate towards the end of flow. This results in relatively high stresses in the gate region as the polymer molecules attempt to recover. This can also lead to dimensional distortion at elevated temperatures.

Polymer molecules do not want to be in this extended chain state, and as a result, a great deal of internal stress is acting on the gate region as indicated by the tension spring analogy shown in Figure 2.9. Internal stresses related to molecular orientation can lead to warpage (when the stresses are high enough to cause buckling) or remain as internal stresses which superimpose on service related stresses, reducing the durability and environmental stress crack resistance of the molded plastic part. The internal stresses can be relieved by annealing the part after molding, however, it is likely that dimensional changes will occur unless the part is properly fixtured. Likewise, the molded part can begin to distort or warp at elevated service temperatures (e.g. in a paint cure oven or on a hot day) if residual orientation levels are high. Frozen-in orientation can also lead to anisotropic behavior with respect to mold shrinkage and end use properties [5, 8-10].

The part shown in Figure 2.10a was produced using a wide fan gate along the short side of the molding. This gating scheme results in a degree of orientation along the flow direction (i.e. along the length of the part). The properties of the part will then vary with the direction of testing. For example, bending or tensile strengths would tend to be greater along the flow direction in comparison with the transverse or cross flow direction strengths. Izod impact specimens cut from the flow direction would tend to exhibit higher impact strength values. In one study done with high impact polystyrene, the Izod impact specimens cut from the part shown in Figure 2.10 (with a 3.2 mm thickness) yielded the following results [5].

Table 2.1. Variation in Impact Strength for a HIPS Molding

Specimen location	Sample direction	Avg Izod impact strength (ft-lbs / in)	(J/m)
Near the gate	Flow	2.53	137
Near the gate	X-Flow	0.95	51
End of flow	Flow	2.21	119
End of flow	X-Flow	0.66	36

The data in Table 2.1 shows that properties can also vary to some degree with distance from the gate. Impact strength values for samples taken at or very close to the gate could also be low due to residual gate stresses. Directional property differences (anisotropy) are expected to be more significant for thinner wall moldings, and with more viscous polymers. The part shown in Figure 2.10b was produced with center gating, which results in radial flow. Radial flow patterns result in a degree of both radial and circumferential orientation due to the expanding flow front. Orientation is a natural consequence of polymer flow, but it must be stressed that net orientation levels in the molding can be minimized by using processing conditions that promote molecular relaxation.

As mentioned earlier, orientation effects are even more significant for fiber reinforced polymers. Figure 2.11 shows the flexural fatigue strength of specimens cut from a molded glass fiber reinforced nylon 6/6 part [11]. The cross flow direction fatigue strength values for the glass fiber reinforced nylon 6/6 part are significantly lower than the flow direction values. The flow direction strength values correlate well with the strength values determined using a standard end gated flexural test specimen (indicating that these standard test specimens provide only a measure of the flow direction properties). It should also be noted that while the fatigue strength values of the cross flow specimens were lower than the flow direction values, they are still greater than the unreinforced nylon fatigue stress values.

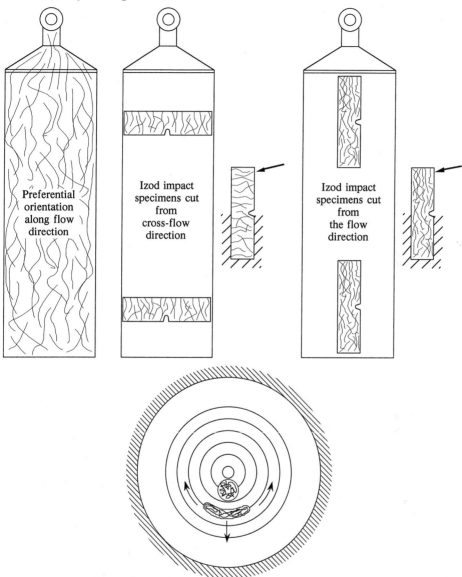

Figure 2.10. (top) Gating into the short side of the rectangular part leads to orientation along the length of the part leading to property differences between the flow and cross-flow directions. The degree of frozen-in orientation is determined by material, design, and processing related factors. (bottom) The center gating scheme results in radial or disc flow with orientation components in both the radial and circumferential directions.

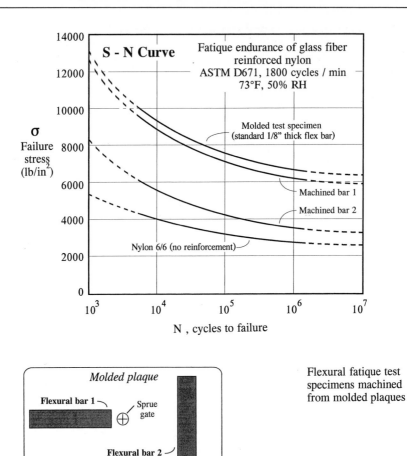

Figure 2.11. The figure shows that the cross-flow fatigue strength values for a glass fiber reinforced nylon 6/6 are significantly lower than the flow direction values.

The previous figures show that residual molecular or fiber orientation does lead to anisotropic behavior, and the part designer must cope with the phenomenon. Whenever possible, the part designer should attempt to position the gate in a location that promotes orientation in the direction of maximum stress associated with the end-use application. The cable tie shown in Figure 2.12 is primarily subjected to uniaxial bending and tensile stresses in the end-use application. Molecular orientation along the length of the part could actually be beneficial in this application. On the other hand, when parts are subjected to multi-axial stresses in service, it is generally best to minimize orientation levels.

The degree of orientation caused by mold filling and packing is influenced by processing conditions, material properties, tool design and part design. For example, large diameter runners, sprues and gates along with shorter flow lengths will tend to reduce orientation.

Faster fill rates and higher melt temperatures tend to reduce the net level of frozen-in orientation by promoting molecular relaxation. The use of hot runner systems is generally advantageous from this point of view as well. Changes in flow direction are a particular concern when it comes to molecular and fiber orientation. Corners, especially the internal corners in the runner system and part, should contain very generous radii whenever possible.

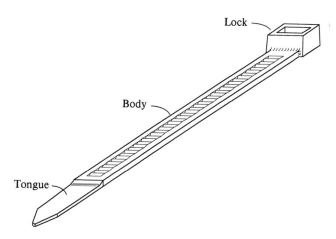

Figure 2.12. For certain types of parts, such as a cable tie wrap, orientation can be advantageous. In general designers should gate parts so that any residual orientation effects are in line with the direction of maximum stress associated with the end-use application.

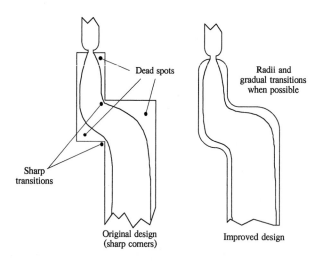

Figure 2.13. Bends or corners, especially internal corners, should contain generous radii to minimize the degree of orientation associated with mold filling.

Sharp internal corners have a tendency to orient and even cause shear degradation of the polymer melt as it flows by at high velocities. Corner radii will also reduce any stress concentrations associated with residual stress or service loading. Ideally, when a plastic part is designed, corners should look similar to the corner highlighted in Figure 2.14. This correct corner design is automatically created if the designer (i) uses a generous radius on the inside corner (core), and (ii) maintains a uniform part wall thickness. This corner design will offer a relatively uniform stress distribution in service, good flow characteristics, and good esthetics.

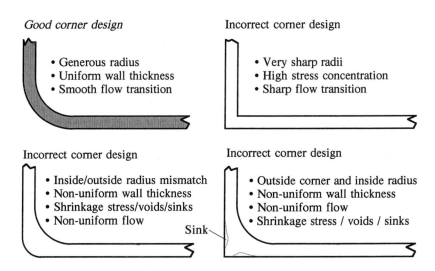

Figure 2.14. Ideally corners should have both internal and external radii. The uniform wall thickness can be maintained if the external radius is equal to the internal radius plus the wall thickness. Thick wall sections at the corners will lead to sink marks, voids, shrinkage stresses, and the potential for race-tracking.

2.2.3   Mold Filling Pressure Losses

Introduction: When selecting a gate location for an injection molded part, the designer must consider all of the various factors associated with mold filling. The cavity filling process for the part begins at the gate, and progresses as the melt follows the path of least resistance. The gate should be positioned in such a way that the mold fills uniformly, and that the pressure drop through the cavity is not excessive. It is important for a designer to obtain an estimate of this pressure drop, in an effort to evaluate the "moldability" of a part with respect to a proposed gating scheme. The pressure drop and filling pattern can be best evaluated using computer aided mold filling simulations [12-15, 134-136]. These process simulations help the designer evaluate the moldability of a product, and alter the design of the part or tool, long before the tool is actually cut. Problems associated with improper gate location, flow hesitation, gas traps, weld positioning and the like can all be addressed at the part design stage, resulting in both shorter overall development time and improved part quality.

The pressure drop or loss associated with mold filling will be influenced by a number of factors. These mold filling variables include:

Material Type	Shear flow properties
	Thermal properties
Molding Machine	Injection pressure capabilities
	Screw / plunger frictional losses
	Barrel cap and nozzle losses
Mold Characteristics	Hot or cold feed system
	Sprue, runner, gate and cavity geometry
	Materials of construction
	Cooling / heating capabilities
	Venting capabilities
Process Conditions	Melt temperature and temperature uniformity
	Tool temperature and temperature uniformity
	Injection rate / mold filling velocity and profile

The "pressure to fill" is then clearly influenced by a large number of variables, including some that may be beyond the control of the product designer. This fact once again stresses the importance of concurrent product engineering. A mold filling simulation done using the cavity geometry is useful, however, a simulation that includes the tool feed (runner) system, and the machine nozzle geometry, will be even more realistic, since all of these geometries influence pressure drop, and temperature distribution as illustrated in Figure 2.16.

Consider an example such as the cable tie shown in Figure 2.17. Gating options for this part include single gates at either end, a single central gate, or perhaps some combination (i.e. multiple gates). The use of multiple gates is often an effective means of cutting down on the effective flow length (and therefore pressure drop); however, in this case, weld lines due to the multiple gates would be a concern as the weld lines form perpendicular to the direction of the service stress. These welds would likely reduce the durability of the product. A single gate into the thin tongue would lead to packing and weld problems for the thicker locking mechanism at the far end of the cavity. It would be difficult to effectively pack and control the dimensions of the thick tight tolerance section at the end of flow with this gating scheme. A single gate into the thicker end of the part would permit control of packing for all sections of the part since the flow path is from "thick to thin". A weld line would be formed, however the streaming weld line would run along the length of the part. Most likely, the strength of the part would not be adversely affected by this weld, since the weld runs along the direction of uniaxial service stress. If the end gate into the lock is selected as the gate location, the designer must determine if the part can in fact be filled with a single gate. Ideally, this should be done using a computer aided mold filling simulation, or alternatively using material supplier moldability data.

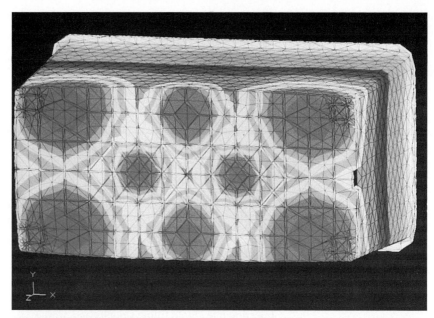

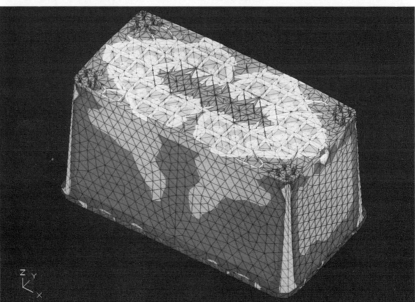

Figure 2.15. Computer aided molding simulations can be used to detect manufacturing problems long before the tool is actually built. These photos show the results of a computerized mold filling and cooling analysis performed on one of the largest parts ever injection molded: a 110 pound refuse container. Because the tool design was optimized using a computer model, good parts were obtained with only minor tool modifications. (Courtesy of Moldflow Pty. Ltd., 2 Corporate Dr., Sheldon, CT 06484)

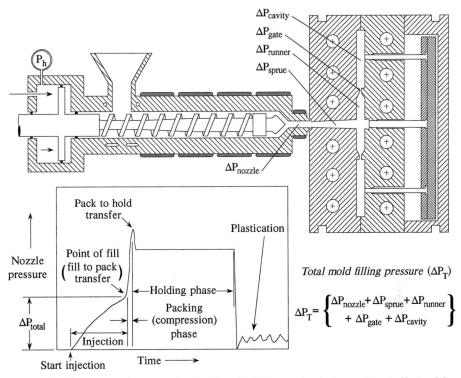

Figure 2.16. The pressure drops associated with mold filling are due to the combined effects of flow through both the machine and the mold.

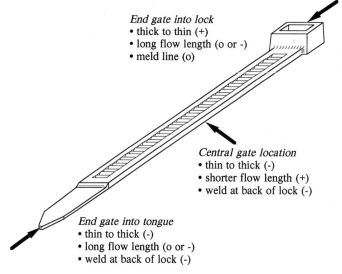

Figure 2.17. Designers should identify the most likely locations for gating injection molded plastic parts and compare the relative advantages and disadvantages of each gating scheme.

Spiral Flow Data: The "moldability" of a specific material grade is often quantified using spiral or serpentine flow molds. To generate this test data, melt is injected into a long spiral type mold cavity under various processing conditions. The maximum flow length that is achievable experimentally is determined as a function of cavity thickness (various cavity depths are typically evaluated using a series of interchangeable cavity inserts). The process variables that are typically evaluated include melt temperature, mold temperature, maximum injection pressure and injection velocity. The experimental data is commonly presented in a manner similar to that shown in Figure 2.18.

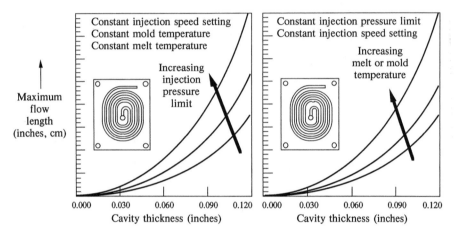

Figure 2.18. Spiral flow curves provide an empirical measure of processability for a particular resin grade. The data is typically presented in graphical form giving maximum flow length as a function of wall thickness for various molding conditions (left). Flow length as a function of injection pressure (right). Flow length as a function of melt or mold temperature.

The flow test results can be used to compare the flow properties, or more specifically, the actual moldability of various resin grades. The data can also assist the part designer in making gating decisions, especially for parts of constant wall thickness. It can be difficult to utilize spiral flow data for parts such as the cable tie shown in Figure 2.17 because the part has a variable wall thickness. The situation is further complicated by the fact that runner systems can account for a significant portion of a mold's pressure drop. Nonetheless, these spiral flow curves, which are available from material suppliers, do provide valuable information on a polymer's flow behavior.

Estimating Mold Pressure Drop: While there is no substitution for computer aided mold filling simulations, there are times where engineering estimates can be used to assist in flow or mold filling related design decisions. Injection mold filling is a complex process as indicated by Figure 2.19. Melt is injected into a "relatively" cold mold at fast injection rates. While most polymers are fairly good insulators, solid layers (skins) do in fact build against the cavity walls as the melt enters the cavity. The flow front behavior is fountain-like, followed by laminar flow tunneling under the solid layer. The melt core stays relatively hot, while the solid / melt interfacial layer temperatures are influenced by both viscous heating and conductive heat loss.

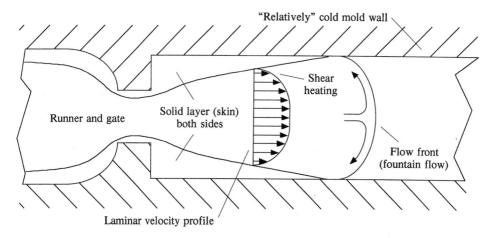

Figure 2.19. Injection mold filling is actually a non-isothermal process involving laminar fountain flow and solid layer formation at the cavity and core walls due to the effects of conductive cooling. The rate of solid layer formation is offset to a degree by viscous heating.

Shear stresses and shear rates at the interface between the solid layer and the melt core can be high, leading to molecular orientation and the potential for shear degradation. The shear stress at a particular layer through the cross section of the part is the product of the shear viscosity times the shear rate associated with that layer.

$$\tau = \eta \cdot \dot{\gamma} \qquad\qquad (2.1)$$

Shear stresses in the boundary region between the solid layer and the melt can be high since (i) the pseudoplastic flow behavior leads to high shear rates at the boundary, and (ii) melt viscosities in the region immediately adjacent to the cool solid layer are high. The shear stresses lead to orientation that is locked into the solid layer as it grows. On the other hand, solid layer formation is offset by heat generated in the boundary region due to viscous heating. The tunneling flow (or underflow) concept is illustrated by the fan gated test part shown in Figure 2.20. The initial portions of the shot were produced with a transparent plastic material (as indicated by the transparent material in the runner cold slug well), while the latter portion of the shot is colored and represents the molten core. The unsteady state injection molding process is in fact so complicated that the coupled fluid flow and heat transfer problems are solved using finite difference or finite element solutions. However, if one assumes that heat transfer effects are not significant during mold filling, then the problem is greatly simplified for regular geometries. While this assumption will no doubt result in error, there is some justification since:

- Mold filling times are relatively short (seconds)
- Most plastic melts have relatively low thermal diffusivities
- Conductive cooling and viscous heating are opposite effects

The magnitude of the error associated with making this assumption would vary with each application. For example, the error for "thin walled" cavities would be greater since the solid layer thicknesses (core and cavity sides) represent a larger percentage of the total wall thickness. Likewise, the error for a mineral filled polymer would be greater than for the unfilled resin due to thermal diffusivity differences. In any case, it is important to know that the pressure drop analysis outlined below provides only a crude estimate of pressure loss for injection molds. However, the simplified approach can be useful for identifying trends and does assist in the understanding of the more sophisticated computer aided mold filling simulations.

Figure 2.20. The fan gated part was produced using transparent material for the initial portions of the shot. The colored material from the latter portion of the shot can be seen tunneling under the transparent solid layers.

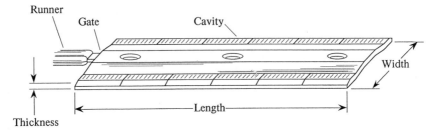

Figure 2.21. When designers alter the geometry or wall thickness of a part such as the ruler molding shown, they should also determine the impact that these changes will have on the manufacturability of the product.

Consider the part shown in Figure 2.21. The designer of the part may be interested to know how a change in wall thickness will influence pressure to fill. For the initial calculation, we will assume isothermal behavior (i.e. constant melt temperature) and steady state flow behavior (i.e. constant injection velocity over the course of the stroke). In reality, melt temperatures do change and injection rates ramp up and down. Additional assumptions as to the regularity of form for the part and runner are also made. In this case, it is proposed that a single cavity, two plate mold will be used to produce the ruler shown in Figure 2.21. While the molding geometry is fairly complex (i.e. it has holes, engraving, curvature etc.), it can be approximated as rectangular flow channel of length, L, width, W, and thickness, H. We will assume that features such as the curvature of the part or the small core pins used to form the holes do not have a significant effect on the pressure to fill the mold. The geometries of the various part and runner sections are described as cylindrical or rectangular flow channels for the steady isothermal analysis.

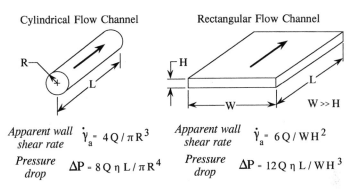

Cylindrical Flow Channel

Rectangular Flow Channel

Apparent wall shear rate $\dot{\gamma}_a = 4Q/\pi R^3$

Pressure drop $\Delta P = 8Q\eta L/\pi R^4$

Apparent wall shear rate $\dot{\gamma}_a = 6Q/WH^2$

Pressure drop $\Delta P = 12Q\eta L/WH^3$

Figure 2.22. Equations for the apparent shear rate and pressure drop for cylindrical and rectangular flow channels. The equations are based upon assumption which include isothermal, laminar, Newtonian flow.

The part will be injection molded using a molding grade high impact polystyrene (HIPS). The shear viscosity behavior of the polymer must be known in order to estimate the pressure drop during mold filling. The shear viscosity data for a particular polymer grade can generally be obtained from the material supplier. In most cases, the viscosity data is presented in tabular or graphical form giving the apparent shear viscosity at the wall as a function of apparent wall shear rate and temperature. If the shear viscosity data provided by the material supplier is described as "apparent", then it is not corrected for the non-Newtonian / pseudoplastic flow behavior exhibited by most polymers. The effects of pressure on viscosity are often neglected.

Table 2.2 Simplified Part and Runner Geometries

Item	Geometry	Dimensions (inches)
Sprue	Cylindrical Flow Channel	0.313 Ø x 2.000 length (average)
Runner	Cylindrical Flow Channel	0.250 Ø x 2.250 length
Edge Gate	Rectangular Flow Channel	0.080 deep x 0.400 wide x 0.120 length
Cavity	Rectangular Flow Channel	0.100 deep x 1.500 wide x 6.030 length

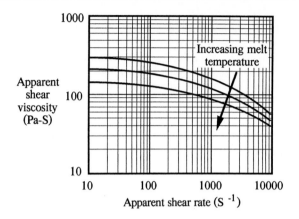

Figure 2.23. Most polymers exhibit pseudoplastic flow behavior. Viscosity curves are used to describe the effect of temperature and apparent shear rate on the apparent shear viscosity of the polymer. The effect of pressure on shear viscosity is often neglected.

For a power law fluid, the true or Rabinowitsch corrected shear viscosity can be determined using:

Cylindrical flow channel $\qquad \eta_T = [4n / (3n + 1)] \, \eta_a$ $\qquad\qquad$ (2.2)

Rectangular flow channel $\qquad \eta_T = [3n / (2n + 1)] \, \eta_a$ $\qquad\qquad$ (2.3)

where n is the power law index (n = 1 for Newtonian fluids, n < 1 for pseudoplastic fluids). It is generally more appropriate to use the corrected viscosity values for engineering calculations. In this case, however, the pressure drop estimates are expected to be low since the effects of the solid layer have not been taken into account. The apparent viscosity and shear rate values will be used here since the calculation is done only to discover trends rather than predict absolute pressure drop values.

It is also important to know if the shear viscosity data obtained for the calculation is end corrected. Shear viscosity data is typically generated on a cylindrical capillary or slit die rheometer as depicted in Figure 2.24. End errors are experimental errors due primarily to capillary entrance pressure losses as the melt flows from the relatively large diameter rheometer barrel into the relatively small diameter capillary die. When shear viscosity data is generated on an instrumented slit die rheometer such as that shown in Figure 2.24b, end errors are eliminated since the pressure drop within the region of defined flow is measured directly. When the viscosity data is generated using the more common circular capillary die rheometer, Figure 2.24a, end errors do influence the test results. The end errors can be minimized (as a percent error) using long capillaries, or corrected for using a correction method such as the Bagley technique [16]. While end correct viscosity data provides a more accurate representation of a polymer's steady shear flow behavior, the uncorrected shear viscosity data (i.e. that without end correction) may be more appropriate for this mold filling pressure estimation since juncture losses are not given special consideration in the analysis. Effectively, the uncorrected data has a

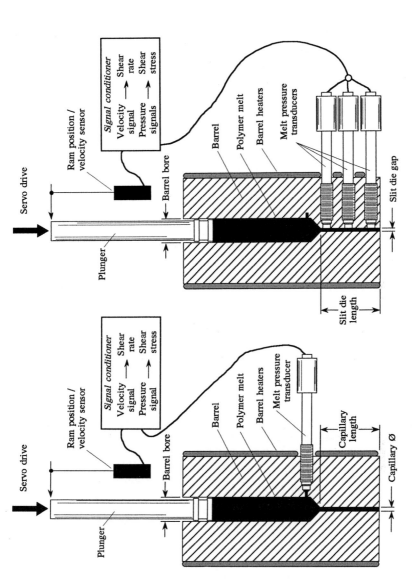

Figure 2.24. Capillary and slit die capillary rheometers are used to generate shear viscosity data at various temperature and shear rates.

"built-in" juncture loss. Similar juncture losses will be encountered during the filling of the injection mold when the melt changes direction or flows through transitions (e.g. from the runner to the gate).

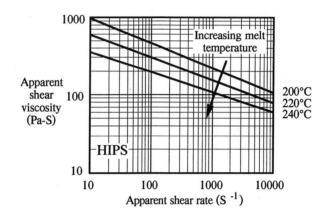

Figure 2.25. Shear viscosity behavior for high impact polystyrene used to produce the part shown in Figure 2.21.

The shear viscosity behavior of the HIPS that will be used to produce the rulers is shown in Figure 2.25. Using this data, the simplified part geometries, and anticipated process conditions (melt temperature and mold filling time), the mold filling pressure can be estimated in the following manner.

Specify Process Conditions: The designer must estimate the processing or molding conditions for the part. For this analysis, a melt temperature and fill time must be selected (for a computer simulation, mold temperature must also be selected). The designer can base his decisions on past experience, or select the worst case conditions for safety (e.g. lowest temperature / highest viscosity). At this stage, the designer can perform a series of calculations in order to obtain a part / mold design that provides for the widest possible processing window. In this case, it will be assumed that the melt will be injected into the mold at the lowest recommended processing temperature, 200°C, using a total fill time of 1.5 seconds.

Determine Part Volumes: The total volume of the molding can be obtained by summing the volumes of the individual geometries that make up the runner system and part:

$$\text{Cylindrical Flow Channel} \qquad V = \pi \cdot R^2 \cdot L \qquad\qquad (2.4)$$

$$\text{Rectangular Flow Channel} \qquad V = L \cdot W \cdot H \qquad\qquad (2.5)$$

Determine Volume Flow Rate: The volume flow rate associated with mold filling, Q, for each section of the molding must be calculated before the pressure drop can be determined. In the special case of the single cavity ruler mold, the volume flow rate through each section of the injection mold is equivalent (assuming an incompressible melt) since the system has only one flow branch. The volume flow rate for the sprue is equivalent to that of the runner and so on.

$$Q_{sprue} = Q_{runner} = Q_{gate} = Q_{cavity} = Q_T \qquad (2.6)$$

Here, the total volume flow rate, Q_T , is simply the total volume (part and runner system) divided by the mold fill time.

$$Q_T = V_T / t_f \qquad (2.7)$$

If, for example, the ruler was produced in a balanced two cavity mold, the volume flow rate through the sprue would be the total molding volume divided by the fill time, while the volume flow rate for each runner, gate and cavity would be one-half that of the sprue since there are two flow branches.

Determine Apparent Shear Rate: The shear viscosity of a polymer is a function of both temperature and shear rate. The temperature of the HIPS melt has been specified earlier as 200°C, however, the apparent shear rate in each flow section must be determined before the shear viscosity in each section can be determined from the set of apparent viscosity curves given in Figure 2.25.

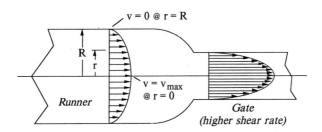

Figure 2.26. Apparent shear rate values vary with both flow rate and flow section geometry. The figure shows that the apparent wall shear rate in the gate is significantly higher than that in the runner system due to the change in the velocity profile caused by the reduced cross sectional area.

Laminar flow can be represented as layer like flow having a velocity of zero at the wall and a maximum velocity at the center of the flow stream. The relative velocity of these adjacent layers results in a shear stress and molecular orientation or deformation. This velocity gradient (or shear rate) is greaterst near the wall, and a minimum at the center of the flow stream. The apparent shear rate at the wall can be determined using:

Cylindrical Flow Channel $\dot{\gamma}_a = [4 \cdot Q] / [\pi \cdot R^3]$ $\qquad (2.8)$

Rectangular Flow Channel $\dot{\gamma}_a = [6 \cdot Q] / [W \cdot H^2]$ $\qquad (2.9)$

The shear rate also varies with volume flow rate and the flow channel geometry. For example, shear rates in the gate feeding the part tend to be higher than those in the runner due to geometry differences as indicated in Figure 2.26. Melt viscosities for most polymers tend to decrease with increasing shear rate due to its effect on molecular alignment (i.e. most plastic melts exhibit pseudoplastic flow behavior). Equations 2.8 and 2.9 have been derived assuming a Newtonian (parabolic) velocity profile. In reality, pseudoplastic polymers tend to have "blunt" velocity profiles, resulting in higher shear rates near the wall and lower shear rates towards the core in comparison with Newtonian fluids.

Determine Apparent Viscosity: The apparent shear viscosity of the polymer melt can be determined once the melt temperature and apparent shear rate values are known. In this case, the apparent shear viscosity values can be taken directly from the set of high impact polystyrene viscosity curves shown in Figure 2.25. Even though we are making the assumption of a constant melt temperature (i.e. 200°C), the viscosity in each section of the mold will be different, since the apparent wall shear rate in each section of the mold is different.

Determine the Pressure Drop: The total pressure drop, ΔP_T, associated with molding filling will be the sum of the individual pressure drops along the branch.

$$\Delta P_T = \sum \Delta P_i = \Delta P_{sprue} + \Delta P_{runner} + \Delta P_{gate} + P_{cavity} \qquad (2.10)$$

The individual pressure drops can now be calculated since the geometries, volume flow rates, and viscosity values are now known.

Cylindrical Flow Channel $\qquad \Delta P = [8 \cdot Q \cdot \eta \cdot L] / [\pi \cdot R^4]$ $\qquad (2.11)$

Rectangular Flow Channel $\qquad \Delta P = [12 \cdot Q \cdot \eta \cdot L] / [W \cdot H^3]$ $\qquad (2.12)$

The results of the isothermal analysis are summarized in Table 2.3. The mold filling pressure determined using equation 2.10 is an indication of the pressure at the instant of fill as indicated in Figure 2.16. While the absolute value determined here will clearly be in error (due to the large number of assumptions), this procedure assists the designer with flow balancing and other trending type design decisions. A computer aided mold filling analysis is recommended whenever the option is available.

Table 2.3 Summary of Isothermal Mold Filling Analysis

Molding section	Section volume (in^3)	Volume flow rate (in^3/s)	Apparent shear rate ($1/s$)	Apparent viscosity		Pressure drop estimate	
				(Pa-s)	(lb-s/in^2)	(MPa)	(lb/in^2)
Sprue	0.154	0.782	259	320	0.046	2.1	306
Runner	0.110	0.782	510	270	0.039	4.9	716
Gate	0.004	0.782	1830	180	0.026	1.0	149
Cavity	0.905	0.782	312	305	0.044	11.4	1650
Total	1.173	-----	-----	-----	-----	19.4	2820

2.2.4   Flow Leaders, Flow Restrictors and Flow Hesitation

Flow Leader / Restrictions: It is generally good practice to gate a part in such a way that the melt flows as uniformly as possible through the cavity. Ideally, melt should flow from the gate region, reaching the extremities of the cavity all at the same instant in time. Consider the sprue gated molding shown in Figure 2.27. The part has a uniform wall thickness, and as a result, a disc or radial flow pattern is observed at the early stages of the mold filling process.

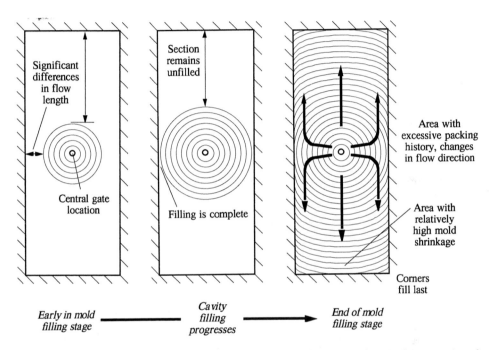

Figure 2.27. Central sprue gating of the rectangular part can result in overpacking in the gate region of the part as well as changes in flow direction as the melt tunnels under the solid layer.

The melt flow front reaches the left and right sides of the molding long before the upper and lower portion of the molding are filled out. This leads to an overpack / underpack situation and a problem with changes in flow direction as the melt tunnels under the solid layer. The net result is a part with variable shrinkage, residual stress, and a tendency to warp. Alternative gate locations for the rectangular molding are shown in Figure 2.28. These gating schemes could be accomplished using a three plate or hot runner tool configuration.

Like the single sprue gated part, the part molded with two gates leads to an overpack situation and flow direction changes, however, to a lesser degree than the part molded with a single sprue gate. Note that when two gates are used, a single weld line is formed when the two flow fronts merge. Figure 2.28 shows that when three gates are used, the filling pattern is more uniform, however, the corner sections of the molding and weld extremities are the last places to fill. Of these three different gating schemes, the three gate option appears to be the best in terms of flow path and packing uniformity, an would be suitable if the welds and the gate vestiges are functionally and esthetically acceptable.

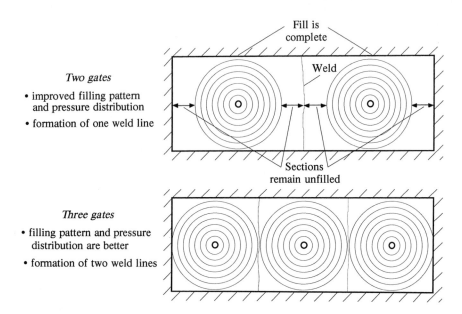

Figure 2.28. Increasing the number of gates improves the flow pattern and pressure distribution, however, this creates weld lines.

While the three gate option in Figure 2.28 is an improvement, the corner sections of the part are still the last sections to fill. This is inevitable when you try to fill a constant thickness rectangular or square shape with a radial flow pattern. However, the filling pattern can be modified so that the melt flow front does reach the extremities of the cavity at the same time. In order to achieve a balanced fill, the filling pressure drop associated with each and every flow path from the gate must be equal (e.g. the pressure drop from the gate to a corner must be equal to that from the gate to an edge). Pressure drops can be balanced by making local adjustments in the part's wall thickness. Local increases in wall thickness (to promote flow) are known as flow leaders or internal runners, while wall thickness reductions (to hinder flow) are known as flow restrictors. On a box shaped molding such as that shown in Figure 2.29, one could thicken the diagonal areas extending towards the corners of the part to promote flow to these areas of maximum flow length. This situation is one of the few instances where a designer purposely deviates from the rule of maintaining a uniform wall thickness. The changes in wall thickness are sometimes very subtle. Computer aided mold filling analyses are useful when designing flow leaders / restrictors, as are the pressure drop calculations outlined earlier in this section (treat the various flow lengths as individual strips of finite width and adjust thickness in an effort to balance the pressure drop). Flow leaders extend from the gate towards the hard to fill sections, while flow restrictors (or dams) can be placed along sections of the cavity that are more easily filled. These wall thickness changes are generally incorporated into non-appearance or less visible surfaces of the molding. The flow leaders or restrictors should be blended and tapered into the part wall to minimize complications created by the introduction of the non-uniform wall thickness (e.g. stress concentration or differential cooling and shrinkage effects). Ribs that are commonly used to stiffen plastic parts can also be used as flow leaders when properly sized and positioned. The melt flow pattern within the cavity will also be influenced by the mold cooling circuit design. Warmer tool temperatures will tend to promote flow.

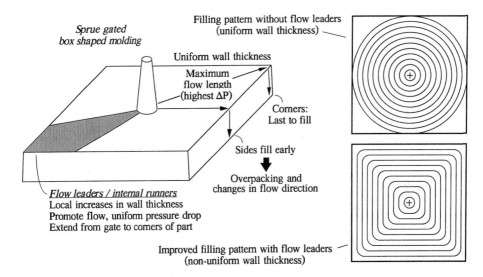

Figure 2.29. Flow leaders or flow restrictors can be used to alter the mold filling pattern in an effort to achieve more balance mold filling.

The mold filling pattern for the part shown in Figure 2.28 could be modified using flow leaders or restrictors. The part shown in Figure 2.30 was produced using three gates and diagonal flow leaders. The properly designed flow leaders eliminate underflow effects and ensure uniform packing, resulting in a higher quality part.

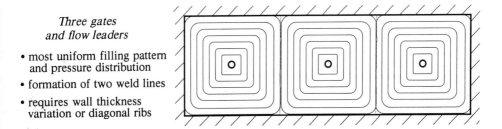

Figure 2.30. A uniform filling pattern is achieved when three gates diagonal flow leaders are used.

However, there are practical limits associated with the use of flow leaders / restrictors. For example, it would be difficult to balance flow for the part shown in Figure 2.27 produced using one gate due to the degree of imbalance.

Flow Hesitation / Race-tracking: Many plastic parts are in fact designed with variable wall thicknesses. This practice should generally be avoided, but sometimes variable wall thicknesses cannot be avoided. Variable wall thicknesses lead to a variety of shrinkage related problems (as discussed later in the chapter), and can lead to a variety of difficulties during mold filling [17]. This point is demonstrated in Figure 2.31.

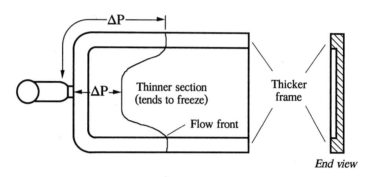

Figure 2.31. When plastic parts have both .thick and thin wall sections, the melt tends to flow preferentially through the thicker sections communicating with the gate since the melt will follow the path of least resistance.

The part in Figure 2.31 has a relatively thin central section surrounded by a thicker frame or rim. The designer has placed the gate along the thicker rim so that the thick section can be packed even if the thin section freezes. Unfortunately, during mold filling, the melt tends to "race-track" or "picture-frame" around the thick rim since the melt follows the path of least resistance. The melt in the central thinner region will tend to "hesitate" until the thicker sections are full, at which time it begins to flow again. This can lead to problems with high residual stress, poor surface appearance, gas trapping and short shots in extreme cases. The thin section is acting like an unwanted flow restrictor. The simplest way to avoid this situation is to avoid the use of variable wall thicknesses. When variable wall thicknesses must be used, the variations should be kept to a minimum. Gating the part in the thinner sections can minimize the filling problems, but may lead to packing problems in the thicker section. A computer aided filling analysis is recommended for parts having variable wall thickness so that flow hesitation or race-tracking problems can be detected in advance. If the problem does arise, the gating schemes can be altered or wall thicknesses can be adjusted until a more balanced flow pattern is achieved.

Multi-cavity vs. Family Molds: Many plastic products actually consist of a series of injection molded parts that must be assembled in a secondary manufacturing operation or by the consumer. When the individual parts that make up the product are produced from different plastic materials, a series of injection molds (or interchangeable insert sets) are generally constructed to produce the individual components. Alternatively, for prototype or low production situations, a single multi-cavity family mold with runner shut offs could be used to mold the individual parts one at a time. If, however, all of the parts that make up the product are produced from the same plastic material, it may be possible to produce all or some of the components in one shot using a family mold.

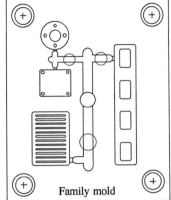

Balanced multi-cavity injection mold (left)

• Naturally flow balanced
• Balanced "H" layout
• Identical core/cavity sets

Four cavity family mold (right)

• Artificially flow balanced
• Individual cooling circuits
• Individual unner shut-offs

Figure 2.32. Multi-cavity and family molds should be flow balanced to avoid flow hesitation or over-packing problems. Runner shut-offs and additional cooling circuit control can assist the process engineer once the mold reaches the production floor.

In most cases, a series of single cavity or balanced higher production, multi-cavity molds is preferable to the family mold option. However, when production volumes are low, a family mold, such as that shown in Figure 2.32, is often a more economical tooling option. It is important that family molds are designed in such a way that each individual cavity fills at the same time (as with a naturally balanced multi-cavity tool). Flow balancing for the family mold can be accomplished with proper cavity layout, and by adjusting runner lengths and diameters in an effort to equalize the pressure drop in each flow branch. Once constructed, it can be very difficult to work with a family mold during production, especially when the tool has not been properly flow balanced. For example, one of the parts may be overpacked and oversized, while another is undersized. Changing molding conditions to bring one part into dimensional specification will most likely magnify the problem for the other part. When parts must be produced in a family mold, it is important to design the tool in such a way that each section of the mold can have its own cooling circuit. In this way, individual mold temperature adjustments can be made for each cavity giving process engineers some additional level of control. It may also be beneficial to include runner shut-offs so that parts can be produced individually as a last resort. The runner shut-offs can also provide a location where flow restrictors are easily inserted. There are a number of disadvantages associated with family molds, but there are also some advantages. For example, color matching problems are effectively eliminated with family molds since all of the parts that make up the product assembly can be molded at the same time (i.e. same machine and same heat / shear history). Parts handling can also be minimized, especially when the entire shot can be shipped as a unit for consumer assembly.

Gating From Thick to Thin: When injection molded plastic parts do have variable wall thicknesses, it is generally good practice to gate into the thickest section of the molding as shown in Figure 2.33. The thicker section of the molding requires more packing / shrinkage compensation and should therefore be located closest to the gate. When this is not done, a thin section located between the gate and the thicker section can freeze off, and the ability to pack the thicker section is lost. It can also be difficult to achieve good surface finishes for parts gated from thin to thick as the melt front tends to cool and jet as it exits the thinner region. If for some other reason, the gate must be positioned in a thin section of the molding, an internal runner or modified rib can be used to keep a flow channel open during the packing and holding phases of the molding process as shown in Figure 2.33 [18].

Part gated from "thin to thick" hinders packing of thicker sections and can create flow problems. *Not Recommended*

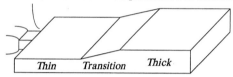

Internal runner to assist / improve the ability to pack the thick section when gating from "thin to thick" is necessary.

Gating from "thick to thin" when possible to improve flow and allow thicker sections to be packed.

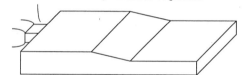

Figure 2.33. Parts with variable wall thicknesses should be gated at the thicker sections whenever possible to reduce the potential for sink marks or voids. If the part must be gated from "thin to thick", internal runners (possibly ribs) can be added to facilitate packing of the thicker sections.

While gating into the thicker wall sections of a plastic part does provide control over packing, it can lead to other molding problems such as "jetting" [19]. Jetting can occur when gating into a thick, open cavity. When jetting occurs, the melt tends to stream into the deep cavity, rather than develop as a fountain flow front. If jetting does occur, the molded part will have a relatively poor surface appearance. The rope-like jet of polymer cools during the early stages of the mold filling process and does not weld together properly. Perhaps more importantly, the mechanical and chemical properties of the parts are also likely to suffer when jetting occurs.

Jetting effects can be minimized with proper gate design. For example, short gate land lengths promote expansion of the melt as it enters the cavity due to elastic / memory effects (an extrusion die designer would do just the opposite, i.e. use long land lengths for an extrusion die, to minimize die swell related dimensional changes as the extrudate leaves the die). Large gates, especially fan gates, and tab gates can be used to minimize the potential for jetting. Gating into some type of flow obstruction (e.g. core pin, etc.) will also help the melt flow front develop, thereby minimizing the potential for jetting.

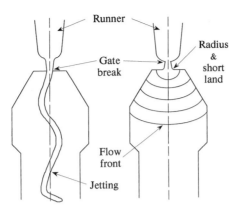

Figure 2.34. Jetting can occur when gating into a thick, open cavity. The potential for jetting can be reduced with proper gate design or by gating into an obstruction. Velocity profiling during the injection phase of the process can also be used to promote melt flow front formation as the melt enters the cavity.

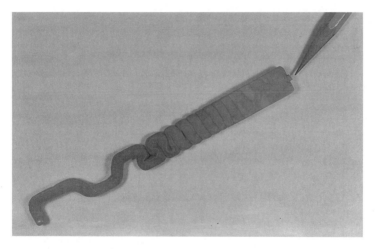

Figure 2.35. When jetting does occur, the parts have a poor surface appearance due to improper welding of the jetting melt as the cavity fills. Jetting can also result in a reduction in mechanical performance.

Summary: Consider the disc shaped moldings shown in Figure 2.36 a to e. The moldings have a thin central disc section surrounded by a relatively thick rim. There are a number of possible gating schemes that could be used for a plastic part with this general type of geometry. Each of these gating schemes offers its own relative advantages and limitations.

Top Center Gating: Central gating offers the advantage of balanced flow, uniform venting at the parting line and no weld lines. However, the part is gated from thin to thick, and it is likely that the thicker section would not be fully packed, resulting in sink marks or shrinkage voids.

Edge Gating: Gating into the edge of the part would facilitate packing of the thick section, however, it is likely that the melt would race-track around the outer rim. This could result in a weld line and the potential for a gas trap or short shot due to flow hesitation. The "roundness" of the part would also be in question with this gating scheme.

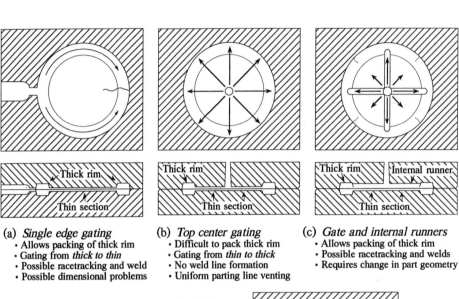

(a) *Single edge gating*
  • Allows packing of thick rim
  • Gating from *thick to thin*
  • Possible racetracking and weld
  • Possible dimensional problems

(b) *Top center gating*
  • Difficult to pack thick rim
  • Gating from *thin to thick*
  • No weld line formation
  • Uniform parting line venting

(c) *Gate and internal runners*
  • Allows packing of thick rim
  • Possible racetracking and welds
  • Requires change in part geometry

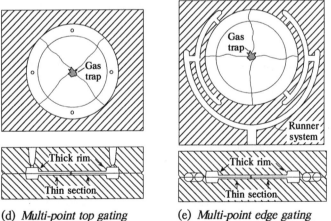

(d) *Multi-point top gating*
  • Three plate or hot runner
  • Gating from *thick to thin*
  • Weld line formation
  • Gas trap (vent pins required)

(e) *Multi-point edge gating*
  • Two plate-cold runner (scrap)
  • Gating from *thick to thin*
  • Weld line formation
  • Gas trap (vent pins required)

Figure 2.36. The disc like part has a thick rim surrounding a thinner central region. Selecting a gating scheme is complicated by the fact that the part has a non-uniform wall thickness. Each of the five options shown have their own relative advantages and limitations.

Multiple Edge Gates: The race-tracking effect is minimized with this gating scheme. The thick to thin gating permits packing of the thicker sections and packing will be more uniform than one edge gate. A series of weld lines are formed with this option. One of the most significant concerns is the fact that the center of the part is the last location to fill. Therefore, parting line vents are not effective and special provisions for venting, such as venting pins, must be incorporated. Large amounts of runner scrap would also be generated.

Multiple Top Rim Gates: This gating option offers the advantages and suffers from the limitations of the previous multiple edge gating option. The top gating option offers the additional advantage of automatic degating in the case of a three plate mold or scrapless molding in the case of a hot runner tool.

Top Center Gating with Internal Runners: The top center gating option with internal runners is an option that can be considered only when the functional and esthetic requirements of the product permit the addition of internal runners. In this case, the internal runners are added to improve the ability to pack the thick section, rather than as flow leaders. In fact, the use of the internal runner could lead to race-tracking and flow hesitation problems. While this option is an improved version of the top center gating option from a packing point of view, it should be evaluated using a mold filling simulation as these internal runners do have an impact on mold fill-up.

2.3   Weld Lines

2.3.1   Introduction

Weld lines (or weld planes) are formed during the mold filling process when the melt flow front separates, and recombines at some downstream location. Separation or division of the melt flow front can be caused by cores / obstructions, variable wall thicknesses (e.g. race-tracking) or runner branching for multi-gated parts. Jetting can also lead to the formation of weld lines on a molded part.

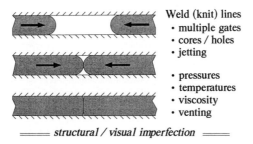

Weld (knit) lines
- multiple gates
- cores / holes
- jetting

- pressures
- temperatures
- viscosity
- venting

structural / visual imperfection

Figure 2.37. Weld lines are formed whenever melt fronts separate and recombine at some downstream location. Weld lines are formed when parts have multiple gates, due to flow around cores, or due to jetting.

Weld lines look like cracks on the surface of the molded part. These crack-like features are often visible to the naked eye, and as a result are considered esthetically unacceptable in many applications. More importantly, however, the local mechanical strength in the area of the weld can be significantly lower than the strengths away from the weld. This is a particular concern for parts subjected to dynamic loads [20,21]. The presence of weld lines is one of the most significant problems associated with designing plastic parts for structural applications due to the potential for failure in the weld area.

While a great deal of research has been conducted in the area of weld line strength and appearance [20-42], there are few hard and fast rules that can be used to assist the designer. The designer must recognize that a weld's strength, chemical resistance and appearance are influenced by:

- Material selection
- Part design
- Mold design
- Processing conditions

Unfortunately, there is only a limited amount of quantitative design data available on weld performance. It is therefore difficult for a designer to predict the structural performance and appearance for plastic parts containing weld lines. This situation is further complicated by the fact that processing conditions can have a large impact on weld performance and appearance. While processing conditions are important, it is the presence of the weld itself that is most significant. Perhaps the most important design rule is to position the weld(s) in locations that are not critical in terms of esthetics or end-use performance. The part designer can vary part geometry, part wall thickness, and gating scheme in order to position welds appropriately.

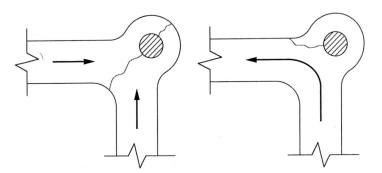

Figure 2.38. Weld lines represent an area of reduced mechanical integrity. This is a particular problem around holes that are used for mechanical assembly.

Weld lines are always a concern when holes are molded into a part for assembly purposes. When holes are used in conjunction with mechanical fasteners for example, local assembly related stresses can be very high. In these applications, designers should ensure that the gating scheme selected minimizes weld line problems. Variables such as flow length before recombination of the flow fronts can have a significant effect on weld performance as shown in Figure 2.39. It may be better to have a larger number of strong weld lines vs. a smaller number of weak weld lines. Unfortunately, the strength differences are difficult, if not impossible to accurately predict in advance. Surface appearance is perhaps even more difficult to predict. Mold surface texturing, combined with the use of lighter colored plastic materials, tends to disguise the surface imperfections associated with the weld line, and painting can be avoided in most, but not all cases.

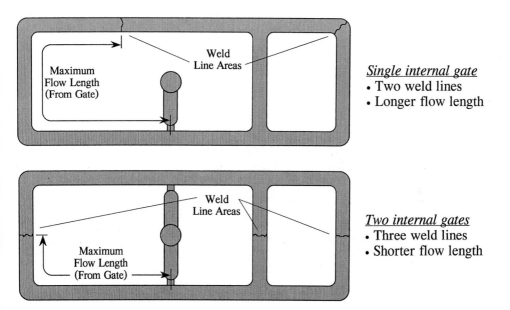

Single internal gate
- Two weld lines
- Longer flow length

Two internal gates
- Three weld lines
- Shorter flow length

Figure 2.39. The gating scheme used for a part determines the number and the locations of the weld lines. While computer aided mold filling simulations can be used to determine the locations of weld lines, it is difficult to predict the quality of the weld in terms of strength or esthetics.

Computer aided injection mold filling simulations are invaluable in assisting the designer with weld related concerns. The mold filling simulations can be used to predict the location of the weld lines, even for parts with extremely complicated geometries. After the initial analysis has been conducted, the part designer can then alter the proposed part geometry or gating scheme in order to position the weld in a less critical area, long before the mold is ever built. In some cases, the compter programs assist in the interpretation of the flow simulation results so that weld locations are automatically identified [22,23]. While mold filling simulations can be used to predict the location of a weld line, they do not explicitly indicate the strength and appearance characteristics of the weld line. However, if the designer evaluates the process simulation output variables such as melt temperature or temperature distribution through the thickness of the part at the weld, and subscribes to the conventional wisdom that "hot" melts produce strong welds, he/she can make qualitative assessments on weld appearance / performance. This is particularly useful when the designer develops correlations based upon past experience.

Weaknesses in the weld line area have been attributed to a variety of factors, all of which are likely to play a significant role. These factors include [22,24]:

- Incomplete molecular entanglement / diffusion
- Unfavorable, frozen-in molecular (or fiber) orientation
- Existence of V-notches at the weld surface
- Presence of foreign substances or microvoids at the weld interface

The significance of each effect is determined by the material type, part design, tool design and process variables.

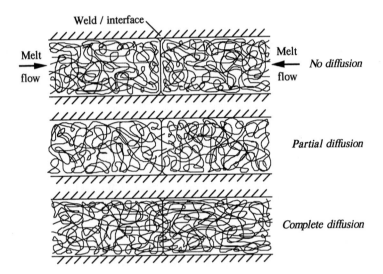

Figure 2.40. In order to achieve strength at the weld interface, molecular diffusion and entanglement must take place.

Figure 2.40 shows that the rich bonding area at the core of the weld plane accounts for the bulk of the weld's strength. Like any welding process, molecular diffusion and subsequent molecular entanglement are necessary in order to achieve good weld strength. It could be reasoned that any part / mold design variable or process variable that increases the temperature of the melt at the weld interface should increase the strength of the weld. Based on similar reasoning, melt pressure at the weld should also be important. Process variables such as melt temperature, injection velocity, and packing pressure have all been shown to have an impact on weld strength. Cavity wall temperature, holding pressure and holding pressure time are also important, however, the importance of a particular process variable is material dependent. Most studies indicate that melt temperature at the weld is the most significant process variable due to its influence on molecular mobility. Hotter melts tend to improve weld strength, but effects due to molecular degradation and outgassing cannot be overlooked. A part (or mold) designer can generally improve weld strengths by keeping flow lengths as short as possible. Shorter flow lengths are more likely to result in a more favorable melt temperature and cavity pressure conditions at the weld.

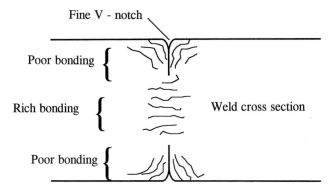

Fine V - notch

Poor bonding {

Rich bonding {   Weld cross section

Poor bonding {

Figure 2.41. The weld line itself is a V-notch observed from the surface of the part. The weld area is actually a plane having areas of both rich and poor bonding. The poor bonding areas have a lack of molecular diffusion, and a degree of unfavorable molecular orientation resulting from the fountain like flow behavior of the impinging melt fronts.

Figure 2.41 shows that there is an area, adjacent to the rich bonding area (top and bottom) of poor bonding described as being in a "precrack state". Significant diffusion does not take place in this area of the weld plane, and a condition of unfavorable, frozen-in molecular orientation may be present due to the fountain flow behavior of the melt fronts prior to welding. In one study [21], the depth of this poor bonding zone was shown to be between 0.2 to 0.3 mm for a polystyrene (depending on exact processing conditions).

A notch like defect (the visible weld line itself) can usually be observed at the weld location. The notch is an esthetic problem and can also act as sharp stress concentrator for parts subject to tensile or bending stresses. The presence of the notch is due to a number of factors including difficulties in venting the air / gasses ahead of the melt fronts as the melt fronts recombine. The use of a pin to vent the weld or gas trap may improve the weld line appearance, however, the pin will leave a witness mark and must be cleaned and maintained periodically during production. Vacuum venting (i.e. evacuating the air / gasses from the mold cavity prior to melt injection) is advantageous in applications where weld appearance and performance are critical. Vacuum venting can also reduce the time required to fill the mold, which should have the added benefits of enhancing the size of the rich bonding area.

2.3.2   Types of Weld Lines

A variety of terms are used to describe weld or knit lines. Weld lines arise due to the splitting and recombination of the melt flow front. The splitting of the flow stream can be due to flow around a core, or due to multiple gates as shown in Figure 2.42. In fact, the cause of the flow stream division is exactly the same in both cases. The mold steel surrounded by the runner system is essentially a core, and the flow stream recombines once the melt flows through the gates.

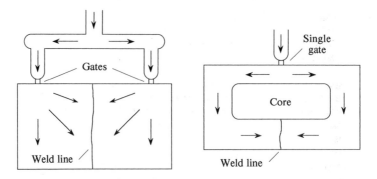

Figure 2.42. Weld lines can be caused by multiple gates or flow around cores.

Welds are more appropriately categorized according to the amount of flow that follows recombination of the fronts. A weld line can be formed when melt fronts traveling in opposite directions meet, and are almost immediately immobilized. This type of weld is typically called a butt weld or cold weld. Other welds involve additional flow in the mold cavity after the melt fronts have recombined. This type of weld is typically called a meldline, a streaming weld or a hot weld. Butt welds are generally considered to be the worst. Examples of both a butt weld and a meld line are depicted in Figure 2.43.

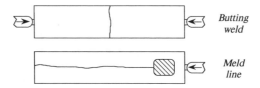

Figure 2.43. One method of characterizing weld lines is to evaluate the degree of flow after the flow fronts combine. In the case of a butt or cold weld, the flow fronts stop after recombining. The terms meld or streaming weld are used to characterize welds with a downstream flow component.

The appearance of weld lines has been correlated to the specific meeting angle between the two flow fronts (Figure 2.44). Studies have shown that weld lines tend to disappear at a particular flow front meeting angle known as the "vanishing angle". Weld lines have been shown to disappear when the weld angle reaches 120° to 150° depending on the material. The weld angle concept is useful since it can be used in conjunction with a mold filling simulation in order to predict the qualitative severity of a weld [29].

A designer must also be concerned with the location and the number of cores / weld lines along the length of a part. For example, a grill type of structure has many small cores, resulting in many weld lines. One would expect that as the distance between a core (flow obstruction) and the gate increases, the strength of the weld would decrease, due to a decrease in average flow front melt temperature. In some cases, this has been shown to be true, while in other studies, weld position (over a somewhat limited range) had minimal effects. Weld strengths have been shown to be influenced by the shape / size of the core, and by the number of cores. Consider the two parts shown in Figure 2.45. The cross flow weld strength values for the part shown in Figure 2.45 (top) were shown to be essentially independent of position. However, the weld strengths for the parts produced in the cavity with multiple cores in Figure 2.45 (bottom) were shown to decrease with distance from the gate.

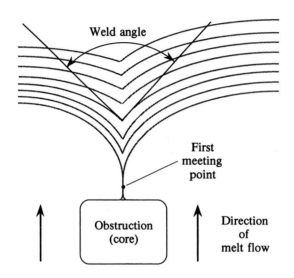

Figure 2.44. The weld angle has been used a measure of weld quality.

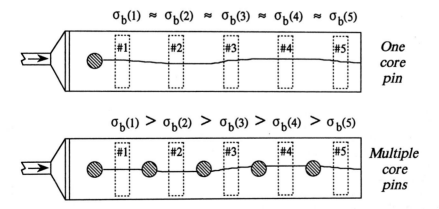

Figure 2.45. Weld lines are a particular problem for grill type structures, where the flow front splits and recombines many times. Weld strengths tend to decrease as the number of flow stream divisions and recombinations increases.

2.3.3   Material Considerations

Weld lines are more of a problem with some plastic materials than with others. Material variables that should be considered include morphology, average molecular weight and additive package. Table 2.4 lists tensile strength retention factors (i.e. tensile strength with weld divided by tensile strength without weld, as a percentage) for a variety of different materials [35]. These weld strength numbers were generated using a double end gated tensile bar mold (butt weld) having a relatively short flow length, and different results would be expected for different mold geometries, flow lengths and weld angles. The numbers can also vary significantly from material grade to material grade, since both average molecular weight and the material's additive package play a major role in weld behavior. The numbers are, however, extremely useful for illustrating several points.

Figure 2.4.   Typical Butt Weld Tensile Strength Retention Values [35]

Material type	Reinforcement type	Tensile strength retention (%) *
Polypropylene	no reinforcement	86%
Polypropylene	20% glass fiber	47%
Polypropylene	30% glass fiber	34%
SAN	no reinforcement	80%
SAN	30% glass fiber	40%
Polycarbonate	no reinforcement	99%
Polycarbonate	10% glass fiber	86%
Polycarbonate	30% glass fiber	64%
Polysulfone	no reinforcement	100%
Polysulfone	30% glass fiber	62%
PPS	no reinforcement	83%
PPS	10% glass fiber	38%
PPS	40% glass fiber	20%
Nylon 66	no reinforcement	83-100%
Nylon 66	10% reinforcement	87-93%
Nylon 66	30% reinforcement	56-64%

* Weld strength data generated on a tensile bar gated at both ends.

The weld strengths retention factors for the unreinforced base resins, both amorphous and semi-crystalline, are generally in the 80-100% range. For unfilled glassy amorphous resins, studies have shown that melt temperature (and to a lesser extent injection speed) is the most significant processing variable that affects weld strength. Mold temperature does not seem to play a very large role for glassy amorphous polymers since even relatively high mold temperatures are still below the Tg of the polymer. However, for semi-crystalline polymers, melt temperature, mold wall temperature, injection velocity and post mold annealing have all been shown to have an effect on weld strength [31]. It should be noted here that good tensile strength retention in and of itself does not necessarily constitute acceptable weld performance. Welds with good tensile strength retention may not offer similar strength retention under impact or fatigue loading, or chemical attack.

While the strength retention for neat polymers can be relatively good when proper design practices and processing conditions are used, polymers containing additives can show very different results. Additives such as external lubricants, mold releases or some flame retardant systems can have a negative effect on weld performance due to a combination of outgassing and contamination in the weld zone. Fillers and reinforcements have a very dramatic effect on weld strength retention as shown in Table 2.4. It should be emphasized here that these are strength retention numbers, not absolute strength values. The degree of strength reduction at the weld varies with filler / reinforcement type, loading level and plastic material type. Generally, the percent loss in strength increases with percent reinforcement, and with aspect ratio. The percent property loss for high aspect ratio reinforcements such as long fibers are most significant, followed by conventional short fibers, then milled fibers and beads. The weld strength reduction for fiber reinforced thermoplastics is due to factors such as local anisotropy at the weld, where fountain flow can cause the fibers to have an unfavorable orientation.

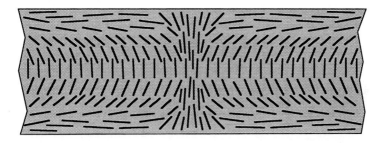

Figure 2.46. Weld line strengths for fiber reinforced polymers can be low for a number of reasons including unfavorable fiber orientation at the weld interface due to the fountain like flow behavior of the impinging flow fronts.

The weld strength retention problem may be most severe for long fiber reinforced thermoplastic materials. Studies have shown that the weld strength retention values for long glass fiber reinforced polymers are relatively low when the fiber concentrations are very high. [30,34]. These reinforced polymers can have outstanding strength, stiffness, creep resistance, and dimensional stability. However, a designer must be concerned with the potential for anisotropy indicating the added importance of gating design decisions.

The results shown in Figure 2.47 for a 42% long glass fiber reinforced styrene maleic anhydride copolymer indicate that the composite material has a flow direction flexural strength of 200 MPa, a cross flow strength of 125 MPa (sample with no weld line) and a meld / weld line strength of approximately 75 MPa. Process variables such as injection velocity have some effect on weld strength, however, it is the presence of the weld line itself that is the most sigfnificant variable. Designers should therefore exercise extreme caution when working with highly filled or fiber reinforced materials and complex part geometries. Heavily reinforced materials might be avoided when part geometries become so complicated that large numbers of welds are inevitable. In these cases, it may be better to work with more lightly reinforced materials (say 10-25% reinforcement). These materials are easier to design with, even though their modulus values are lower, because anisotropy is less of a problem and weld strength retention factors are higher.

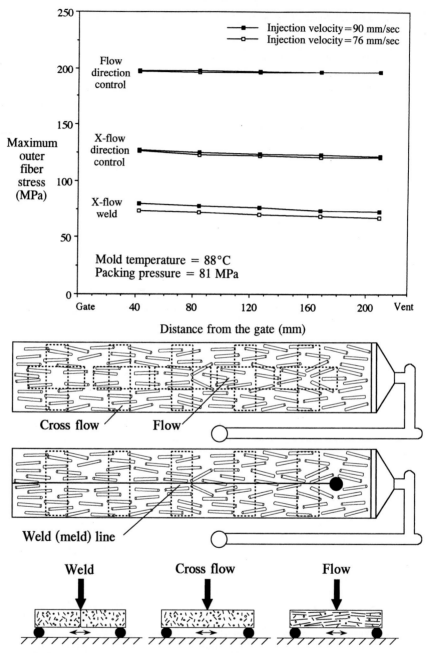

Figure 2.47. Anisotropic behavior and weld line strengths are a particular concern for fiber reinforced polymers. The results of an experimental study done using a long fiber reinforced styrene maleic anhydride copolymer show that bending strength values in the flow direction are significantly greater than the cross flow values, which in turn are greater than the weld strength values.

2.3.4   Improving Weld Performance and Appearance

The strength and appearance of a weld line can be altered to some degree by adjusting processing conditions such as melt temperature as described above. Any variable that increases the temperature and pressure at the plane of recombination is likely to have some positive effect on weld performance by promoting entanglement across the weld interface. Tool design variables, especially runner and gate designs, can also have a large impact on weld performance. Extended nozzles or hot runner systems are beneficial because they provide improved control over melt temperature. Computer aided mold filling simulation should be used when designing the feed system for parts containing weld lines so that the relative effects of viscous heating and conductive cooling on the temperature of the melt can be evaluated.

Consider the part shown in Figure 2.48. The rim shaped part could be produced using a single edge gate in a two plate mold. This gating scheme would result in a potentially weak butt weld opposite the gate, especially in the case of a large diameter part (i.e. long flow length prior to welding).

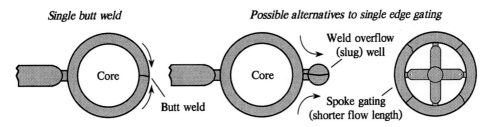

Figure 2.48. Butt welds can be an area of reduced strength, especially when flow lengths are long. The rim shaped part produced with spoke gating has a larger number of welds, however, the welds are associated with shorter flow lengths. It is also possible to add a weld slug well, which effectively changes the butt weld into a meld.

One method that could be used to improve the strength of the weld is to add an overflow well adjacent to the weld. This effectively changes the butting weld line to a stronger meld line having a downstream flow component. The addition of the weld slug is a potential solution for an existing part experiencing failure at the weld, since it is a relatively simple modification to an existing tool. Unfortunately, the weld slug represents additional material consumption and must be removed in a secondary operation after molding. An alternative gating scheme for this type of part would be internal spoke gating. This multiple gating scheme (typically 2, 3 or 4 gates) produces more butting weld lines, however, each weld line is likely to be stronger (compared to the part with a single edge gate) due to the reduction in melt flow length in the cavity. Tangential gating, as shown in Figure 2.49, is an alternative to conventional edge gating for parts with weld lines.

Vacuum Venting: The injection mold cavity must be vented at the parting lines and in deep mold crevices (e.g. rib cavities or boss cavities) to allow air and melt front volatiles to be pushed from the mold as the melt fills the cavity. Parting line vents are suitable for

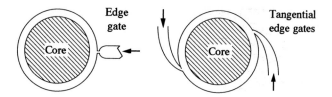

Figure 2.49. Tangential gating schemes can sometimes be used in place of conventional edge gating to alter the filling pattern and weld characteristics.

weld lines that are located adjacent to the parting line. Venting pins are required when the weld lines are isolated from the parting line. Unfortunately, the venting pins (or vented ejector pins) have several disadvantages associated with their use. Venting pins can: leave a witness mark on the molding, can clog due to external lubricants, juicing and plate out, are more difficult to clean / maintain than parting line vents, and can interfere with the mold cooling layout. It can also be difficult to position venting pins precisely in the weld area, since the position of a weld line can change from shot to shot due to variations in one of the many mold filling related process variables.

Vacuum venting, a process where the cavity air is forcibly evacuated during mold filling, is an improved venting method that overcomes the limitations of venting pins [43,44]. A typical vacuum venting system consists of a vacuum pump, a vacuum reservoir (tank), and a solenoid operated valve between the mold and the vacuum reservoir, which is interfaced with the molding machine controls. It is important that air flow restrictions between the mold cavity and the vacuum system be minimized to facilitate air movement. Ideally a vacuum is drawn before the melt enters the cavity, and must be maintained up until the last vent is sealed off. The solenoid valve opens at the start of (or slightly before) injection and closes once filling is complete. During the remainder of the molding cycle, the vacuum reservoir is evacuated so that it is ready for the injection phase of the next molding cycle begins. Vacuum levels in the vacuum reservoir must be maintained throughout the filling phase of the process, even during the initial rush of air when the solenoid valve is open, necessitating the use of a relatively large vacuum reservoir. Vacuum venting systems can be physically connected to the mold through wide parting line vents, or through sealed ejection boxes. Air infiltration from outside sources (e.g. through the parting line, ejector pin holes etc.) must be minimized. This can be accomplished using o-rings and seals of various type.

Solvents: One study [33] has shown that controlled solvent vapor exposure after molding can improve the weld line strength for an amorphous polymer such as ABS. The process is basically the same as the practice of vapor polishing that is used to restore a high gloss surface to a scratched ABS part. Exposure to solvent vapor, for a period of up to several seconds, can relieve orientation and promote molecular entanglement, if a sufficient level of solvent penetration is achieved. The solvent also tends to blunt the V-notch of the weld line. The combination of these weld healing factors has been shown to improve the impact performance of weld lines for ABS parts but has limited practical application.

Multi-Live Feed Injection Molding: A relatively new process modification to the conventional injection molding process is know as Shear Controlled Orientation Injection Molding or SCORIM®[45-48]. The ancillary process, that can be retrofit to an existing conventional injection molding machine, can be used to essentially eliminate weld lines, minimize sink marks and microvoid formation, and control or manage both molecular and fiber orientation.

The system shown in Figure 2.50 has three major components. The mechanical head or activator attaches to the end of the conventional injection unit barrel, replacing the standard machine nozzle. The unit is powered by a self-contained hydraulic power pack and is controlled using the systems electronic controller. The molds that are used with the process must have at least two gates. The molding shown in Figure 2.50 has two gates, along the top. The initial phase of the process is essentially equivalent to that of conventional injection molding process . Melt is injected through the heated head and into the mold (using one or both gates). Once the mold is filled, the multi-live feed system's hydraulic pistons begin moving forward and backward in an alternating fashion. As one live feed piston pushes downward, it forces melt through the runner and cavity up into the second live feed cylinder. The process then reverses, and the melt flows in the opposite direction, effectively washing out any weld lines that might be present in the molding. This reversing flow continues for several cycles. Since only the molten core flows, it is possible to control molecular orientation (or fiber orientation for reinforced polymers) through the cross section of the part. When four gates are used (say one on each edge of a rectangular molding), the gates are paired, and controlled biaxial orientation can be obtained. After a series of alternating strokes, the two live feed pistons act together, in and out, for one or more cycles imparting compression forces, ensuring maximum and uniform packing of the cavity. In the final mode of the process, the pistons act together and downward to pack and hold melt in the cavity until the gates freeze (i.e. a conventional holding cycle). This unique process has been shown to be very effective at healing weld lines, particularly for fiber reinforced polymer grades, and as a molecular / fiber orientation management process.

Push-Pull Molding: A similar process, known as push-pull injection molding, has also been recently developed [49-51]. The process can be used to heal weld lines, and provide a means for controlling both molecular and fiber orientation. This process utilizes an injection molding machine with two injection units; a master injection unit and a secondary companion injection unit. These are used in concert with a multi-gated mold cavity. In the simplest case, a mold with two gates is used for the process. The master injection unit is used to overfill the mold through one gate, while the excess melt flows through the second gate into the second injection unit, providing a cushion like volume of melt for that injection unit. After the initial mold filling, the cycle is reversed, the second injection unit pushes on the melt, and the master injection unit receives the excess melt. This reversing process can be repeated many times during the molding cycle. Weld lines are effectively flushed out or healed due to melt flow across the weld interface. Any weld lines that exist within the individual push - pull layers are dispersed throughout the thickness of the part (much like a series of finger joints), thus minimizing their effect. The plastic parts must be thick enough to permit movement of the melt for several cycles before complete solidification occurs. The process can also be used in orientation control applications using molds with more than two gates, when used in conjunction with valve gating systems capable of mechanically opening / closing gate on demand.

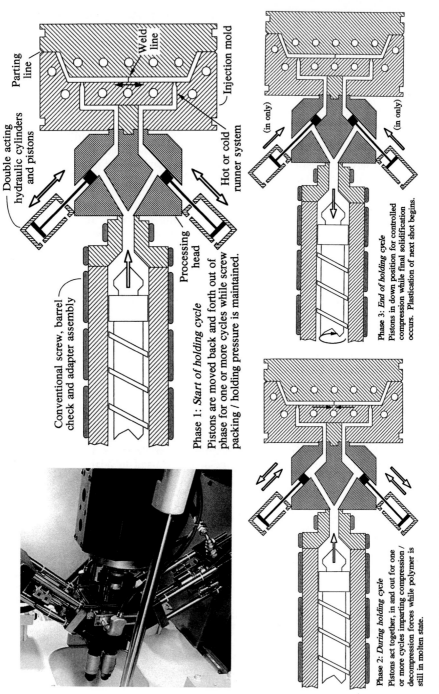

Parting line

Weld line

Injection mold

Double acting hydraulic cylinders and pistons

Hot or cold runner system

Conventional screw, barrel check and adapter assembly

Processing head

Phase 1: *Start of holding cycle*
Pistons are moved back and forth out of phase for one or more cycles while screw packing / holding pressure is maintained.

(in only)

(in only)

Phase 3: *End of holding cycle*
Pistons in down position for controlled compression while final solidification occurs. Plastication of next shot begins.

Phase 2: *During holding cycle*
Pistons act together, in and out for one or more cycles imparting compression / decompression forces while polymer is still in molten state.

Figure 2.50. Novel molding processes such as multi-live feed injection molding can be used to improve weld line strengths and to manage fiber and molecular orientation. (Photo courtesy Scortec Division, British Technology Group USA, Gulph Mills, PA 19406)

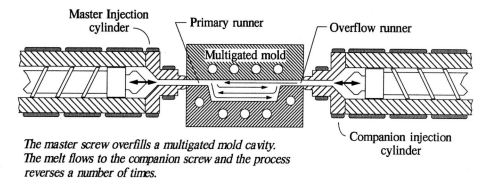

The master screw overfills a multigated mold cavity.
The melt flows to the companion screw and the process
reverses a number of times.

Figure 2.51. The push-pull molding process uses primary and secondary injection units to move the molten core and to pack the part. The process can be used to wash out weld lines and to control molecular or fiber orientation.

In-mold Reciprocating Pins: It is also possible to improve the strength characterics of weld lines using moving mold sections such as a rotating core (for cylindrical plastic part geometries) or using reciprocating pins [52]. In the case of the reciprocating pins, it is possible to use either one pin located adjacent to the weld line, or two pins located on either side of the weld line. The pins move "up-and-down" (or reciprocate) as the melt flows past during the mold filling stage of the process. This action creates lateral flow across the weld zone, which has been shown to improve the weld's strength. The reciprocating pin's movement can be controlled using a hydraulically driven cam that causes the pin to move from a position flush with the cavity surface, to some distance below the surface (creating a temporary well). After a specific number of reciprocating cycles, the pin (or pins) return to their home position flush with the cavity surface. The cam movement can be triggered in a variety of different ways. The movement can be triggered using a timer, the injection ram position signal, or an in-mold pressure sensors signal.

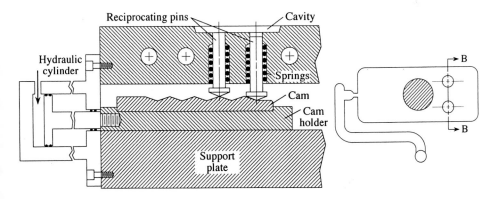

Figure 2.52. One or more cam operated reciprocating pins can be used to create a transverse flow component across the weld as the mold fills.

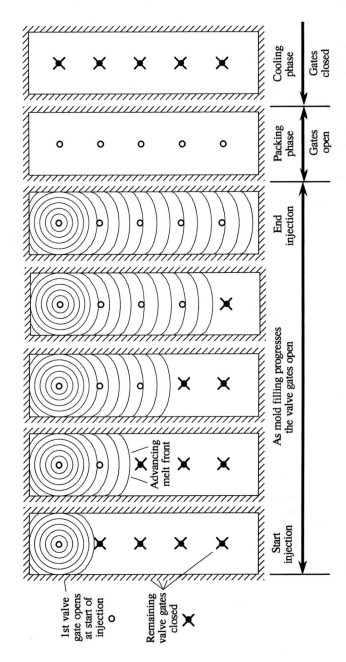

Figure 2.53. A series of mechanical, valve gates can be used to control the mold filling pattern for a mold cavity. The valve gates can be opened and closed on demand, and can be sequenced during the injection phase to avoid weld line formation. The valve gates can be programmed to open after the melt flow front has crossed over the gate opening.

Sink marks or voids are also common problems for parts containing reinforcing ribs on the underside of the molding [58]. Thick ribs provide improved structural benefits and are easier to fill, however, the level of sink associated with thick ribs can be excessive. The sink problem is magnified if large radii are used at the intersecting walls to reduce stress concentration factors and improve flow. In practice, rib wall thicknesses are typically 40-80% as great as the wall from which they extend, with base radius values from 25-40% of the wall thickness. The specific rib designs are material dependent, and are influenced primarily by the shrinkage characteristics of the material.

Visible sink mark   Grooves opposite rib   Beads opposite rib   Surface texture

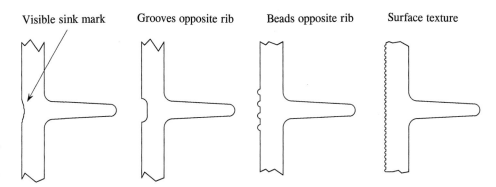

Figure 2.59. A variety of methods can be used to disguise the sink marks that occur opposite ribs and bosses.

When proper guidelines are followed, the size of the sink associated with a feature such as a rib is minimized, but some degree of sink will generally be noticeable. Localized mold cooling in the area of the sink mark can be beneficial in reducing the severity of the sink. Various methods can be used to disguise the sink mark as indicated in Figure 2.59 [59].   One of the most common reasons that surface textures are used with injection molded plastic parts is to disguise esthetic defects such as sink marks or weld lines. As a last resort in the fight against sink marks, molders will sometimes add small quantities of blowing agent to the base resin, and produce a conventional injection molded part, with structural foam like regions in the thicker section of the molding (the sink is eliminated due to the internal foaming action).

2.4.3   Pressure - Volume - Temperature Behavior of Polymers

Plastic materials have positive coefficients of thermal expansion, and are highly compressible in the molten state. As a result, the volume that a given mass of material occupies will change with both temperature and pressure. Spencer and Gilmore developed equations of state that could be used to describe the expansion and contraction of amorphous polystyrene [60]. This generalized equation of state for polymers is given by:

$$(P + a) \, (\upsilon - b) = RT / M \qquad\qquad (2.13)$$

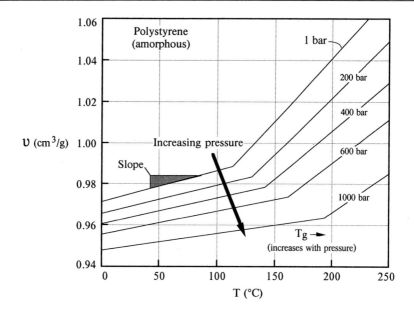

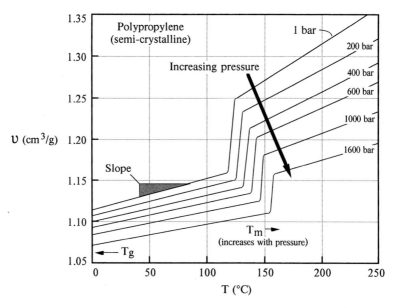

Figure 2.60. Typical pressure - volume - temperature (P - υ - T) curves for an amorphous polymer, polystyrene (top) and a semi-crystalline polymer, polypropylene (bottom).

where P is the hydrostatic pressure, v is the specific volume, R is the universal gas constant, M is molecular weight, T is the absolute temperature and a & b are material constants. The equation simply states that pressure, temperature, and specific volume are dependent on each other such that for any particular condition of temperature and pressure, there is a related specific volume. The relationship between pressure, temperature, and specific volume can be determined experimentally. Pressure - volume - temperature data is commonly presented in a two dimensional graphical format that gives specific volume as a function of temperature at various constant pressure values (isobars).

The P-v-T curves show that plastic materials are in fact very compressible at the temperatures and pressures encountered in the injection molding process. Process variables such as packing pressure or holding pressure (or more precisely, cavity pressure) should then have a significant influence on part dimensions or mold shrinkage. The pressure - volume - temperature behavior for a semi-crystalline polymer, such as polypropylene or nylon 6/6, is very different than that of an amorphous polymer such as polystyrene. Like amorphous polymers, semi-crystalline polymers show an increase in specific volume with increasing temperature (at constant pressure) due to thermal expansion, and a decrease in specific volume with pressure (at constant temperature) due to compressibility effects. However, unlike amorphous polymers, semi-crystalline polymers exhibit a step like change in specific volume at their melting temperature. As a semi-crystalline polymer cools in a mold cavity, the "amorphous melt" cools and solidifies as it reaches its crystallization temperature. The significant volume decrease associated with the phase change occurs as the polymer molecules pack closely together in ordered crystalline regions as shown in Figure 1.2.

This phase change, from an amorphous melt, back to a partially ordered semi-crystalline morphology accounts for the higher shrinkage of semi-crystalline polymers in comparison to amorphous polymers (where shrinkage is due primarily to pressure compensated thermal contraction). The shrinkage for unfilled semi-crystalline polymers such as polypropylene can be five times greater than that of an unfilled amorphous polymer such as PMMA [61].

The volumetric shrinkage of a plastic part can be predicted theoretically, if the P-v-T characteristics of the polymer, and processing conditions are known [2]. Unfortunately, the process conditions (and therefore the mold shrinkage) are to a large degree beyond the control of the designer, however, the concept can be used to gain a better understanding of how the various phases of the injection molding process affect the volumetric shrinkage of the material.

The molding process begins with the injection of hot melt into a relatively cool mold. The polymer begins to cool, and its specific volume begins to decrease. During this time, the injection ram (screw and check valve) are packing additional material into the tool cavity, thereby compensating for the shrinkage effects. This process can continue until one of the sections between the injection unit and the cavity (usually the gate) solidifies. At this point, the central core sections of the molding remain molten, and continue to shrink without compensation. Once the part is rigid enough to keep its own shape (without distorting due to ejection related stresses, internal stress or gravity) the mold opens and the part can be ejected. After ejection, the part continues to cool and shrink until ambient temperature is reached.

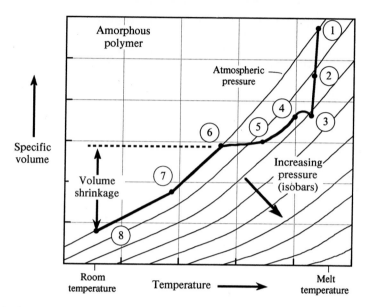

Figure 2.61. The injection molding process can be represented in terms of the material's pressure, volume and temperature.

The injection molding process steps described above are tracked on the P-υ-T curve shown in Figure 2.61.

1.   Melt pressure builds as material enters the cavity
1-2. Filling of the mold cavity
2.   The instant of fill (zero pressure at the end of the flow)
2-3. Packing or compression phase
3.   Peak cavity pressure is achieved and transfer to holding pressure is initiated
3-4. Switch-over to holding pressure with some pressure loss due to back flow (discharge) of material when pressure switch-over occurs
4.   Holding pressure phase begins
4-5. Pressure drop due to cooling and an increase in the solid layer thickness. Material flow continues to compensate for contraction resulting in a specific volume decrease
5.   Gate freeze-off (solidification of gate) preventing material flow, end of holding phase
5-6. Pressure drops as the part cools and shrinks without compensation
6.   Atmospheric pressure is reached indicating that the part size equals that of the cavity, and "mold shrinkage" (as defined) begins
6-7. Isobaric cooling in the mold
7.   Mold open-part ejection
7-8. Post mold isobaric cooling
8.   Thermal equilibrium - final part volume (neglecting any morphological or moisture related volume changes)

2.4.4   Linear Mold Shrinkage

While concepts such as that shown in Figure 2.61 are useful in determining volumetric shrinkage, it is linear shrinkage that is of interest to most product and tool designers. For an isotropic material that is free to shrink, linear shrinkage, S_L, is given by [57]:

$$S_L = 1 - (1 - S_v)^{1/3} \qquad (2.14)$$

where S_v is the volumetric shrinkage (the isotropic linear shrinkage is approximately 1/3 of the volume shrinkage). Unfortunately, there are a number of factors that cause the mold shrinkage behavior of plastic materials to be anisotropic. For example, restraint in one direction will lead to an increase in shrinkage in another direction. Linear shrinkage will also vary due to differences in orientation, cavity pressures, and cooling rates throughout the cavity. Volume shrinkage can be predicted, however, the length, width and thickness shrinkage components that lead to a specific volume change must be established experimentally or simply approximated.

Linear mold shrinkage values are determined experimentally by molding parts and evaluating the differences in part and cavity dimensions. Shrinkage values are determined by subtracting the dimension of the molded specimen from the corresponding dimension of the mold cavity in which the specimen was molded and dividing by the latter [62]. Mold shrinkage values are essentially thermal strain values, and are reported in units of inch / inch, mm / mm, or as a percent (mold shrinkage x 100). Given the experimental linear values of mold shrinkage, a tool designer can determine the appropriate cavity dimensions using:

$$\text{Cavity Dimension} = \text{Part Dimension} / (1 - \text{Mold Shrinkage}) \qquad (2.15)$$

where mold shrinkage is in units of (inch / inch) or (mm / mm). The standard testing method for mold shrinkage [62] is used to generate linear "in-flow" and "cross-flow" shrinkage values using standard test specimen geometries.

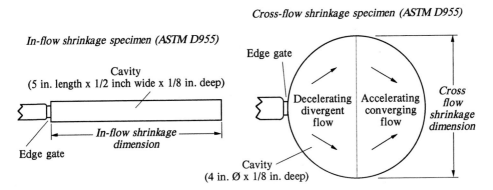

Figure 2.62. One standard test provides only a rough indication of flow and cross flow mold shrinkage.

The information that can be generated with this shrinkage test procedure is fairly limited, especially in the case of the cross flow specimen where flow is never really fully developed [63]. It is also important to note that the test standard emphasizes the importance of conditioning the parts before the part dimensions are taken. The "normal" shrinkage data is reported after 48 hours of conditioning at standard conditions of temperature and relative humidity. This is particularly important for semi-crystalline and hydroscopic polymers. The dimensions of parts produced from a glassy, amorphous polymer such as polystyrene can stabilize in as little as 20-30 minutes [64]. On the other hand, morphological changes for semi-crystalline polymers can go on for hours or even days after molding. The dimensional changes that occur in a part after molding are also affected by moisture reabsorption for hygroscopic polymers [65,66].

Hygroscopic polymers such as PBT or nylon 6/6 are dried prior to molding, and as a result the molded part is "dry" as it is ejected from the tool. Over time, the part will reabsorb moisture from the atmosphere, however, it can be days or weeks before an equilibrium moisture level is reached (depending on part thickness). As moisture is reabsorbed, the parts tend to swell or grow.

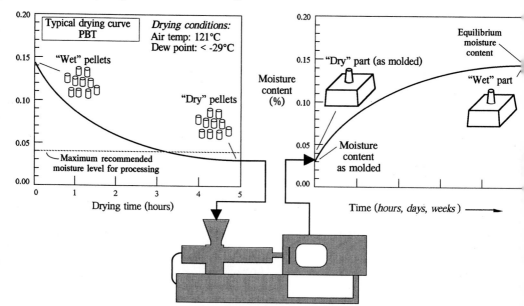

Figure 2.63. Molded parts produced from "dried" hygroscopic polymers will reabsorb moisture over time. The rate of moisture pick-up will be influenced by the part geometry and the ambient conditions.

The post molding dimensional changes for semi-crystalline polymers are complicated by the fact that many semi-crystalline polymers continue to shrink after molding due to secondary crystallization [65]. This secondary crystallization can be due to the crystallization of amorphous regions or a reordering of the crystalline morphology. The

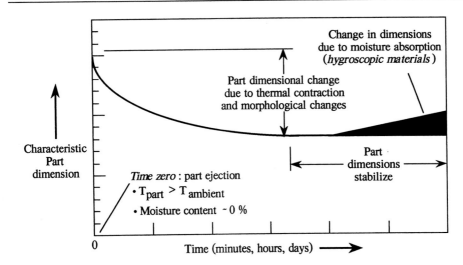

Figure 2.64. The dimensions of amorphous polymers stabilize within a relatively short time. Semi-crystalline polymers can continue to shrink for longer times due to changes in the crystalline morphology. Hygroscopic polymers can tend to grow slightly as they pick up moisture from the surroundings.

dimensions of a hygroscopic semi-crystalline polymer such as PBT, acetal or nylon 6/6 will decrease initially due to thermal contraction and morphological changes, and can then increase over the longer term as the hygroscopic material reabsorbs moisture from the atmosphere. The moisture does cause a degree of swelling, and has a plasticization effect, making the polymer tougher and more ductile. Both ductility and dimensions are important in an application such as the cable tie wrap shown in Figure 2.65. Ductility is important due to a possible tight bending radius associated with the end-use application, while dimensions are important considerations for the self locking mechanism. When the parts are packaged immediately after injection molding (without conditioning), the packaging can act as a moisture barrier to moisture, keeping the parts dry and brittle for a longer time. To overcome this problem, a premeasured quantity of water (based on the weight of the molded parts) can be sprayed in with the molded parts before the packaging is sealed, to ensure that there is an adequate supply of moisture during the period of storage.

The overall tolerances that can be achieved for injection molded parts are to a large extent determined by the ability to predict shrinkage values correctly. The dimensional tolerances that can be achieved in practice are influenced by both the injection molding process conditions and the tool dimensions [67]. An accepted tolerance on a mold dimension is generally less than 50% of the part tolerance (for example 25%). A 50/50 tolerance split would give the mold builder and the molder equal tolerance to compensate for variations in tool construction / shrinkage prediction and molding conditions respectively [68].

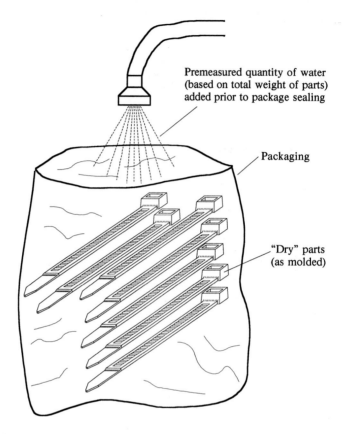

Figure 2.65. Premeasured quantities of water can be added when "dry" parts are packaged immediately after molding to promote moisture reabsorption.

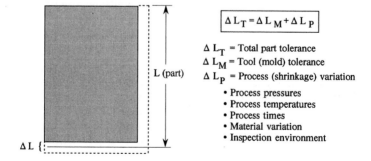

Figure 2.66. The tolerances associated with a particular part dimension are influenced by both the tool tolerances and processing related shrinkage variations.

High quality tools are built to tighter dimensional specifications and limit the degree of elastic distortion due to cavity pressure or clamp tonnages. It is important to remember that significant tool deflections can occur under high cavity pressures. It is also easier to hit the target dimensions when the plastic material shrinkage is both low and predictable (such as in the case of filled amorphous polymer). Unfortunately, there are a number of parameters that make it difficult to predict shrinkage and can cause anisotropic shrinkage behavior resulting in the potential for warpage and internal stress.

2.4.5   Anisotropic Shrinkage and Part Distortion / Warpage

Anisotropic mold shrinkage behavior is an undesirable phenomenon in injection molding since it can lead to: difficulties in hitting the target dimensions, internal stress levels, and warpage when the internal stress levels are sufficient to cause deformation of the part. Computer aided process simulation software packages can be used by the part designer to optimize the part and tool designs, and minimize the potential for shrinkage and warpage long before the tool is ever built. A variety of factors are responsible for the complex, non-uniform shrinkage behavior of injection molded plastic parts. These factors include: (i) asymmetric thermal shrinkage due to uneven cooling of the part, (ii) non-uniform planer volumetric shrinkage, (iii) anisotropic material behavior due to flow induced orientation, and (iv) differential thermal strain due to geometry effects [69].

Directional Shrinkage: The degree of orientation imparted to the melt during the mold filling process has a large influence on the shrinkage exhibited by the plastic material. During mold filling, the polymer molecules undergo a stretching that results in molecular orientation and this anisotropic shrinkage behavior. Neat plastic materials tend to shrink more along the direction of flow (in-flow shrinkage) compared to the direction perpendicular to flow (cross-flow shrinkage), while the shrinkage behavior of reinforced materials is restricted along the direction of fiber orientation. In general, mold shrinkage will tend to be more isotropic when the degree of orientation imparted to the melt during mold filling is minimized and favorable conditions for molecular relaxation exist [8].

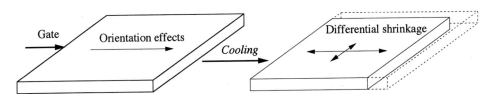

Figure 2.67. Flow induced orientation effects will cause the in-flow mold shrinkage to be different than that in the cross flow direction.

Differential Cooling: Differential shrinkage through the thickness of the part can be caused by differences in the cooling rate between the cavity and core. Due to the complexity of many part and mold designs, it is difficult to achieve completely uniform cooling in practice. Non-uniform cooling causes differential thermal contractions of the polymer across the thickness of the part as it cools from the initial processing temperature down to room temperature. The hotter surfaces of the part will continue to shrink more than the cooler surfaces after gate seal off and part ejection. This differential shrinkage causes internal moments that are likely to warp the part after it is ejected from the tool [69].

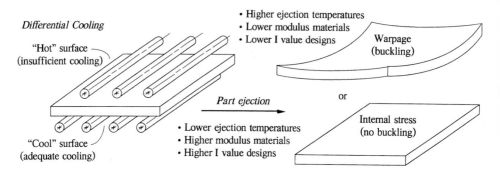

Figure 2.68. Warpage or internal stress can be caused by differential cooling, which leads to differential shrinkage through the thickness of the part. The hotter surface tends to shrink more once the part is ejected from the tool.

When the part is rigid enough to prevent buckling, because it has a high modulus or geometrical stiffening features (e.g. edge stiffeners or ribs), it will keep its shape, but it will be stressed internally. This is important because internal stress levels can lead to reduced environmental stress crack resistance, reduced impact performance, and the potential for warpage if the part is exposed to elevated temperatures (where modulus is reduced) at some point during assembly, decorating or in service.

Differential shrinkage through the thickness of the part can also be caused by differences in the cavity and core geometry that occur in areas such as corners. Compared to the cavity side of a tool, the core side has a reduced surface area and can be difficult to cool effectively in practice due for example, to structural concerns. The core side of the molding tends to stay hotter, and therefore shrinks more when the part is ejected. As a result, a moment is created that causes the part to warp inward after it is ejected from the mold.

The differential cooling problem can be minimized with proper mold cooling system design. Some of these warpage problems can be corrected during production, if the tool has been built in such a way that the different cavity and core sections of the tool have individual cooling circuits, allowing the process engineer to make local tool temperature adjustments in order to control the cooling rate of each surface.

Cavity Pressure Differences: The magnitude of the packing and holding pressures used during processing will have a significant effect on mold shrinkage. Higher packing and holding pressures lead to a global reduction in mold shrinkage, while lower pressures increase shrinkage. Unfortunately, pressures in the cavity vary from a maximum at the gate to minimum at the end of flow due to melt compressibility. The pressure differential

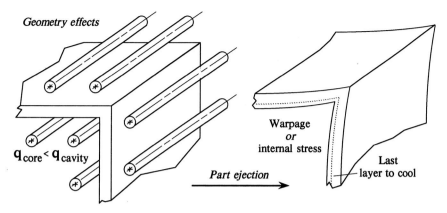

Figure 2.69. Differential cooling through the thickness of the part can also be due to differences in the cavity and core geometry. Cores are typically more difficult to cool than cavities. The hotter (core) side of the molding shrinks more after ejection, leading to warpage or internal stress.

over the length of the cavity can be very significant, particularly for longer flow lengths or thinner walled parts. This pressure history differential, which occurs over the course of the cycle, results in mold shrinkage values that tend to be greater towards the end of the cavity, away from the gate area(s). Differential mold shrinkage due to cavity pressure history differences can also lead to dimensional distortion or warpage of the molding.

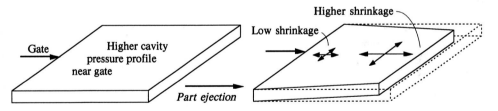

Figure 2.70. Mold shrinkage values near the gate are lower than those at the end of flow.

This differential shrinkage also complicates the cavity sizing procedure for the tool designer. One way to get around the problem is to use many gates. In this way, the flow length is cut down, and cavity pressures tend to be more uniform (therefore mold shrinkage is more uniform) since all areas of the part are then "near" the gate. Alternatively, the cavity dimensions can be cut to compensate for the different shrinkage values, if the appropriate shrinkage data is available (not a common practice). Shrinkage data that is generated on larger plaque type test molds with well defined linear flow is preferred to that generated using the oversimplified, standard ASTM testing technique [62]. Using these larger parts, materials suppliers can generate both in-flow and cross-flow shrinkage values close to and far away from the gate region.

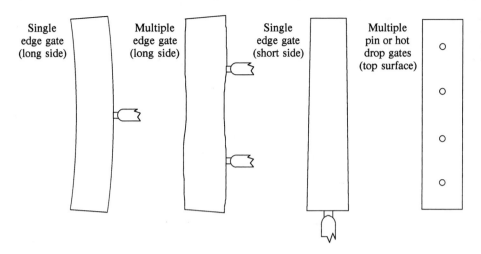

Figure 2.71. Parts produced in cavities that are simply scaled up versions of the part print can have dimensional variation due to the reduced mold shrinkage near the gate. The correct part geometries can be obtained if a larger number of gates are used in an effort to minimize cavity pressure variation and shrinkage variation.

With this type of shrinkage data, the dimensions of the edge gated cavity (gate on the short side) in Figure 2.71 could be altered such that the end of flow cavity width was greater than that near the gate, to compensate for the pressure induced differential shrinkage.

Radial Flow: Parts produced using top center gating (e.g. using a sprue gate, pin gate, hot drop etc.) fill via radial or disc type flow. In radial flow, the radius could be viewed as the flow direction, while the circumferential direction is essentially the cross flow direction. If there is differential shrinkage, then center gated parts can remain flat, warp into a dome shape, or warp into a saddle shape. If the molded parts do not warp, it is an indication that either the shrinkage is uniform, or that the stiffness of the part (due to the combined affects of modulus and geometry) is great enough to resist the shrinkage stresses caused by differential shrinkage. However, in this case, the part remains internally stressed.

If differential mold shrinkage is present, and the plastic part does not have sufficient stiffness to withstand the shrinkage stresses, warpage or dimension distortion will occur. Dome like warpage is likely to occur when the circumferential mold shrinkage is greater than the radial mold shrinkage. Saddle type warpage such as that shown in Figure 2.72 can be caused if inner region shrinkages are greater than those of the outer region, or when radial mold shrinkages are higher than those in the circumferential direction [57]. In any case, warpage of the part can be minimized by minimizing the degree of differential shrinkage due to the combined effects of packing, orientation or differential cooling.

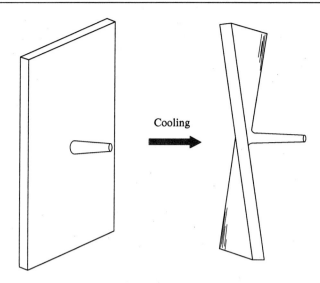

Figure 2.72. The central sprue gated part exhibits differential shrinkage due to (i) differences in the radial and circumferential shrinkage as a result of orientation, (ii) differences in shrinkage along the length of flow due to packing pressure differences, and (iii) flow length differences from the sprue to the short and long sides. The differential shrinkage can lead to the out-of-plane saddle shape shown.

Material Considerations: All injection molded thermoplastic materials have the potential to exhibit differential mold shrinkage due to orientation, packing, or cooling rate differences. Flow / cross flow shrinkage differences tend to become more significant as the average molecular weight of the polymer increases. Cooling related shrinkage differences exist for all polymers, but are a particular concern for semi-crystalline polymer. As the name implies, semi-crystalline polymers are only partially crystalline, with the remainder of the matrix being amorphous. The ability of a semi-crystalline polymer to pack neatly into a crystalline lattice is improved when the polymer is cooled more slowly. The mold shrinkage that a semi-crystalline polymer exhibits will therefore be influenced by the rate of cooling due to its effect on percent crystallinity. This cooling rate / percent crystallinity relationship also accounts for variations in the crystalline morphology of the material through the thickness of an injection molded part.

The shrinkage behavior of a semi-crystalline polymer is then far more complicated than that of an amorphous polymer. The effect of part thickness on mold shrinkage is very significant with semi-crystalline polymers. The general type of behavior that can be expected is shown in Figure 2.73. Higher (normalized) mold shrinkage values can be expected for semi-crystalline polymers when thicker wall sections are used, due to the increase in cooling time (and time for crystallization) associated with the thicker wall. This can be a particular concern when molding parts with variable wall thickness. For example, in applications where reinforcing ribs are used to stiffen plate-like parts, the ribs are typically thinner than the nominal wall thickness from which they extend. This practice limits the size of the sink opposite the rib, however, the slower cooling rate for the nominal wall (thicker section) will lead to an increase in shrinkage, and the potential for warpage in a direction away from the ribs. Crystal orientation and shear induced crystallization also complicate the shrinkage behavior of semi-crystalline polymer [57].

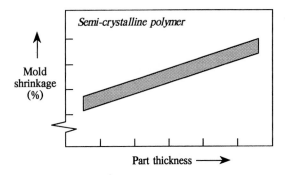

Figure 2.73. The mold shrinkage values for a semi-crystalline polymer increase with increasing wall thickness.

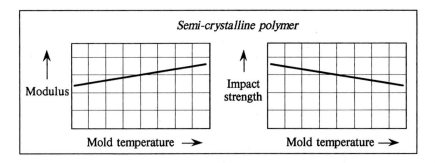

Figure 2.74. Like mold shrinkage, the mechanical properties of a semi-crystalline polymer vary with part thickness or processing conditions. Processing conditions that promote crystallization lead to an increase in stiffness at the expense of ductility.

Process conditions that influence cooling rate will also influence the mold shrinkage of a semi-crystalline polymer. Process variables that reduce the cooling rate will tend to promote crystallization and therefore these variables can be used by a process engineer to control mold shrinkage to some extent. This gives molders the ability to alter part dimensions using variables such as mold temperature. However, it should also be noted that changes in morphology will also affect the end-use properties of the material as indicated in Figure 2.74.

In general, mold shrinkage values for unfilled semi-crystalline polymers are several times greater than those for unfilled amorphous polymers. Along with the higher shrinkage values is an increase in the potential for differential shrinkage, which can lead to internal stress and warpage. The part shown in Figure 2.75 has a non-uniform wall thickness, and would most likely warp due to the additional mold shrinkage associated with the relatively thicker bottom section. The potential for warpage can be minimized by "coring out" thicker sections whenever possible in an effort to achieve a more uniform wall thickness and cooling rate. When variable wall thicknesses must be incorporated into the part design, the tool cooling layout and materials of construction (i.e. thermal properties) must be altered so that a more uniform rate of cooling can be achieved.

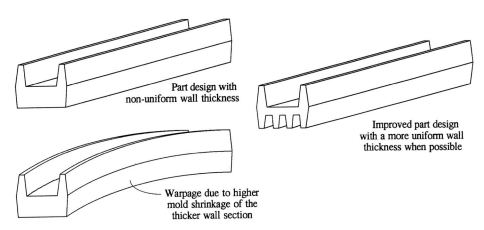

Part design with
non-uniform wall thickness

Improved part design
with a more uniform wall
thickness when possible

Warpage due to higher
mold shrinkage of the
thicker wall section

Figure 2.75. It is especially important to maintain a uniform wall thickness when parts are produced from semi-crystalline polymers since the shrinkage value of a semi-crystalline polymer is thickness dependent.

Mold Shrinkage for Filled or Reinforced Polymers: Fillers, flakes or fibers are commonly added to plastic materials to selectively modify mechanical properties. The additives are generally added to increase the rigidity and creep resistance of the polymeric system for applications requiring stiffness. Most fillers and reinforcements are inorganic in nature, and have relatively low coefficients of thermal expansion. The fillers and reinforcements tend to shrink significantly less than the polymeric matrix to which they are added. Particulate fillers and flake type reinforcements both tend to reduce shrinkage when added to amorphous or semi-crystalline polymers. The reduction in shrinkage is approximately proportional to their concentration, and no significant problems with anisotropic shrinkage are introduced. This is not the case when fibrous type reinforcements are used as the reinforcing element in a polymer matrix. When properly coupled, fibers produced from materials such as glass or graphite, offer a number of advantages in terms of end-use performance, however, their use can lead to several processing related problems. For example, compared to particulate or flake filled polymers, the shrinkage differential between the in-flow and cross-flow directions for fiber reinforced polymers can be a significant concern as indicated in Figure 2.76 [70]. The anisotropic shrinkage can make it difficult for a mold designer to determine the appropriate cavity dimensions. The anisotropic shrinkage for glass fiber reinforced polymers can be attributed to the fact that glass fibers become oriented in the shear field as the polymer flows during injection, in much the same way that the polymer molecules

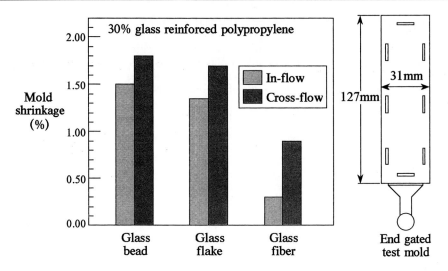

Figure 2.76. Differential mold shrinkage tends to be more of a problem for fiber reinforced polymers compared to polymers that contain lower aspect ratio fillers.

become oriented. However, unlike polymer molecules, fibers have no tendency to rerandomize (even when favorable conditions for molecular mobility exist), and the flow induced fiber orientation is retained as the polymer cools. The orientation distribution for the fibers will be influenced by both shear and elongational flow. Variables such as mold filling rate, cavity thickness, melt viscosity, and the gating scheme used, are all significant factors [71,72]. As a result, flow related design decisions, such as gate type / location, are even more critical when the plastic parts will be produced using fiber reinforced polymers.

Fibers tend to align along the direction of flow and restrict shrinkage in that direction. Figure 2.77 is indicative of how the mold shrinkage behavior of a glass fiber reinforced semi-crystalline polymer, such as acetal, can be characterized. When the semi-crystalline polymer is unfilled, the in-flow shrinkage value tends to be somewhat greater than the cross flow value, and both values are relatively high (e.g. 1.5 to 2.0 %) which is typical for a semi-crystalline polymer. As the concentration of glass fiber reinforcement increases, the in-flow mold shrinkage is greatly reduced, while the cross-flow mold shrinkage value decreases by only a small amount. The differences between the flow and cross flow mold shrinkage values increase with increasing fiber content. This flow / cross-flow shrinkage difference tends to be more pronounced with semi-crystalline polymers although differential shrinkage problems can also exist with fiber reinforced amorphous polymers [72]. It suffices to say that there is a tendency towards anisotropic shrinkage behavior with fiber reinforced polymers. Designers should at least consider the potential for differential shrinkage and warpage when fiber reinforced grade polymers are used. Unfortunately, there are many factors to consider. For example, a highly reinforced grade may exhibit greater differential shrinkage, yet the additional rigidity imparted by the fibers may minimize the potential for warpage.

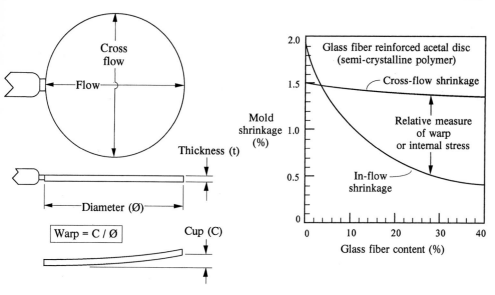

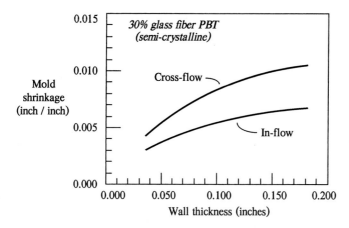

Figure 2.77. Differential shrinkage can occur with fiber reinforced semi-crystalline polymers. Fiber orientation lowers the flow shrinkage value, while the cross flow shrinkage value remains relatively high.

Figure 2.78. The mold shrinkage for a reinforced semi-crystalline polymer, such as glass fiber reinforced PBT, varies with direction (flow vs. cross flow) and with part thickness.

The shrinkage behavior of fiber reinforced semi-crystalline polymers becomes even more complicated when different wall thicknesses are considered. As mentioned previously, the longer cooling times associated with thicker wall sections tend to promote crystalline growth, which will lead to an increase in mold shrinkage. Changes in wall thickness will affect both flow and cross flow mold shrinkage values. This concept is illustrated in Figure 2.78 [73]. It should also be noted, that the mold shrinkage characteristics of reground or recycled fiber reinforced polymers can be different from those of the virgin resin due to the effects of regrinding and reprocessing on fiber length distributions [63].

A number of techniques can be used to minimize the potential for warpage of fiber reinforced polymers due to differential shrinkage. One of the more common approaches is to use a polymer composite that contains both fibrous and flake or particulate (filler) reinforcements. These hybrid materials offer a unique balance in terms of mechanical performance and more isotropic mold shrinkage (compared to purely fiber reinforced grades) and as a result, are widely used in tighter tolerance applications [63, 72].

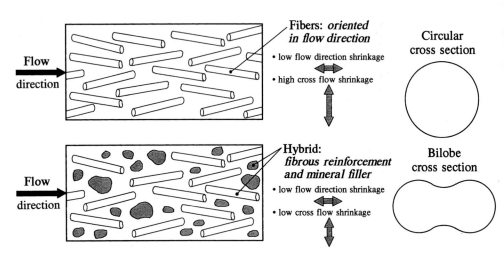

Figure 2.79. Hybrid composite materials that incorporate both fibrous and flake reinforcements have mold shrinkage values that tend to be more isotropic in comparison with conventional fiber reinforced polymers. The use of fibers having bilobal cross sections has also been shown to be beneficial in providing more uniform mold shrinkage when compared with fibers of circular cross section.

Fibrous reinforcements with non-circular cross sections have also been shown to be useful in controlling warpage for fiber reinforced polymers. One study has shown the use of glass fibers having a bilobe cross section has resulted in a 30-40 % reduction in warpage for semi-crystalline polymers when compared with circular fibers of similar cross sectional area, while maintaining similar mechanical performance [74]. Design features such as edge stiffeners or ribs can also be helpful in minimizing the tendency towards warpage for fiber reinforced polymer, as are structural foam molding processes. Gating schemes that minimize preferential fiber orientation are also preferred. A part produced with a large number of gates distributed uniformly over the surface of the part will have reduced flow lengths, fill primarily with radial flow, and ensure more uniform packing. These are all factors which can reduce anisotropic shrinkage for fiber reinforced polymers, and therefore the potential for warpage. When fiber reinforced polymers are to be used for plastic parts with tight dimensional and flatness requirements, computer aid mold filling / shrinkage / warpage analyses are recommended. These simulations can provide in depth information on how fibers are oriented during mold filling, and their impact on shrinkage and dimensional distortion.

2.5 Cooling and Solidification

The cycle time for injection molded parts is influenced by a number of factors including the time required to close the injection mold, fill the mold cavity, cool the molding, open the mold, and eject the finished part. In most cases, part cooling accounts for the majority of the molding cycle time, and therefore the rate at which parts can be produced. Plastic parts must be cooled down to a temperature that is low enough that the part does not become permanently distorted due to the forces associated with part ejection (e.g. local deformation due to ejector pins) or due to the relaxation of residual molding stresses that can cause the part to warp or distort after ejection. The rate at which a molding will cool and resolidify will be influenced by a large number of part design, tooling, material, and processing related variables. For example, tooling variables include the materials used for construction of the mold, and the layout of the cooling channels. Important process variables include the melt's temperature, and the cavity and core surface temperatures. Due to the large number of variables involved, it is impossible to specify with certainty the exact cooling time that will be required for a given part design in advance, however, it is possible to obtain an estimate of the cooling time that can be expected. Cooling time estimates can be very helpful to the designer of an injection molded plastic part, particularly when considering economics. For example, the designer can determine how a proposed change in the wall thickness for the part, or a material change, will affect the cooling time for the part (or cycle time) and therefore the cost of the final product.

The best estimates of part cooling time are obtained when an integrated computer aided process simulation is performed. An analysis of this type combines the results of a mold filling analysis with those of a mold cooling analysis, generating a complete view of the heat transfer processes that occur over the course of the injection molding cycle. These analyses provide information on cooling time, but more importantly, allow the cooling system design to be optimized in an effort to achieve balanced and efficient cooling for all areas of the injection molded part. Without an analysis of this type, it is likely that certain sections of the injection mold will run hotter than others, leading to delays in the cycle and the potential for differential shrinkage and part warpage. It is, however, useful for a designer to obtain rough estimates of cooling time using approximate solutions for the problem of unsteady state conductive heat transfer for parts having regular geometries. For example, many parts can be approximated as having a plate like geometry, and cool primarily by conduction through the relatively large top and bottom surfaces. While the flat plate cooling equations assume infinite width and length, the error will be relatively small if the length and width of the plate are greater that 10-15 time the plate thickness (i.e. the wall thickness of the molding) since the quantity of heat conducted through the sides of the plate is relatively small. Similar relationships hold for cylindrical parts, where the length of the cylinder should be 10-15 times greater than the diameter in order to avoid significant error [2,75,76]. These equations also assume that the temperature of the melt entering the cavity is uniform, and that the part is cooled uniformly from both sides (or uniformly around the circumference in the case of the cylinder). An additional assumption is that the mold cooling system is capable of removing heat from the tool steel as fast as the plastic part can transfer heat to the steel, and therefore, constant cavity and core wall temperatures are maintained. However, in practice, the mold surface temperature is likely to run somewhat hotter. The time required for the center of the part to reach the ejection temperature and the time required for the average part temperature to reach the ejection temperature are given in Figure 2.80 for both plate-like and cylindrical part geometries [75].

Plate

Centerline
reaches T_e

$$t_c = \frac{h^2}{\alpha \pi^2} \ln\left[\frac{4}{\pi}\left(\frac{T_m - T_w}{T_e - T_w}\right)\right]$$

(2.16)

Average
reaches T_e

$$t_a = \frac{h^2}{\alpha \pi^2} \ln\left[\frac{8}{\pi^2}\left(\frac{T_m - T_w}{T_e - T_w}\right)\right]$$

(2.17)

Cylinder

Centerline
reaches T_e

$$t_c = 0.173\frac{R^2}{\alpha} \ln\left[1.6023\left(\frac{T_m - T_w}{T_e - T_w}\right)\right]$$

(2.18)

Average
reaches T_e

$$t_a = 0.173\frac{R^2}{\alpha} \ln\left[0.6916\left(\frac{T_m - T_w}{T_e - T_w}\right)\right]$$

(2.19)

t_c is the time required for the centerline temperature to reach the ejection temperature (s)

t_a is the time required for the average part temperature to reach the ejection temperature (s)

h is the plate like part wall thickness (m)

R is the radius of the cylindrical molding (m)

T_m is the melt temperature at the start of cooling (°C)

T_w is the cavity / core wall temperature during cooling (°C)

T_e is the ejection temperature of the polymer (°C)

α is the thermal diffusivity of the polymer = $k / \rho c$ (m²/s)

k is the thermal conductivity of the polymer (W/m°K)

c is the specific heat of the polymer (J/kg°K)

ρ is the density of the polymer (kg/m³)

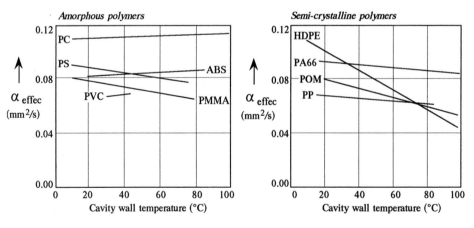

Figure 2.80. Designers can use cooling time equations to estimate how changes in part wall thickness or material selection will influence cooling / cycle time.

In order to utilize the equations given in Figure 2.80, the designer must specify a number of terms. The thickness or radius of the part are generally known, or the designer is attempting to establish a relationship between part thickness and cooling time. It is typical to work with the thickest section of the molding when the part has a variable wall thickness since this section of the molding will require the longest cooling time. The melt and mold temperature values used in the calculation are to be representative of those that can be expected in production. Ideally, a designer would perform a series of cooling time calculations to cover the entire window of recommended processing conditions for the material. The ejection temperature of the molding must also be specified, and lies somewhere between the melt and the cavity wall temperatures. The part must be cooled to the point where it can withstand the action of the ejectors, and maintain its shape after ejection. Temperature values such as the material's glass transition temperature (for amorphous polymers), *Deflection Temperature Under Load* [77] or Vicat *Softening Temperature* [78] are commonly used as an indication of the maximum part temperature at ejection. These standard tests provide an indication of the temperature range at which the plastic material goes from being rigid (able to support a load) to a more flexible, leathery state. In the context of the cooling calculation, these property values are viewed in reverse, as an indication of the temperature at which the material goes from being soft or flexible to rigid. The *Vicat Softening Temperature* is generally the preferred value of *maximum part temperature at ejection* for the mold cooling time calculations, since this standard test provides a measure of the temperature at which a flat pin penetrates into the molded test sample, and is thought to be analogous to the process of pin ejection. Regardless of the property value used, it is important to recognize that there is a temperature gradient through the thickness of the molded part as it cools. Initially, the melt is assumed to be at a uniform temperature, namely the melt temperature selected for the calculation. If one was to wait long enough, the entire part would eventually reach the cavity wall temperature. In practice, plastic parts are ejected long before the entire cross-section of the molding reaches the tool temperature. Equations 2.16 and 2.18 give the time required for the centerline of the molding to reach the ejection temperature, while Equations 2.17 and 2.19 give the time required for the average part temperature to reach the ejection temperature value selected.

The thermal properties of the polymer that will be used to produce the part will also have a significant effect on mold cooling time. The thermal diffusivity of the polymer provides the quantitative value required for the mold cooling time calculation. Unfortunately, all of the material properties that are associated with thermal diffusivity, namely thermal conductivity, density, and specific heat, are a function of both temperature and pressure (both of which change significantly over the course of the molding cycle). This is especially true for semi-crystalline polymers, such as nylon or polypropylene, that undergo a true phase change during the cooling process. It is possible to get a rough estimate of cooling times if average values of thermal diffusivity are used. The effective thermal diffusivity values given in Figure 2.80 have been shown to be useful in calculating the mold cooling times for both unfilled amorphous and semi-crystalline polymers [75].

Finally, it should be noted that the part thickness or radius terms in Equations 2.16 to 2.19 are squared. Part thickness does influence material consumption (to the first power), but the effect of part thickness on cycle time is dramatic. Even a small reduction in part thickness can lead to significant molding cycle time related savings. On the other hand, if a designer was to double the wall thickness of the part, the theoretical cooling time would increase by a factor of four, although in practice, the cycle increase would be somewhat less because thicker parts are generally stiff enough to be ejected before the center of the molding solidifies. It suffices to say that the relationship between part thickness and cooling time should be kept in mind when selecting the nominal wall thickness for the plastic molding.

2.6   Part Ejection

2.6.1   Introduction

In the final phase of the injection molding process, the mold opens and the part is ejected from the tool. Ideally, this ejection phase of the process is accomplished without imparting any damage or distortion to the molded part as it is stripped from the cavity or core. While it is generally the responsibility of the tool designer to design a suitable ejection system for a given part geometry, it is the part designer that establishes ease or difficulty associated with this stage of the plastic part manufacturing process. The plastic part must be designed with ejection considerations in mind. This can be done if the product designers work closely with (or consult with) the tool designer right from the early stages of product development, when the part begins to take shape. The tool designer can comment on specific ejection related concerns and possible part design changes. Plastic part design considerations that influence the ease of ejection and ejection related tooling costs include:

- Draft angles or tapers
- Surface finishes
- Esthetic requirements
- The presence of undercuts or holes
- Stationary or moving half ejection
- Parting line location

Almost all of the features associated with a particular part geometry will have some impact on the ability to eject the part. Ejection systems for even a relatively simple plastic part can be expensive (in terms of tooling cost) if the part is not "designed for ejection".

2.6.2   Draft Angles

Cavity Draft: Draft angles or tapers are generally used to facilitate ejection of any molded part that has a significant depth of draw. When parts are produced using the standard cavity and core configuration, the cavity is stationary while the core is attached to the moving platen. In most cases, the part tends to stay with the core when the mold opens since (i) material shrinkage causes a contact pressure and normal frictional forces between the part and the core, and (ii) material shrinkage through the wall thickness tends to pull the part away from the cavity wall. It should also be noted that the area of contact between the part and the cavity can be greater than that of the part and the core, however, contact pressures with the cavity are likely to be lower due to shrinkage through the wall thickness of the part. Draft angles are typically added to the cavity side of the tool to assist in releasing the part from the cavity when the mold opens at the end of the molding cycle. The draft also reduces the potential for scuffing or abrasion to the outer (cavity) sidewall surfaces of the part when the tool opens.

Cavity draft angles reduce the effects of undercuts, eliminate sliding friction and part damage after the initial break away as the tool opens, and facilitate air movement to compensate for vacuum effects as the tool opens. Typical cavity draft angles range from a fraction of a degree to several degrees. The draft angle that is required varies with parameters such as depth of draw, material rigidity, surface lubricity, mold surface roughness and material shrinkage. Parts can be produced with a "zero draft", however, special mold action, such as a split cavity, must then be used to pull the cavity away from the part as the mold opens.

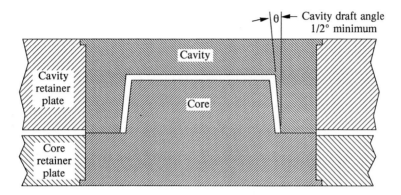

Figure 2.81. Cavity draft angles are used to facilitate release from the cavity and the tool opens while core draft angles are added to facilitate release from the core during ejection.

The split cavity action reduces mold opening forces, essentially eliminates the potential for the part sticking to the cavity, and eliminates the potential for part sidewall damage or scuffing due to sliding friction as the mold opens. The split cavity segments are essentially large side actions, and can also be used to produce textured sidewalls, holes, slots and other undercut features. However, split cavity tools are significantly more costly than more conventional open and shut tools, and additional parting witness lines, and potentially flash, will be visible on the molding.

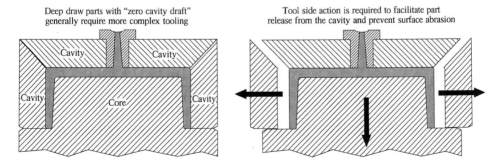

Figure 2.82. It is possible to produce parts with a zero cavity draft, however, special side action tools must be used to facilitate part release from the cavity and prevent surface abrasion when the mold opens.

Core Draft: Once the mold has opened and the molding has been removed from the cavity, it must then be stripped or ejected from the core. Plastic parts tend to grip tightly onto the core, and the forces required to eject the part can be very significant. The initial breakaway forces are the highest ejection forces. The magnitude of these ejection forces is influenced by factors such as material shrinkage, material modulus, coefficient of friction, surface roughness, contact area, and draft angle. Parts with zero core draft angles are difficult to eject, and have high ejection forces throughout the course of the ejection cycle. Draft angles from 1/4° to 2° are commonly used or cores for essentially the same reasons that they are used on cavities. Larger draft angles will improve the release characteristics even further, however, larger draft angles begin to have a significant effect on the shape of the product. Draft angles reduce the initial (breakaway) ejection forces and therefore simplify ejection system design, which may in turn result in a reduced cycle time by allowing placement of additional cooling lines.

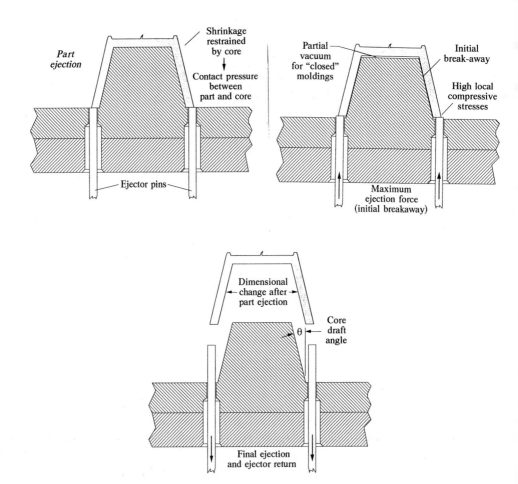

Figure 2.83. Once the tool opens, the part must then be stripped from the core. The force required to eject the part is due to the combined effects of shrinkage, vacuum, and undercuts.

If ejection forces are low, it may also be possible to eject a part sooner, even though the part is "softer", provided the ejection forces can be distributed evenly over the surface of the part. Perhaps more importantly, draft angles result in a loss in contact between the part and the core after the initial breakaway and as a result, the ejection forces drop off rapidly after breakaway. This loss of contact pressure also facilitates air flow up around the core to compensate for vacuum effects that add to ejection force, and can result in part damage. For very large or deep draw parts, air valves or venting pins are used to break the vacuum and blow the part from the core after initial break away. In most cases, the draft angles used on the core are equivalent to those used for the cavity (i.e. a parallel draft is used). It is generally considered good practice to use parallel draft, since this results in a uniform part wall thickness.

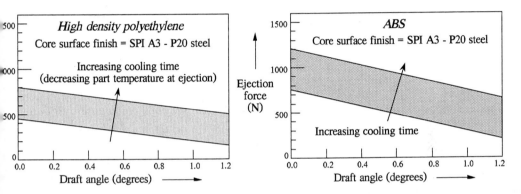

Figure 2.84. Experimental results have shown that the peak forces associated with ejecting a molding from a core decrease with increasing draft angle. The use of a draft angle also minimizes scuffing or surface abrasion during ejection.

Experimental studies have shown that draft angles do reduce the forces associated with part ejection. Figure 2.84 summarizes the results of an experimental study [79] conducted to evaluate the effect of draft angle on the release forces for both ABS and high density polyethylene moldings. In each case, an increase in draft of even a fraction of a degree resulted in significant reductions in ejection force.

Draft angles do have a significant influence on the shape of the plastic part. This can often be a point of conflict between the plastic part and tool designer. Even features such as ribs, bosses and depressions or holes must be drafted. Design features such as the reinforcing ribs should have a draft angle on both sides of the cavity that forms them. Unfortunately, the only positive benefit of adding this draft angle to the rib is to reduce the force of ejection. The rib will be more difficult to fill, and from a structural design point, it will have less of a stiffening effect. The draft angle that is used in practice is a compromise between that which results in improved ejection without causing an excessive loss in stiffness. While the ejection forces for the drafted rib are lower, there is a reduction in the surface area on which the ejection components can act on. Small diameter ejector pins tend to be fragile and have such small surface areas that local compressive stresses on the part can become so high that the pins push into the rib as it is ejected. Blades (rectangular ejectors) provide the best method of ejecting ribs, but they are relatively expensive in terms of tooling costs.

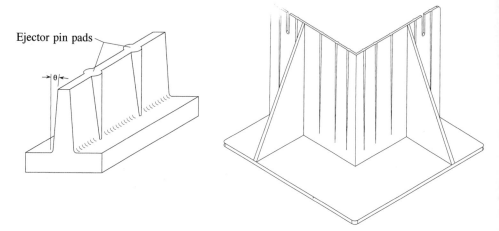

Ejector pin pads

θ

Figure 2.85. Ejector pin pads are commonly used on deep ribs as a method of increasing the area on which the ejector pins can act. This reduces the local compressive stress at the pin and the tendency for the pin to indent the part during ejection.

Figure 2.86. Section of a molding showing the use of ejector pin pads.

Ejector pin pads, such as those shown in Figures 2.85 and 2.86, provide a practical alternative for the ejection of ribs or internal wall sections. The ejector pin pad is essentially a solid, circular boss integrated into the rib. The ejector pin pad has a larger surface area on which the pin can act, but will not have a significant impact on the size of the sink mark on the wall opposite the rib, since the wall thickness at the base of the boss like feature (where it meets the nominal wall) is equal to or close to that of the rib itself.

Part designers should be very careful to avoid ambiguities when specifying rib or other feature details on a part print. For example generalized statements regarding "minimum", "maximum", "nominal" and "allowable" should be used with caution. The print notation

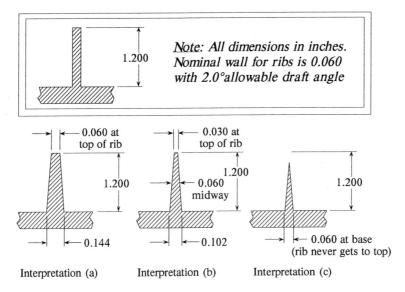

Figure 2.87. Details such as rib wall thickness and draft angle must be specified clearly on a part print to avoid the potential for misinterpretation. Several interpretations are possible due to a lack of specific information.

in Figure 2.86 specifies a rib with a nominal wall of 0.060 inches and 2° allowable draft [80]. This note could be interpreted in a variety of ways including those shown in Figure 2.87. In order to avoid the potential for misinterpretation, the part drawing should include more detailed dimensional specifications on features such as ribs in conjunction with more descriptive notations. The use of 3D wire frame and solid model databases has effectively eliminated design ambiguities of this type.

2.6.3   Effect of Cavity and Core Surface Finish

Surface Roughness: The surface finish on both the cavity and core have a significant influence on release characteristics of a plastic part. The type of tool steel or surface plating, surface roughness and direction of polish are all important factors. For example, the direction of mold polishing has been shown to have a significant impact on the ability to eject a part. Polishing a core or cavity in the line of draw (parallel to the direction of ejection) is preferred, especially in deep draw applications where little or no draft is used. This is an important point because it is sometimes much easier to polish a mold core or cavity perpendicular to the direction of ejection. While the cylindrical core shown in Figure 2.88 is most easily polished in a spinning lathe, it is important that at least the final polishing steps be done along the direction of part ejection (i.e. in the line of draw) to improve release. A similar polishing problem exists for ribs, which are generally easier to polish from side to side, which is the direction perpendicular to the direction of ejection. Draw polishing minimizes the negative effects of undercuts caused by surface polishing by keeping any polishing related undercuts in the line of draw, thereby reducing ejection forces.

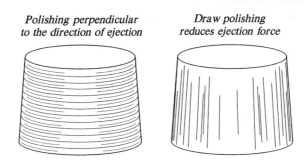

Figure 2.88. Cavities and cores should be polished in the line of draw to reduce release forces by minimizing the effects of polishing undercuts.

The experimental results shown in Figure 2.89 show that the ejection forces for even a ductile polymer such as high density polyethylene are significantly lower when the core is polished in the line of draw rather than perpendicular to the line of draw [79]. The results in Figure 2.89 also show that ejection forces decrease as the part temperature at ejection increases (i.e. when the part is ejected sooner). This ejection force reduction can be attributed to a reduction in shrinkage and modulus at the instant of ejection, which in turn reduce the contact pressure between the part and the core.

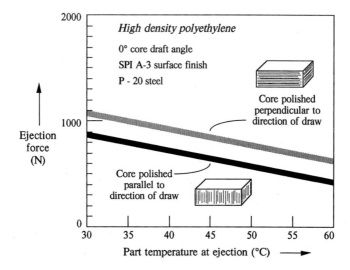

Figure 2.89. Experimental results have shown that draw polishing does reduce the forces of ejection.

The average surface roughness / topography of the core or cavity is also an important ejection parameter. Surface finishes or roughnesses are typically specified using one of the 12 SPI standard surface finishes (A1 through D3) [81]. These 12 surface standards have replaced the older SPE / SPI surfaces designated #1 to # 6. Surface roughnesses are measured using a profilometer which utilizes a stylus and analyzer to detect the differences in height between the peaks and valleys. The surface roughness is then reported as a weighted average (RMS value) of these distance values. In most cases, smoother, more highly polished surfaces assist in part release. This is especially true for brittle, rigid or glassy polymers. In other cases, lightly textured or bead blasted surfaces can reduce ejection forces. This tends to hold for certain grades of elastomeric or ductile polymers. While this may seem contradictory, factors such as wetting and venting can be used to explain the phenomenon. The surface finish on a molded part cannot be better than that of the tool. The best surface finishes are generally achievable when lower viscosity (higher MFR) polymer grades are used. These fluid melts are able to wet out the surface of the tool. However, it is more difficult to achieve a good surface finish with the higher viscosity (lower MFR) polymer grades. The more viscous polymers may not be capable of thoroughly wetting the tool surface.

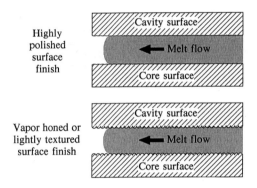

Figure 2.90. In most cases, highly polished surfaces improve release characteristics by minimizing the size of polishing related undercuts. However, in other cases, for example with some elastomeric or ductile polymers, lightly textured or bead blasted surfaces can improve release.

If the polymer does not fully wet the surface, then the actual surface area of contact is reduced, and the forces of ejection are reduced, provided the polymer is flexible enough to deflect as it releases from the undercuts which are ideally gentle hills and valleys rather that sharp scratches. Poor wetting is also likely to facilitate air flow (assist venting) as the part is stripped of the core or pulled from the cavity. While this phenomenon is sometimes observed with viscous, flexible polymers, more highly polished surfaces are generally preferred, especially for the higher modulus glassy amorphous or reinforced polymers.

Surface Textures: Parts that are produced using textured surfaces require additional draft to facilitate release. Cavities with random texture require about 1° - 1 1/2° of draft (per side) for each 0.001 inch (0.025 mm) of texture depth as a rule of thumb. Directional patterns, such as a wood grain that runs perpendicular to the direction of draw, can require greater draft. When surface textures are used, they are generally used on the "outside" surface of the molding (i.e. the surface texturing is applied to the cavity side of the tool). "Inside" surface textures, formed on a textured core, are significantly more difficult to eject since the material shrinks tightly around the core. If textured cores must be used, even greater draft angles are generally required [82].

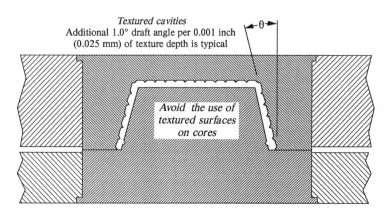

Figure 2.91. When textured surfaces are used on the cavity side walls, additional draft is required to facilitate release from the cavity and reduce scuffing. In addition, it may be necessary to add undercuts to the core to ensure that the parts stays with the core when the tool opens.

Frictional Factors: The friction forces between the plastic part and the tool during ejection (i.e. the forces associated with sliding the part over the mold cavity or core) can be reduced using (i) lubricants, or (ii) by altering the tool surface coating.

Lubricants and Release Agents: Lubricants or release agents are commonly added to plastic materials to improve flow and facilitate release [83,84]. It is common for lubricants to be classified as either internal or external, however, it is unlikely that either is completely internal or external. It is more appropriate to classify lubricants as predominately internal or predominately external. Predominately internal lubricants are additives that have a good affinity for the polymer and reduce the polymer's viscosity in the melt state. Predominately external lubricants, on the other hand, are additives with a very low solubility in the base polymer. They tend to migrate from the bulk polymer melt during processing to the metal interface of the processing equipment, creating a lubricating boundary layer. Metal soaps are commonly used external lubricants. External lubricants are used to reduce the ejection forces encountered in the injection molding process, particularly for brittle materials such as polystyrene. These external lubricants are a good alternative to mold release sprays, which can lead to cycle delays, inconsistent processing, decorating and assembly problems.

Mold Surface Coatings: Another approach to reducing release forces involves the use of low coefficient of friction mold platings or surface treatments [85-94]. Some of these surface treatments provide the additional benefits of improved surface hardness, abrasion resistance, resistance to plate out, and improved corrosion protection. These coatings act as dry lubricants essentially eliminating the need for mold release agent or external lubricant removal prior to secondary operations such as printing, bonding or welding. Conventional surface platings such as electroless nickel plating or electrolytic chrome plating offer improved abrasion resistance and offer a degree of corrosion protection (depending on the polymer), however, their effect on release forces is not well documented.   Specialty hard surfacing treatments such as plasma chemical vapor deposited titanium nitride (TiN) have been shown to reduce ejection forces for polymers such as acetal, nylon, styrenics, and acrylic [86]and improve melt flow during injection [93].   Similar advantages have been reported for molybdenum disulfide, tungsten disulfide coatings [90] and amorphous boron carbide coatings [91].   Another coating that is commonly used to reduce release forces is a PTFE impregnated electroless nickel plating [88].   The latter coating consists of PTFE particles, approximately 1 to 3 μm diameter, suspended within an electroless nickel solution.   The PTFE particles are caught or trapped in the nickel matrix as it forms on the mold cavity or core steel as indicated in Figure 2.92.

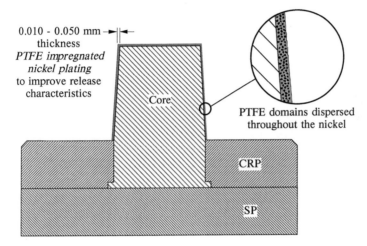

Figure 2.92. Finishes, such as PTFE impregnated nickel, can be used to reduce ejection forces.

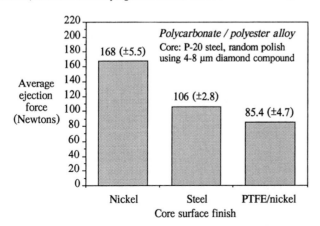

Figure 2.93. Surface coatings such as PTFE impregnated nickel are effective in reducing release forces.

The PTFE forms a thin dry lubricating film on the cavity or core surface. The coating has been shown to reduce coefficient of friction and release forces for a variety of polymers including high impact polystyrene, polycarbonate, and polypropylene [92].

2.6.4   Esthetic Considerations

Part ejection systems utilize moving mechanical components such as ejector pins, blades, sleeves, lifters etc. that leave witness lines on the molding. It is generally the responsibility of the tool designer to design a suitable ejection system for a particular part configuration. However, the part designer must recognize that the ejection components in contact with the molding will result in surface imperfections. The part designer should therefore indicate which locations on the part are not suitable for ejection placement for esthetic reasons. In some cases, such as on a lens type molding shown in Figure 2.94, objectionable ejection defects are not permitted on any surface.

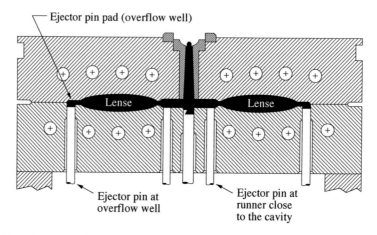

Figure 2.94. Ejector pins, sleeves, lifters and the like do leave witness marks on the molding and must therefore be placed in esthetically acceptable areas.

On such a shallow draw part, it might be possible to eject the part with ejector pins located in the runner system, if the gate is deep (or strong) enough. Ejector tabs can also be added to facilitate ejection as shown in Figure 2.94, however, the tabs require an additional secondary operation for removal.

In most cases, the design of the ejection system for an injection mold is not a stand alone design process. Design decisions associated with part ejection are closely related to parting line location, gate location, and cooling considerations. Consider once again the part shown in Figure 2.5. This part could represent the top half of a clamshell appliance or business machine housing. In the case of a single cavity mold, the simplest way to produce the part would be to have a sprue gate and the standard cavity / core set up (i.e. the cavity is attached to the stationary platen of the molding machine while the core is attached to the moving or force platen of the molding machine). It is generally preferred to have the part stay with the moving half of the mold so that the molding machine's knockout system can be utilized to activate the molds ejector system. However, if the outer surface of the part is an appearance surface, sprue gating into the top exterior surface is esthetically unacceptable. As an alternative, the part could be gated on the underside , however, because parts tend to stay with the core (they shrink onto the core) and the ejector marks must be hidden, the tool must then be designed with ejection provisions on the stationary side of the tool. While this can be accomplished, it is not standard practice, and will result in additional tooling costs. The designer should recognize that there are other possible options or alternatives to stationary side ejection in this case. For example, the conventional cavity and core set up could be used with a cavity side sprue gate was used, if the sprue gate vestage was covered up using a label or logo.

2.6.5 Undercuts and Holes

Ideally, a plastic part should be designed so that it can be ejected from the mold without any special mold actions. Special mold movements such as side action, side coring, angle pins, collapsible cores, unscrewing mechanisms and the like should be avoided whenever possible. These special mold actions can be expensive to tool, add to mold maintenance, may interfere with the mold's cooling layout, and may ultimately add to the overall cycle time for part production. While it may not be possible to eliminate special mold movements, their use should be limited whenever possible. If side actions must be used, movement in a direction perpendicular to the mold opening direction is preferred. Actions at oblique angles should be avoided whenever possible. As an example, the hole in the sidewall of the part shown in Figure 2.95 would require side action to pull the small core pin (that produces the hole) from the hole before the part can be released from the cavity as the mold opens. The side action, and added tooling cost, could be eliminated if the part is designed with consideration towards ejection. For example, the hole could be replaced by a slot in the line of draw, and as a result, no special side actions or core pulls are required.

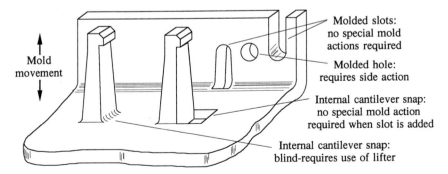

Figure 2.95. Whenever possible, part features such as holes or cantilever snap beams should be "designed for ejection". For example, changing a hole in a part sidewall to a slot will eliminate the tooling costs and maintenance problems associated with side action.

Figure 2.95 also shows that the undercut associated with the cantilever snap beam can be eliminated, if the part design is modified so that the cantilever snap beam is formed with a shut-off, rather than a lifter (see section 6.3.3 for details). The shut-off is the preferred alternative only in applications where the resulting cored slot in the part wall at the base of the snap beam is esthetically and functionally acceptable.

In another example, the part shown in Figure 2.96 has a slot or window in the side wall that is produced using a shut-off rather than a side core pulling action. From a tooling point of view, this approach is preferred since no special mold actions are required. However, it can only be used in applications where the part's sidewall draft angles are sufficient to permit the use of this simple open and shut approach.

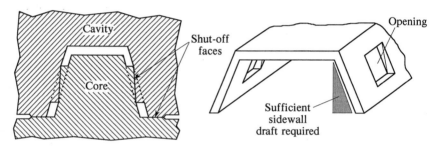

Figure 2.96. The opening in the sidewall of the part is produced using a cavity/core shut-off, eliminating the need for any type of special mold action.

It is essentially impossible to pull parts with external undercuts from the cavity as the mold opens (split cavities or side actions must be used). However, it is possible to eject parts from a core with some degree of internal undercut, since at this stage of the process, the cavity has been withdrawn and the part can deform outwards as the internal undercut rides over the core. The amount of undercut that is permissible is dependent upon the undercut design, material properties at the ejection temperature, and on the dimensional tolerances required. For example, it is possible to "strip" a threaded polyethylene closure from a core, if the part is free to deflect (the cavity is clear) and the threads have been designed with angles that facilitate gradual ejection and minimize the potential for shear failure at the thread root. The polyethylene enclosure will distort and recover as it is ejected or stripped from the core and will continue to shrink after ejection. The dimensional tolerances for parts with undercuts that are stripped from cores can be difficult to predict because there is a strong probability that some permanent distortion will occur. Materials such as thermoplastic elastomers can generally be molded with very large undercuts, however, it may be difficult to design an effective automated ejection system. In some cases, the elastomeric parts must be stripped from the core by hand. Looking at the other extreme, the permissible amount of undercut for rigid, glassy polymers such as polystyrene is very low. In some cases, internal undercuts are purposely cut into the core solely to ensure that the part stays with the core as the mold opens (i.e. to keep the part from sticking in the cavity) as shown in Figure 2.97.

Parts with internal undercuts can be produced to tighter tolerances than those achievable by simply stripping the parts from the cores, if special mold actions are used. In addition,

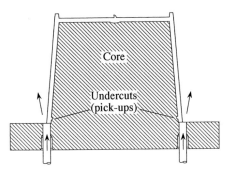

Figure 2.97. In situations where the part is difficult to pull from the cavity, such as when the cavity sidewalls are textured, undercuts are sometimes added to the core side of the tool to ensure that the parts stay on the core when the tool opens.

the relative size and shape of the undercut feature are no longer limited by the plastic material's ductility when special tool actions are used to release the undercut. A variety of mechanisms can be utilized for the purpose of releasing internal undercuts. Commonly used methods include unscrewing mechanisms, removable insert sets, lifters (section 6.3.3) and collapsible cores. Unscrewing mechanisms can be used to produce plastic parts that incorporate an advancing thread design (e.g. closures). Removable inserts are sometimes used for very complex geometries or low production / prototype runs. Removable inserts are metal cavity / core components that are placed in the mold prior to injection and are removed along with the part as the part is ejected. A second set of interchangeable inserts is then placed in the injection mold and the molding process continues, as the first set of inserts is removed by an operator. Insert sets of this type can be used to produce parts with very complicated geometry. While the process is labor intensive, it is particularly popular for low production or prototype molding runs, since it is possible to use relatively simple and low cost tools to produce parts with very complex geometries.

Lost or Fusible Core Molding: In recent years, several processes have been developed that allow the production of extremely complex parts. Parts with extensive internal undercuts that cannot be released using conventional injection molding technologies can be produced using the fusible (or lost) core molding process. The fusible core process has been used to produce parts such as valves, pumps, tennis rackets and automotive air intake manifolds [93-98]. While the process is capital intensive, it can produce very complex parts in one shot, eliminating parts and the cost / quality problems associated with secondary assembly operations.

The fusible core molding process begins with the loading of a mass produced, die or gravity cast metal core into the injection mold (i.e. the core that will produce the complex internal geometry). The tool closes and the plastic part is then molded over the cast core in the usual manner. When the mold opens, the core and the part are ejected together, and a replicate core is loaded into the tool for the next cycle. After molding, the core (usually a low melting point metal alloy) is then melted from the plastic part. Melting can be accomplished using a variety of methods. The hot liquid inductive heating method is preferred since the core can be melted quickly, and the potential for metal oxidation is minimized. The melting of the metal core can be accomplished using a variety of methods, including:

- Circulating hot fluid through the core (for hollow cores)
- Immersing the part and core into a bath of hot fluid ("swimming pool method")
- Inductive heating (likely to result in oxidation of the metal)
- Inductive heating in a hot liquid

After the core is melted, the parts must be inspected using metal detectors to ensure that a complete melt out has been accomplished. The metal alloy is then recast to produce "temporary" cores for subsequent molding cycles.

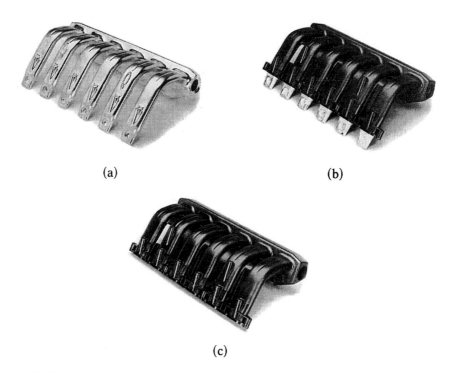

(a)   (b)

(c)

Figure 2.98. Very complicated part geometries can be produced using the fusible or soluble core molding processes. (a) Low melting metal alloy core ready to be loaded into the mold. (b) The molded part and the core are removed from the mold as one piece. (c) Plastic molding after the core has been melted out.

The metal alloys that form the core must have relatively low melting temperatures so that the plastic part is not damaged or distorted during the core melting operations. On the other hand, the cores must also be able to withstand the thermal loads and pressures associated with the injection molding process. In practice, eutectic tin-bismuth alloys are typically used. These alloys exhibit low shrinkage and are relatively easy to work with. Even though these alloys have melting temperatures in the range of 138°C, they can be used for the molding of materials such as glass fiber reinforced nylons at processing temperatures as high as 290°C. This is possible because the thin frozen layer in contact with the core is enough to sustain a temperature gradient within the plastic material. In addition, the heat transfers from the relatively hot core surface towards the cooler central region of the core. The net result for a properly designed process is a core surface temperature that remains below the core melting temperatures. The soft, fusible core must also be able to withstand the mechanical loads associated with molding. The runner design / gate location must be optimized to ensure balanced filling and minimize the potential for core damage due to excessive bending or compressive stresses.

Although this process involves two molding operations, one for the metal core and one for the plastic part, and the core melting steps, it can be used to produce plastic parts with extremely complex internal geometries. An example of such a part is the automotive air intake manifold shown in Figure 2.98 [93]. The air intake manifold is molded from a glass fiber reinforced nylon. Compared to a die cast aluminum manifold, the nylon part offers a number of advantages including:

- Lighter in weight (30-60% lighter than the metal casting)
- Offers improved surface finish resulting in less resistance for the intake air
- Offers exact dimensions without machining
- Tends to keep air cooler due to thermal insulation

The lost or fusible core molding process is used when the structural integrity of a one piece molding is required. In applications where the end-use requirements are less severe, it is more common practice to produce the complex geometry by injection molding two or more separate parts and assembling the parts using a secondary process such as ultrasonic welding.

Collapsible Cores: Collapsible cores provide another method for producing plastic parts with internal undercuts [96-101]. Collapsible cores are segmented cores with flexing elements that collapse inward during the initial stage of ejection to release the internal undercut. Once the collapse has been achieved, the part is easily pushed clear of the core in a second ejection stage. Like unscrewing molds, collapsible cores can be used to produce threaded closures and fittings. However, unlike unscrewing molds, collapsible core molds can also be used to produce parts with internal features such as O-ring grooves, dimples, and even holes in the sidewall of a part (eliminating the need for external side action). Collapsible cores are available as premanufactured "blanks" in a variety of sizes [99,100]. The larger size standard cores have diameters that range from 25 - 90 mm and offer a collapse of 1.20 mm to 3.75 mm per side (permissible depth of undercut feature). Smaller cores, having diameters of 13-24 mm, are also available with collapse distances of 1.32 - 1.50 mm per side. These smaller "mini-cores" cores are limited to applications where the thread or undercut is interrupted (i.e. not continuous over 360°) [101].

Parting Line Location: In certain cases, undercut sections can be avoided simply by altering the orientation of the part within the mold itself. The part shown in Figure 2.100 has ribs extending at an angle from the nominal wall. The part orientation in Figure 2.100a requires a moving core or lifter to facilitate ejection. If the part is set into the tool on an angle as shown in Figure 2.100b, it can be ejected without any special difficulties [102]. However, in general, it is best to avoid any type of projection that is not perpendicular to the nominal wall.

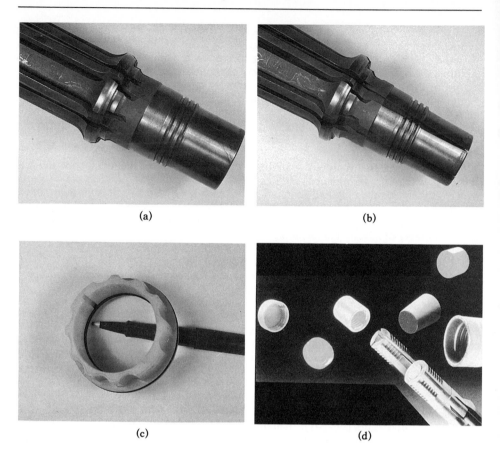

Figure 2.99. Collapsible cores can be used to produce parts with internal undercuts (a) Collapsible core is used to produce a series of internal grooves. (b) Core in the "collapsed" position. (c) Plastic part with an O-ring groove was molded on a collapsible core. (d) Smaller size collapsible cores (mini-cores). Collapsible cavities produce parts with external undercuts. (Courtesy Roehr Tool, Hudson, MA 01749)

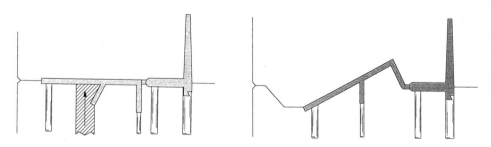

Figure 2.100. In some case, altering the orientation of the part within the tool can simplify part ejection by eliminating undercuts.

2.6.6   Predicting Part Release Forces

The forces associated with ejecting a plastic part from a mold core can be estimated in much the same way that "push-on" forces can be estimated for press fit parts (section 6.2). For example, the forces required to push an undersized gear or hub over a metal shaft can be determined if the geometry, interference, modulus and friction properties are known. Part ejection is essentially the reverse of a press fitting operation. During the cooling phase of the molding process, the parts cool and shrink. The metal core limits the dimensional change for the plastic part, resulting in a level of internal strain (i.e. restrained shrinkage). When the part is pushed from the core during ejection, it exhibits an immediate dimensional change due to elastic contraction.

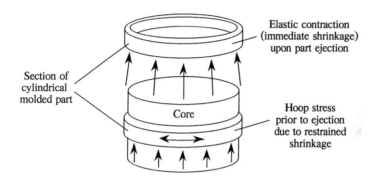

Figure 2.101. Plastic part shrinkage during the cooling phase of the process is restrained by the core. Once the part is ejected, its dimensions change due to elastic contraction.

This immediate dimensional change (core dimension minus the part dimension immediately after ejection) is analogous to the interference value for the press fit part. The frictional ejection forces can be estimated if the following values can be defined [2]:

- Part geometry
- Shrinkage at the time of ejection
- Polymer modulus at the time of ejection
- Frictional characteristics of the core / polymer pairing

The forces of ejection for a plastic part are actually due to the sum of the frictional, vacuum, and mechanical undercut force contributions. Vacuum forces are the result of the pressure differential that forms when closed sleeve or box type moldings are stripped from the core. The magnitude of the vacuum related force is determined by the relative size of the part, and by the ease in which air can enter into the displaced volume between the part and the core (through ejection pin holes etc). The forces of ejection for an open sleeve molding (which has no top and therefore no vacuum forces) with no mechanical undercuts is then due only to the friction forces associated with the vertical wall sections. The breakaway ejection or frictional forces can be determined using:

$$F_e = \mu \cdot P \cdot A \qquad\qquad (2.20)$$

where μ is the static coefficient of friction, P is the contact pressure between the plastic part and the core (due to restrained shrinkage), and A is the sliding surface area of contact between the part and the core. Of the three variables in the equation, the area, A, is most easily obtained. Consider the example of an open cylindrical sleeve such as that shown in Figure 2.101. The initial area of contact is:

$$A = \pi \cdot \varnothing_c \cdot L_c \tag{2.21}$$

where $\varnothing_c$ is the core diameter and L_c is the axial length of the core.

The contact pressure, P, between the plastic part and the core will be influenced by both the degree of restrained shrinkage and the tensile modulus of the polymer at the time (or part temperature) of ejection. Contact pressures are greatest for high shrinkage, high modulus semi-crystalline polymers. Any variable that decreases the shrinkage or modulus at the time of ejection will reduce contact pressure, and therefore ejection force. For example, a decrease in mold close time would reduce ejection force by reducing both the degree of shrinkage and polymer rigidity at the time of ejection. It may, however, be a potential problem ejecting the part at the higher temperature (even though the forces are lower) because the part is softer and may tend to distort as it is ejected.

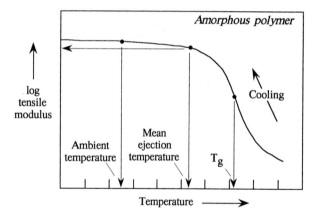

Figure 2.102. Plastic parts must be cooled to the point where they reach a state of rigidity that is sufficient to prevent permanent deformation due to ejection forces and internal stress release.

In practice, plastic parts are ejected as soon as they cool to the point of sufficient rigidity to prevent permanent distortion. This cooling time is determined experimentally by a process engineer. As mentioned previously, the *Vicat Softening Temperature* or the *Deflection Temperature Under Load* are sometimes used as an estimated value of average part temperature at ejection for design related calculations.

The tensile stress through the wall of the part, due to the restrained shrinkage at the time of ejection can be obtained if the tensile modulus of the polymer and the linear shrinkage at the time (temperature) of ejection are known. Unfortunately, the shrinkage value associated with the time of ejection is not easily determined, since parts will continue to shrink after ejection. Pressure - volume - temperature diagrams or computer aided shrinkage simulations can assist in determining the shrinkage value at ejection, or as a practical solution, a percentage of the nominal "mold shrinkage" value can be used.

$$\sigma_T (T_e) = E_T (T_e) \cdot \varepsilon_T (T_e) \qquad (2.22)$$

In the case of a thin walled cylindrical sleeve, the tensile stress is a hoop stress, and can be used to estimate the contact pressure for a sleeve of radius R and wall thickness h.

$$\sigma_H (T_e) = \sigma_T (T_e) = P \cdot R / h \qquad (2.23)$$

In the case of the thin walled open sleeve, the initial breakaway ejection force is then:

$$F_e = 2 \cdot \pi \cdot \mu \cdot E (T_e) \cdot \varepsilon (T_e) \cdot L_c \cdot h \qquad (2.24)$$

The μ value is the static coefficient of friction for the polymer / core pairing. Unfortunately, this value is dependent upon both temperature and normal stress level for most polymers. This is further complicated by the fact that the polymer is molded over the core surface, and the initial breakaway friction value during ejection will involve some degree of polish related undercut release. Friction values generated under realistic molding conditions would be most appropriate, yet are not readily available. Even with all of these uncertainties, the predicted ejection force value provides a rough estimation of the behavior that can be expected during this phase of the process. The ejection force estimate for the cylindrical sleeve was done assuming a zero draft. The value can be corrected for draft angles using Figure 2.103. The figure provides a rough indication of the reduction in ejection force with increasing draft angle. A more detailed discussion and coverage of part ejection forces given by Menges and Mohren [2].

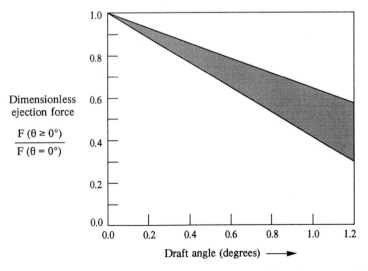

Figure 2.103. The figure can be used to provide a rough indication of the reduction in ejection forces that can be expected when draft angle is added to a core.

2.7   Other Injection Molding Processes

2.7.1   Gas Assisted Injection Molding

Introduction: The gas assisted injection molding process has added new level of flexibility to the design and manufacturing of injection molded plastic parts. Like structural foam molding, the gas assisted injection molding process is a modification of the conventional injection molding process, however, the gas assist process avoids most of the surface finish, part weight, and long cycle time limitations of the structural foam molding process. The gas assist molding process is capable of producing stiff, nearly stress free, sink free moldings, with a relatively good surface finish. The clamp force requirements for the gas assist process are also lower than those associated with the conventional injection molding process. The process offers a great benefit in terms of part design freedom, and is being widely used in automotive, business machine, and consumer product markets. While the process does offer a number of advantages, it is relatively new; hence, there is a learning curve associated with processing / part design and optimization. Compared to conventional injection molding, the gas assist process is more critical in terms of process control, especially for multi-cavity applications. Unlike conventional injection molding, where the wall thicknesses of the part are determined by the tool geometry, the distributions of wall thickness for the gas assisted molding process are determined both by the tool (for the thinner sections of the part) and by process variables such as the degree of underfill, gas injection conditions and mold temperature (for the hollow gas channel areas), indicating the added importance of precise process control. In addition, a licensing fee is generally required for gas assisted molding processes.

A limited description of the gas assisted molding technology is given here, however, a more complete description of the process can be found in the literature [103-109]. The gas assist molding process is most commonly used for (i) thick wall parts such as tubes, handles, or channel type frames, or (ii) larger parts such as television / computer enclosures, panels, shelves or chassis. The primary advantage of the process for the thick wall moldings is that problems associated with excessive material consumption, sink, stress and cycle time can be avoided by coring out the center sections of the molding. These *contained channel flow* applications are generally the easiest to work with because the gas has a clearly defined flow path. In the latter case, the process is applied to thinner walled moldings in an effort to reduce warpage, reduce sinks associated with reinforcing ribs and bosses, and reduce the pressures required to fill the tool. For these thinner walled applications, known as *open channel flow* applications, thicker gas channels are integrated into the part design to provide a predefined flow path for the compressed gas. The thicker gas channels also serve as means for stiffening the part, in much the same way that ribs are used to stiffen conventional injection molded parts. Parts involving open gas flow are more difficult to design and process because the gas must be prevented from penetrating the thinner nominal wall sections of the molding (since the gas is free to travel in any direction that represents the flow path of least resistance). The gas flow channels must be sized, and strategically placed in such a way that both balanced filling and the desired stiffening effect are achieved.

Table 2.5 summarizes the fundamental advantages of the gas assisted injection molding process relative to other molding processes. The table contrasts the characteristics of large polystyrene television enclosures (i.e. a large injection molded part that must have both good esthetics and the ability to support external loading) produced using conventional, structural foam, and gas assisted molding processes [110].

Table 2.5 Comparison of Various Injection Molding Processes as Related to the Manufacture of a Polystyrene Television Enclosure

Molding process	Design flexibility	Product rigidity	Molding cycle time	Product weight	Surface appearance
Conventional injection molding	Good	Fair	Good	Good	Good
Low pressure structural foam	Good	Excellent	Poor	Poor	Poor
Counter pressure structural foam	Good	Excellent	Poor	Poor	Fair
Gas assisted injection molding	Excellent	Good	Good	Excellent	Good

Gas Assist Molding Process Overview: In the simplest terms, gas assist molding processes begin like any conventional injection molding process with the injection of polymer melt into a well vented cavity. The gas channels act as internal runners along the part to fill from a single gate, thereby eliminating weld lines associated with multiple gates. However, only a fixed short volume of melt is injected, and a short shot is purposely produced. At the end of this polymer injection stage (or after a short delay), compressed gas, usually nitrogen due to its relative inertness and availability, is injected through the central core of the melt. The gas pressure acts on the fluid melt core, completing the mold filling process. The gas takes the path of least resistance, penetrating and hollowing (coring out) a network of predesigned thick flow leader sections (gas channels), displacing molten polymer at the core , filling out the entire cavity. This phase of the process is described as the primary gas penetration phase. Since this is a short shot process, packing is not accomplished by the injection ram / cushion, but rather by the gas pressure itself. After mold filling, the gas pressure is maintained in order to pack the part and compensate for volumetric shrinkage (secondary gas penetration). After the part has cooled to the point where it is rigid enough to eject, the gas is vented off through a pin or by sprue breakaway (and sometimes recycled) prior to mold opening and part ejection. The basic phases of the gas assisted injection molding process are depicted in Figure 2.104 [115].

Several gas assisted molding technologies are available. One primary distinction between these processes is based on where the compressed gas is injected. Depending on the specific process, gas can be injected through the molding machine nozzle, or directly into the tool through the runners or cavities. When nozzle gas injection is used, all gas channels must begin at the nozzle, while with direct gas gating into the cavity, the gas channel can be placed into the cavity, independent of melt gating location. While direct gas injection processes are more versatile, the designer must cope with the esthetic problems associated with both melt injection and gas injection / venting when these processes are used.

(1) *Melt injection:* A fixed, short volume of polymer melt is injected into the mold cavity (short shot).

(3) *Packing phase:* After filling, packing is accomplished by maintaining the gas pressure.

(2) *Gas injection:* Compressed gas is injected into the core of the melt. The gas displaces the melt causing the melt to fill the cavity.

(4) *Part ejection:* The compressed gas is vented before the part is ejected.

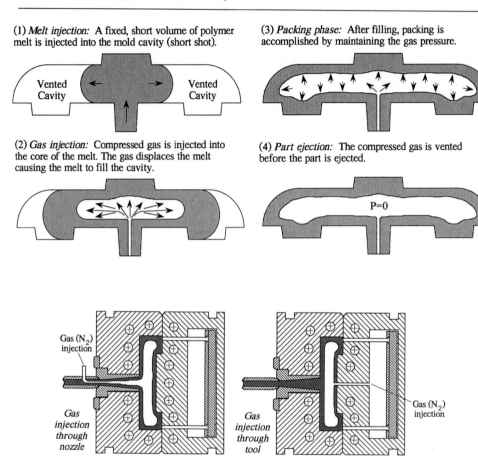

Figure 2.104. (top) Schematic showing the various stages of the gas assisted injection molding process. (bottom) Schematic showing both nozzle and mold gas injection locations.

Gas Assist Molding Process Stages: There are a variety of gas assisted molding technologies available, and their four basic stages of the process are similar, namely; melt flow, melt / gas transition, gas flow (primary gas penetration), and gas packing (secondary gas penetration). Like the conventional injection molding process, the basic stages of the gas assisted process can be represented in terms of cavity pressure profiles over the course of the molding cycle as shown in Figure 2.105.

Mold Filling : In this initial stage of the process, a fixed volume short shot is injected into the mold cavity. This first stage of the gas assisted molding process is essentially equivalent to the early stages of mold filling for the conventional injection molding process (e.g. solid layer formation etc.). Compared to the conventional molding process, the filling pressure requirements are reduced since the cavity is only partially filled, and because the thicker gas channels facilitate flow. It is important for the polymer melt to be evenly distributed within the cavity during the melt filling stage of the process if the final distribution of the polymer is to be successfully completed during the gas flow stage [105]. If the relatively thick gas channels are improperly positioned, or are too large in diameter, the melt will tend to race-track along the thicker gas channel before gas injection, defeating the purpose of the channel, and creating the potential for gas traps. Computer aided flow analysis packages are invaluable here, since they can be used to make wall thickness and channel location decisions before the tool is built, eliminating costly trial and error development procedures [112].

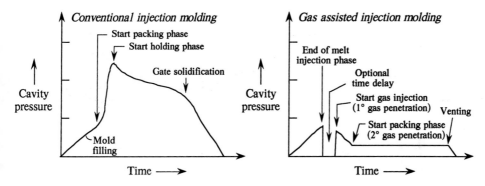

Figure 2.105. Typical cavity pressure profiles for the conventional (left) and the gas assisted (right) injection molding process.

Melt / Gas Transition : The timing of the transition from melt injection to gas injection can have a significant effect on the final quality of the part. In the nozzle gas injection processes, the flow of melt (melt injection phase) is complete before injection of the compressed gas. When the compressed gas is injected directly into the cavity, it is possible to initiate gas flow prior to the end of the melt filling stage. It is sometimes desirable to delay gas injection for a fixed period of time after melt injection, so that the polymer cools and becomes more viscous, reducing the tendency for the gas to permeate outside of the gas channels, into the adjacent wall sections of the molding. Unfortunately, when a delay is used, the surface quality of the molding is likely to suffer due to the stop/start action (flow hesitation effect) or in the worst case, freeze-off can occur [111].

Gas Injection Phase : The final phase of mold filling is accomplished using compressed gas injection at pressures that typically range from 0.5 - 30 MPa (70 - 4500 psi) using either a pressure or volume based gas injection system [112]. The gas pressure used is sufficient to overcome the viscous resistance of the polymer melt, advancing forward in the cavity toward the unfilled areas of the part as indicated in Figure 2.106 [113]. As the gas flows through the gas channels (the gas should remain contained within the channels), it displaces molten polymer ahead of it into the remaining empty regions of the cavity. This portion of the mold filling phase is typically short in duration, since the gas moves rapidly through the channel until all empty sections of the cavity are filled with molten polymer [108]. The part wall thickness surrounding the hollow gas channels will

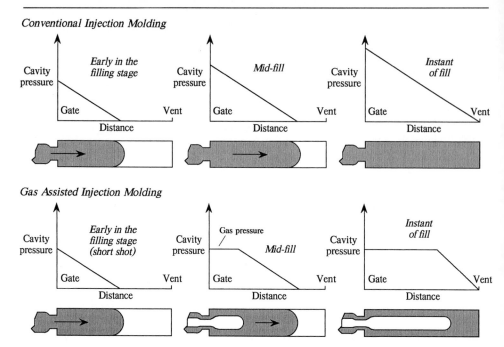

Figure 2.106. Simplified concept of cavity pressure distributions for the conventional and gas assisted injection molding during the mold filling stage of processing.

be influenced by a number of variables including the degree of cavity underfill, tool temperature, and by the overall uniformity of gas distribution within the gas channels.

Problems that can occur during the gas filling phase include: blow through (due to insufficient polymer ahead of the gas bubble), gas traps (due to race-tracking), hesitation marks (due to gas injection delay time), short shots (due to low pressure or poor design), or gas penetration into thin sections of the molding (due to race-tracking, which leads to high pressure differential along channel) [105]. Gas penetration into the thinner sections is a particular concern since it will adversely affect the mechanical performance of the part.

Gas Packing : After filling, pressure is maintained on the gas within the channels, which in turn acts on the polymer melt. Because the pressurized gas channels are distributed throughout the various sections of the part, cavity pressure distributions tend to be fairly uniform, thereby reducing the potential for warpage. As the part cools and shrinks during the gas packing phase, additional gas penetration occurs. The outer surfaces of the thick sections of the part do not sink because the sections are cored out, and are pushed against the mold surface by the gas as the part solidifies. Any sink in these sections takes place internally, rather than on the exterior surface of the part [103]. Improper packing pressure can also lead to problems. For example, overpacking can cause the gas to permeate outside the gas channel into the adjacent wall (fingering) leading to the same types of defects associated with gas filling related permeation into thin sections [111].

Gas Assist Design Principles: When designing parts for the gas assisted injection molding process, it is imperative that both manufacturing concerns (moldability) and end use requirements be considered. This means that part design, tool design, and process design must all be done simultaneously (i.e. concurrent engineering). It is also advantageous to utilize computer simulations of the gas assisted molding process prior to cutting the tool with the goal of optimizing the design and process conditions. The use of process simulation is widespread in the gas assist area because (i) the process is more complex than conventional injection molding, and (ii) the process is relatively new, and as a result, few designers have extensive experience with it. While there are some basic guidelines associated with the design of gas assist parts, the rules of thumb do not apply in all situations due to the complexity of the process [111].

Materials: The gas assisted injection molding process has been used successfully with most classes of thermoplastic materials, including filled and reinforced grades. Because the filling phase of the gas assisted process is so critical (both melt and gas flow), the rheological behavior of the polymer has a large impact on processing [111,113,114].

Gas Channel Layout: The layout of the gas channels is perhaps the most critical design decision associated with gas assisted processing. The layout will affect both product stiffness and processing behavior. The gas channel layout will predetermine gas flow, and influence the flow of melt during the initial short shot injection phase of the process. Closed loop gas flow channels that loop back together should be avoided [103]. The gas (and melt) flow paths should be as balanced as possible since both the melt and the gas flow will follow the path of least resistance. The channels should be oriented in the general direction of flow and positioned in such a way that they end near the last area of the part to fill (where the pressure during fill is lowest). For example, diagonal gas channels would be most appropriate for a centrally sprue gated rectangular part. In terms of mold filling, the addition of the relatively thick gas channels can be a problem since their introduction will likely change the filling pattern, with the potential problem of race-tracking along the channels. Race-tracking must be avoided since it can result in gas traps, and because the gas cannot fill channels that are completely filled with polymer. Race-tracking is less likely to occur when a larger number of smaller cross section gas channels are used. Alternatively, melt can be injected into the thinner sections of the molding when a direct gas injection option (into the gas channels) is available [113].

Gas Channel Geometry: Gas channels can have a variety of geometries, and like ribs, are generally located on the non-appearance surface of the molding. The part thickness in the gas channel area must be greater than that of the adjacent wall in order to create a well defined flow path for the compressed gas. The local thickness associated with the gas channel is at least two to three times the nominal wall thickness at a minimum. Thicker gas channels provide additional stiffness, but when the gas channels become too thick, race-tracking becomes a problem. It is generally better to use more, smaller cross section gas channels to eliminate this problem. Reinforcing ribs can be added to the gas channels for added stiffness as shown in Figure 2.107 and 2.108 [103, 110-113].

Design Methodology: Methodology for the design of open channel flow gas assisted moldings are described in various sources [111-113]. All of these approaches rely heavily on the use of computer aided mold filling (for the short shot portion of the process) and gas assisted molding simulation software. The general design process involves developing a proper layout or network of gas channels throughout the part and sizing the gas channels such that uniform mold filling and gas penetration are achieved.

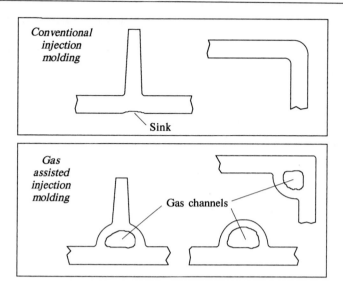

Figure 2.107. Typical gas channel geometries for the gas assisted injection molding process. Gas channels are commonly integrated into corners, ribs or other design features.

Figure 2.108. Photo showing a typical gas channel cross section.

2.7.2   Structural Foam Molding

Introduction: The thermoplastic structural foam molding process is a modified version of the conventional injection molding process which yields thermoplastic parts consisting of solid external skins over the surfaces of the molding surrounding an inner cellular (or foam) core [116-127]. The structural foam process is particularly suited for the production of large, relatively thick thermoplastic parts. The skin / foam core / skin material distribution which results from the structural foam process is ideally suited for bending applications, since the outer fibers (or skins) are subject to the highest tensile and compressive stresses, while the neutral axis runs through the weaker inner foam core. A typical structural foam cross section is shown in Figure 2.109 [116].

Figure 2.109. Typical structural foam cross section showing the integral skins and the foam core. (Courtesy General Electric Plastics, Pittsfield, MA 01201)

The structural foam process also offers a number of advantages from a manufacturing point of view. The process is capable of producing complex, thick parts that are essentially sink free, have a very low level of internal stress, and as a result, less of a tendency to warp or distort. In addition, the clamp force requirements for most structural foam molding processes are an order of magnitude lower than those associated with the conventional injection molding process due to the relatively low cavity pressures associated with the process. As a result of the lower cavity pressures and clamping forces, softer tools can be used (aluminum or soft steel tools for production runs) and larger parts (in terms of projected area) can be produced. As a result of these advantages, the structural foam process is widely used in the manufacturing of large moldings such as business machine housings, chassis, computer housings, large storage bins, pallets and other large products where bending stiffness is a primary requirement. Structural foams also offer improved thermal insulation and good sound dampening characteristics. While the general term "thermoplastic structural foam" is used to describe thermoplastic parts having a cellular core and integral skins, there are a number of molding processes that can be used to achieve this construction.

Low Pressure Structural Foam Molding: The low pressure structural foam molding process is by far the most commonly used process for the manufacturing of structural foam parts. The process can be carried out using standard injection molding presses or special low pressure foam molding machines (typically having larger platen sizes, reduced clamp capacity, larger platens, larger shot size, and faster injection capabilities). This modified injection molding process is commonly used with polymers such as HDPE, PP, ABS, PC, ABS/PC blends and modified PPO, although virtually any thermoplastic material can be processed in this manner [117-121]. The resins that are used with the low pressure foam molding process contain a small quantity of blowing or foaming agent, typically a chemical blowing agent (CBA) having a decomposition temperature that has been closely matched with the processing temperature of the base resin. During processing, these CBAs decompose to yield large volumes of gas (carbon dioxide, nitrogen, etc.) to provide the foaming action. In special cases, physical blowing agents or compressed gas are used in place of the CBA. The resin used for the process can be purchased as a precompounded structural foam-grade containing the CBA, or the CBA can be added on-site using (i) precompounded master batches (contain higher concentration of CBA) or (ii) by dry blending the CBA powder directly with the base resin pellets. While the latter methods introduce additional processing and handling steps, they allow a processor to easily alter and optimize the blowing agent concentration in the formulation for each application. Structural foam resins may also contain other additives such as finely divided inorganic powders that have been added as nucleating agents to promote uniform foam cell structure. The low pressure structural foam process is a short shot process that begins with plastication of the resin / CBA material system (the shot is typically 10-35% short depending on the cavity size, cavity thickness, and the desired density reduction). During plastication, the CBA thermally decomposes to yield gas, most of which remains in solution, under pressure at this stage of processing. The short shot is then rapidly injected into the mold cavity. Skins are formed as the gas bubbles near the surface collapse as they are forced against the mold surface [118]. The mold cavity is well vented, and the expanding gases continue to push the short shot out to the extremities of the cavity (creating the foam core) in order to complete the fill. After filling, the gas pressure continues to push equally in all directions, forcing the solid skins against the mold surface as the part cools, effectively eliminating sink marks. Compared to the conventional injection molding process, shrinkage stresses and warpage are greatly reduced for the low pressure structural foam process. This is due to the relatively uniform cavity pressures and the shear compliance of the foam core. There can, however, be significant density gradients along the flow length depending upon the part geometry and processing conditions used. Before ejection, the part must be cooled to the point where it has sufficient rigidity to resist the stresses associated with ejection, and the internal gas pressure, which unlike gas assisted molding, cannot be vented off. Residual gas pressure can cause post blowing (an increase in part thickness after ejection) if the part is not sufficiently rigid.

While the low pressure structural foam process is capable of producing large thick, stiff, sink free and nearly stress free moldings, it also has a number of disadvantages in comparison to the conventional injection molding process. The relatively thicker foam walls associated with structural foam molding will inevitably lead to a significant increase in molding cycle time. The thicker wall may also lead to an increase in material consumption since the density reduction may be less than the wall thickness increase (in comparison with a thinner wall but ribbed conventional solid molding). The wall thickness used in most structural foam applications ranges from about 4.0 mm (thin walled structural foam molding) to 9.0 mm, with density reductions in the 10 - 35% range, although density reductions of 15 - 20% are most common. It generally becomes more difficult to achieve the higher density reductions with the thinner walled foam parts, but the thinner walled parts tend to have an improved surface appearance.

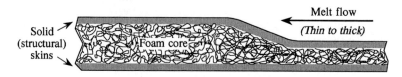

Figure 2.110. Schematic representation of a thermoplastic structural foam molding showing a tapered wall thickness transition and direction of melt flow.

When low pressure structural foam parts have variable wall thicknesses, it is generally better to gate into the thinner section of the molding since it is easier for the gas pressure to fill out the thicker sections of the cavity. Unlike conventional injection molding, there is no problem with premature solidification of the thin section between the thicker section and the gate, since this is a short shot foam process and packing is the result of internal gas pressure.

Without question, the most significant limitation of the conventional, low pressure structural foam process is the relatively poor surface quality that is achievable. During mold filling, as the expanding mass of melt travels through the mold cavity, the bubbles or cells that come in contact with the mold surface tend to rupture. Due to problems with venting and skin formation, a discolored, relatively rough swirl pattern forms over the surface of the molding [122]. Thinner wall structural foams tend to have a better surface appearance due to their higher filling pressure requirements, which tends to pack out the swirled surface to some degree. Process modifications that lead to faster injection rates will tend to improve surface appearance for structural foam parts, however, surface quality problems are a major issue for most appearance parts. In some instances, the swirl look is purposely imparted to create a wood grain like appearance (textured tools can also be used), however, the specific swirl pattern / surface appearance that is desired is not always achievable. In most cases, low pressure structural foam parts slated for appearance applications are painted in order to improve their surface appearances. The painting operations typically involve a number of sequential steps including sanding / filling, priming, primary color application, and surface texturing, and therefore can add a significant cost to the part. In addition, a time delay between molding and painting is generally required to provide adequate time for outgassing before paint application.

Design guidelines for structural foam parts are in most ways similar to those associated with conventional injection molded parts (e.g. adequate draft angles etc.) Structural foam moldings must incorporate adequate radii and flow transitions to facilitate flow and minimize stress concentrations due to service loads. Other mold filling concerns such as weld lines and race-tracking must also be considered. Weld line integrity can be a particular problem in foam molding due to gas venting problems and the relatively low cavity pressures associated with the process. Flow obstructions such as the louvers shown in Figure 2.111 should be positioned in such a way (relative to the gate) that flow in enhanced and thin weld areas are avoided.

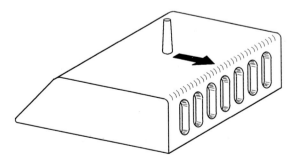

Figure 2.111. Features such as depressions, grills and louvers should be oriented along the direction of flow whenever possible to assist in mold filling.

Certain aspects of structural foam design, such as structural design, become more complicated due to the "composite" nature of the structural foam. Like conventional moldings, orientation effects and morphology are important considerations, but a structural foam designer must also consider the effects of factors such as skin thicknesses, overall density reduction, and cell structure on the mechanical properties of the molding. The mechanical performance of a structural foam part, especially impact performance is greatly influenced by skin / core structure. Whenever possible, structural foam parts should be designed in such a way that they are subject to bending loads, where the integral solid skins are subject to the highest stresses. The strength properties of the inner structural foam core are greatly reduced in comparison with the solid skins. This can present a problem in areas such as self threading screw assembly. Inserts are generally recommended for structural foam parts subject to repeated.

Unlike conventional solid injection moldings, the deflection and stresses associated with the loading of a particular structural foam part design are difficult to predict in advance due to uncertainties associated with the skin / core structure. The most common approach for deflection predictions is to use a bulk modulus value associated with a particular density reduction and part thickness. Alternatively, designers could use composite layer bending theory if the properties of the individual skin and foam core layers are known. Unfortunately, the individual layer thickness and densities are not easily predicted by the designer in advance. In addition, the layers are not clearly defined (there is a transition region at the solid / foam core interface) and as a result, this approach is not easily applied. Regardless of the method used, it is important for structural designers to recognize that there can be very significant density variations throughout the part which lead to localized property variations. Density variations are a particular problem for multi-cavity structural foam tools that do not fill evenly (e.g. family molds).

Structural foam resins are sometimes reinforced with fibers, such as glass, to provide additional stiffness and strength [121-125]. The addition of the fibers can lead to anisotropic mechanical behavior, but does not result in the same degree of anisotropic shrinkages that occur during conventional injection molding of fiber reinforced polymers. The degree of anisotropy due to flow induced orientation has been shown to be less significant at lower fiber loading levels.

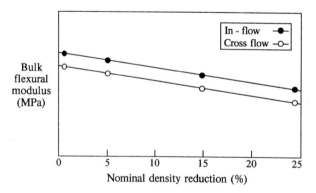

Figure 2.112. The mechanical properties of fiber reinforced structural foams are influenced by both density reduction and fiber orientation.

Counterpressure Structural Foam Process: The counterpressure structural foam molding process is a modification of the more conventional low pressure structural foam process that is capable of producing structural foam parts with improved surface appearance and mechanical performance. While the counterpressure foam process is somewhat more complex than the conventional low pressure process (in terms of ancillary equipment and process steps), the savings associated with reduced secondary finishing / painting costs can be very significant [117, 120, 122, 123].

The counterpressure process differs from the conventional low pressure structural foam process in that the cavity of the tool is pressurized (typically using compressed nitrogen gas) before the resin and blowing agent are injected into the mold. Injection of the melt into a pressurized tool delays expansion of the compressed blowing agent gases until most of the shot is in the tool when the counterpressure gas is vented. The expansion delay allows the skins (outer surfaces) to form before expansion (or foaming) occurs, resulting in a relatively swirl free surface. While the counterpressure process may not completely eliminate the need for painting when appearance is critical, its finishing procedure is generally simplified to the point where only one finish coat of paint is required. The process has also been shown to produce foam parts with a more uniform cell structure and thicker skins. The density reductions that are achievable with the counterpressure process are typically 3 to 8% lower than those associated with the conventional low pressure structural foam process. The higher density, improved surface finish, and more uniform skin / core structure lead to significant improvements in mechanical properties compared to the conventional low pressure process. For example, significant increases in the breaking strain for counterpressure parts provide additional safety and design flexibility in areas such as snap fit design [122, 123].

The counterpressure structural foam process, however, is more complex, and requires precision sequencing for the pressurization, mold filling and venting stages. The tools that are used with the process must be capable of being pressurized. This is generally accomplished using O-rings around the tool faces, core pins, ejection pins, etc. (existing low pressure structural foam tools can generally be modified) and as a result, the additional tooling and maintenance costs must be considered. In addition, the maximum flow lengths that are possible with counterpressure processes are typically reduced by as much as 10 - 20% due to the added resistance to filling [122]. While there are a few limitations, the counterpressure structural foam process retains the fundamental benefits of the traditional low pressure structural foam process (i.e. high bending stiffness to weight ratios, reduced sinks, reduced warpage, low cavity pressure), but offers very significant improvements in both surface quality and mechanical performance.

High Pressure Foam Processing: While low pressure foam molding techniques are used most commonly for the production of structural foam parts, there are several high cavity pressure processes that are used to a lesser extent. The cavity pressures encountered in these processes are similar to those encountered in conventional injection molding and as a result, the clamp tonnage (and tooling strengths / hardnesses) required for these high cavity pressure foam molding processes are greater than those associated with the conventional low pressure structural foam process. A typical process begins with the injection of a foamable melt into the mold cavity. The cavity is completely filled and packed in a manner equivalent to solid molding. Once the solid skins are formed sufficiently, the cavity then undergoes a controlled expansion (using a moving core, slide or through platen movement) and foaming takes place. The process offers excellent control over part weight / dimensions, and excellent surface finish / color.

Unfortunately, the process can only be used with parts of limited complexity and tooling cost are relatively high [116, 120].

2.7.3   Co-injection Molding

A variety of co-injection molding technologies exist for the production of plastic parts. These technologies are very specialized and require specially constructed co-injection molding machines. While these processes offer many advantages, their use has been limited due to the limited availability of co-injection molding machines. All co-injection processes utilize two (or more) reciprocating screw injection units, each of which plasticates and injects a different material (e.g. different grade, color, etc.). The various co-injection processes are categorized according to where and when the individual shots are injected.

For example, two (or more) color molding (two shot molding) is a process that is used for parts such as computer keys or multicolored automotive taillight lenses. The process is essentially an in-mold welding or assembly process where one part is molded using one resin, and the second resin is molded onto the first part after a section of the tool retracts or the part rotates to a second larger cavity (see section 6.4.2.3).

Another co-injection process is categorized as the sandwich molding process [128-130]. This type of co-injection process is analogous to the co-extrusion process where a multi-layered structure is formed. This process also uses a molding machine with two velocity controlled, reciprocating screw injection units. During the injection phase of the process, both material components are shot through a common nozzle assembly and feed system (sprue and runners) into the cavity. The nozzle is essentially a feedblock that causes one of the resin components to surround the other, and a skin-core construction is achieved.

A typical co-injection process begins with the injection of the solid outer (skin) component. Shortly after skin injection begins, the other solid or foam component (the core) injection begins. This starts a period of simultaneous injection. At some point during the fill, skin injection is complete, and the core injection continues until the filling phase is complete. The layered skin core structure is maintained during the fill due to the fact that the flow through the feed system and cavity is laminar. This prevents intermixing of the various layers, and results in complete encapsulation of one material with another, with predictable and repeatable skin / core ratios [125,127].

While co-injection molding specialized molding equipment it can offer a number of appearance, performance, and economic advantages. The skin material that is used with the process is selected with consideration towards color, surface quality, abrasion resistance, weatherability, chemical resistance, friction characteristics and other surface properties. The core material is commonly a chemically blown foam (for thicker parts) or can be a solid, often a dimensionally stable, or stiff reinforced material. In the case of the foam core, the co-injection process results in a "structural type" foam part with very good esthetics. For thinner solid core / solid skin moldings, a variety of performance advantages can be achieved. Common applications include the production (i) stiff, dimensionally stable high surface quality moldings produced with neat skins and fiber reinforced cores, (ii) molded housings with electromagnetic interference shielding capabilities produced using a conductive metal fiber reinforced core and neat skin resins,

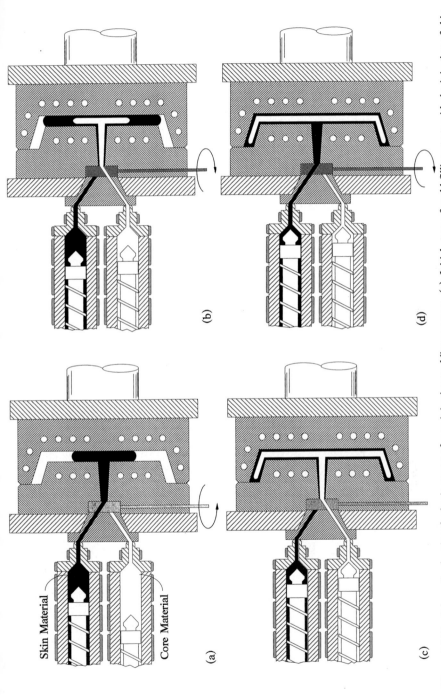

Figure 2.113. Schematic showing the basic stages of a co-injection molding process: (a) Initial stage of mold filling starts with the injection of skin material. (b) Injection at an intermediate stage: core material flows through the center part. (c) At competion of core injection, the core is nearly full. The skin is unbroken and uniformly encapsulates the core. (d) After core injection is complete, the valve returns to the starting position and is cleared of core material in preparation of next shot.

and (iii) the production of high surface quality moldings using virgin resin for the skin and recycled or off-specification resin for the core. The latter application is particularly attractive since the core makes up as much as 50 - 60% of the molding volume, resulting in a significant cost savings in many applications. While most tool geometries and materials are suitable for the co-injection process, there are limitations in the material combinations that can be used. Material variables that are of particular concern are melt viscosities and mold shrinkage values (they should be closely matched) and mutual adhesion [129]. It may also be difficult to achieve complete skin / core uniformity throughout the part, particularly in areas such as ribs and bosses which tend to fill with skin resin. Though the co-injection process has been available for many years, it is not widely used, but there is no doubt that the versatility and benefits of the process will lead to more widespread use.

2.7.4   Injection-Compression Molding

A variety of injection-compression molding processes have been developed over the years which address some of the fundamental problems associated with the conventional injection molding process. The primary advantage of these injection-compression processes is their ability to produce dimensionally stable, relatively stress free moldings at low clamp tonnages (typically 20-50% lower). The processes are particularly useful for thin wall applications where significantly greater flow lengths can be achieved, and internal stress / warpage problems are minimized, even when more viscous resin grades are used. The internal stress reduction also makes the process ideal for optical media and molded lens type applications [131-133].

The basic injection-compression process is an extension of the convention injection molding process, and in concept is much like early transfer molding processes, where a volume of plasticated melt is fed into an open cavity and subsequently compressed. While there are many process variations, the basic processes have common process phases. The process known as sequential injection-compression molding (using a preset gap) begins with the injection of a predetermined volume of melt into a partially open mold cavity. The gap between the cavity and core is typically two times the nominal wall thickness. The thick gap minimizes mold filling pressure drops and faster injection rates can be used. After injection, the clamp is then activated and closed, forcing the melt to flow into the unfilled sections of the tool. Shear edge tooling is used to prevent the melt from flowing beyond the cavity during the compression phase of the process. Sequential injection-compression processes are similar, except that the compression phase is triggered earlier in the injection cycle so that portions of the injection and compression phases occur simultaneously. Both strokes are complete when the screw reaches the desired cushion point [131].

The injection-compression process is most appropriate for shallow draw parts, but can be used for many part geometries with gating practices that ensure a balanced fill. The process has been applied to the manufacture of products such as optical media discs and automotive wheel covers (sprue / disc gated circular parts are ideal for this process due to the balanced radial flow). In the case of the optical discs, high quality optics can be obtained, while the wheel covers exhibit advantages such as improved impact performance. One potential disadvantage of the process is a ring like flow mark or dull area (known as a halo) which can appear on the surface of the molding due to the stalling of the flow (and flow front cooling) which occurs between the injection and compression phases of the process. Changes in process sequencing and process conditions can be used to minimize the problem [131]. An additional limitation of the process is the need for modified tooling and injection-compression molding machines, which are essentially conventional molding machines that have been modified with the appropriate controls and precise clamp positioning capabilities.

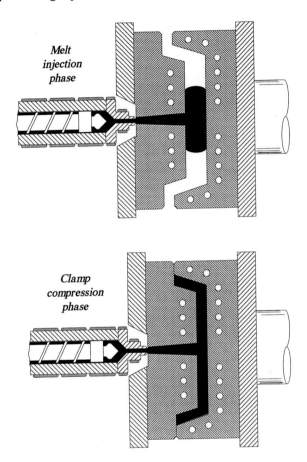

Figure 2.114. Basic schematic of the injection-compression molding process.

2.8   References

1.   Catoen, B., *Plastics Engineering* , **49**, (2), 21 (1993).
2.   Menges, G. and Mohren, P., *How to Make Injection Molds* , Hanser, NY (1986).
3.   Liou, M. and Suh, N., *Polymer Engineering & Science* , **29**, (7), 441 (1989).
4.   Fritch, L., *SPE Annual Technical Conference*, **36**, 302 (1990).

5. Prakash, R., "Development of Molding Area Diagram Analogs", M.S. Thesis, Department of Plastics Engineering, University of Massachusetts Lowell (1991).
6. Willey, S. and Ulmer, A., *SPE Annual Technical Conference*, **32**, 173 (1986).
7. Thompson, M. and White, J., *Polymer Engineering & Science* , **24**, (4), 227 (1984).
8. Cox, H. and Mentzer, C., *Polymer Engineering & Science* , **26**, (1), 488 (1986).
9. Siegmann, A., Kenig, S., and Buchman, H., *Polymer Engineering & Science* , **27**, (14), 1069 (1987).
10. Criens, R., Handler, M. and Mosle, H., *Kunststoffe* , **75** (8), 507 (1985).
11. Cloud, P. and Alvord, R., *Plastics Design Forum*, **4**, (5), 85 (1979).
12. Moldflow Pty. Ltd., 2 Corporate Drive, Sheldon, CT 06484.
13. Structural Dynamic Research Corporation, 2000 Eastman Drive, Milford, OH 45150.
14. AC Technolgy, 31 Dutch Mill Road, Ithaca, NY 14850.
15. Plastics and Computer Inc., 14001 Dallas Parkway, Suite 1200, Dallas TX 75240.
16. Rauwendaal, C., *Polymer Extrusion* , Hanser Publishers, NY (1990).
17. Mehta, K., *Annual Structural Plastics Conference* , Society of the Plastics Industry, 242 (1993).
18. Technical Bulletin, "Engineering Materials Design Guide", General Electric Plastics, Pittsfield, MA (1989).
19. Gastrow, H., *Injection Molds, 102 Proven Designs* , Hanser Publishers, NY (1983).
20. Miller, E., *Plastics Product Design Engineering Handbook* , *Part A*, Marcel Dekker, Inc., NY (1981).
21. Tomari, K., Tonogai, S. and Harada, T., *Polymer Engineering & Science* , **30**, (15), 931, (1990).
22. Jong, W., and Wang, K., *SPE Annual Technical Conference*, **36**, 197 (1990).
23. Lautenbach, S., Wang, K., Chiang, H., and Jong, W., *SPE Annual Technical Conference*, **37**, 372 (1991).
24. Kim, S., and Suh, N., *Polymer Engineering & Science* , **26**, (17), 1200, (1986).
25. Fisa, B., and Rahmani, M., *SPE Annual Technical Conference*, **37**, 396 (1991).
26. E. Bernhardt, ed., *CAE for Injection Molding* , Hanser, NY (1983).
27. Janicki, S., and Peters, R., *SPE Annual Technical Conference*, **37**, 391 (1991).
28. Knasnecky, D., *SPE Annual Technical Conference*, **37**, 363 (1991).
29. Yokoi, H., Murata, Y., Oka, K., and Watanabe, H., *SPE Annual Technical Conference*, **37**, 367 (1991).
30. Lalande, F., *SPE Annual Technical Conference*, **37**, 404 (1991).
31. Dharia, A., and Wolkowicz, M., *SPE Annual Technical Conference*, **37**, 1149 (1991).
32. Worden, E., and Kusion, S., *SPE Annual Technical Conference*, **37**, 2653 (1991).
33. Brewer, G., *SPE Annual Technical Conference*, **33**, 252 (1987).
34. Malloy, R. and Brahmbhatt, S., *SPE Annual Technical Conference*, **38**, (1992).
35. Technical Bulletin, Cloud, J. and McDowell, F., *Reinforced Thermoplastics: Understanding Weld-Line Integrity* , LNP Engineering Plastics, Exton, PA.
36. Rahmani, M. and Fisa, B., *SPE Annual Technical Conference*, **37**, 400 (1991).
37. Liou, M, Fang, L., and Ishii, K., *SAMPE Symposium*, New Materials & Processes, Tokyo, Japan, 1509 (1989).
38. Hagerman, E., *Plastics Engineering* , **29**, (10), 67 (1973).
39. Malguarnera, S., and Manisali, A., *SPE Annual Technical Conference*, **27**, 775 (1981).
40. Wendt, U., *Kunststoffe*, **78**, (2) 10 (1988).
41. Boukhili, R. and Gauvin, R., *Plastics & Rubber Processing Applications*, **11**, (1) 17 (1989).
42. Criens, R., and Mosle, H., *Polymer Engineering & Science* , **23**, (10), 591, (1983).
43. Wright, R., *Thermosets*, Hanser, NY (1991).
44. Technical Bulletin, Hulls Corporation, Hatboro, PA.
45. Bevis, M., *SPE Annual Technical Conference*, **38**, 442 (1992).
46. Technical Bulletin, Scortec, Inc., Gulph Mills, PA.
47. Kirkland, C., *Plastics World*, **49** , (2), 37, (1991).

48.   Malloy, R., Gardner, G., and Grossman, E., *SPE Annual Technical Conference*, **39**, 521 (1993).
49.   Theberge, J., *Plastics Engineering*, **47**, (2), 27, (1991).
50.   Klockner Ferromatik Desma, Erlanger, KY.
51.   Michaeli, W., and Galuschka, S., *SPE Annual Technical Conference*, **39**, 534 (1993).
52.   Gardner, G. and Malloy, R., *SPE Anual Technical Conference*, **40** (1994).
53.   Austin, C., *SPE Annual Technical Conference*, **34**, 1560 (1988).
54.   Potsch, G. and Michaeli, W., *SPE Annual Technical Conference*, **36**, 355 (1990).
55.   Lee, M., et. al., *SPE Annual Technical Conference*, **34**, 288 (1988).
56.   Santhanam, N. and Wang, K., *SPE Annual Technical Conference*, **36**, 277 (1990).
57.   Austin, C., *Warpage Design Principles*, Moldflow Pty. Ltd., Kilsyth, Victoria, Australia (1991).
58.   Liou, M., et. al., *SPE Annual Technical Conference*, **36**, 288 (1990).
59.   Bralla, J., ed., *Handbook of Product Design and Manufacturing*, McGraw Hill, NY (1986).
60.   Spensor, R., and Gilmore, C., *Modern Plastics*, **28** (___) 97 (1950).
61.   Whelan, A., *Injection Molding Materials*, Applied Science Publishers, 168 (1982).
62.   ASTM D955, Standard Test Method for Measuring Shrinkage from Mold Dimensions of Molded Plastics, Annual Book of ASTM Standards, **8.01** (1991).
63.   Noller, R., *Plastics Engineering*, **49** (5), 23 (1991).
64.   Sepe, M., *SPE Annual Technical Conference*, **37**, 238 (1991).
65.   Rohn, C. and Herh, P., *SPE Annual Technical Conference*, **34**, 1135 (1988).
66.   Anonymous, *Plastics Design Forum*, **4**, (2), 61 (1979).
67.   Bernhardt, E., *Plastics Design Forum*, **14**, (5), 61 (1989).
68.   *Customs and Practices of the Mold Making Industry: Classification of Injection Molds for Thermplastic Materials*, Society of the Plastics Industry, Washington DC (1989).
69.   Chiang, H., et. al., *SPE Annual Technical Conference*, **37**, 242 (1991).
70.   Sanschagrin, B., *SPE Annual Technical Conference*, **35**, 1051 (1989).
71.   Gupta, M. and Wang, K., *SPE Annual Technical Conference*, **39**, 2290 (1993).
72.   Cloud, P. and Wolverton, M., Technical Bulletin, "Predicting Shrinkage and Warpage of Reinforced and Filled Thermoplastics", LNP Engineering Plastics, Exton, PA.
73.   Technical Bulletin, "Valox Injection Molding", General Electric Plastics, Pittsfield, MA (1988).
74.   Gallucci, R., et. al., *Plastics Engineering*, **49** (5), 23 (1993).
75.   Sors, L. and Balazs, *Design of Plastic Molds and Dies*, Elsevier Publishers, NY (1989).
76.   Ballman, R. and Shusman, T., *Modern Plastics*, **37**, 126 (1959).
77.   ASTM D648, Standard Test Method for Deflection Temperature Under Flexural Load, Annual Book of ASTM Standards, **8.01** (1991).
78.   ASTM D1525, Standard Test Method for Vicat Softening Temperature of Plastics, Annual Book of ASTM Standards, **8.01** (1991).
79.   Burke, C. and Malloy, R., *SPE Annual Technical Conference*, **37**, 1781 (1991).
80.   Tobin, W., *Plastics Design Forum*, **14**, (5), 25 (1989).
81.   Society of the Plastics Industry, Washington, D.C.
82.   Technical Bulletin, Mold-Tech Division of Roehlem Industries, Chicopee, MA 01013.
83.   Gachter, R., and Muller, H., eds., *Plastics Additives Handbook*, Hanser, NY 300 (1985).
84.   Daoust, H., and Stepek, J., *Additives for Plastics*, Springer-Verlag, NY, 39 (1983).
85.   Siegman, T., *Kunstostoffe*, **73** (___), 25 (1983).
86.   Hoffmann, H., *Kunststoffe*, **81** (10), 59 (1991).
87.   Daniels, V., Hamer, B., and Hannebaum,, A., *Kunststoffe*, **79** (___), 15 (1989).
88.   Technical Bulletin, Poly-Plating, Inc., Chicopee, MA 01022.
89.   Technical Bulletin, General Magnaplate Corporation, Linden, NJ 07036.
90.   Technical Bulletin, E / M Corporation, West Lafayette, IN 47906.
91.   Technical Bulletin, Carolina Coating technologies, Inc., Conover, NC 28613.
92.   Balsamo, R., Hayward, D. and Malloy, R., *Society of Plastics Engineering Annual Technical Conference*, **39**, 2515 (1993).

93.   Fallon, M., *Plastics Technology*, **36** (6), 41 (1990).
94.   Dowler, B., *Injection Molding*, **1** (2), 42 (1993).
95.   Albrecht, F., Hirschfelder, K., Jaser, K., and Jeschonnek, P., Automobil - Industrie, 5, 449 (1990).
96.   Hauck, C. and Schneiders, A., *Kunststoffe*, **77** (12), 1237 (1987).
97.   Sattler, E., *Modern Plastics*, **71** (1) (1993).
98.   Galli, E., Plastics Design Forum, 1**7**, (4) 24 (1992).
99.   Technical Bulletin, Roehr Tool Corporation, Hudson, MA
100. DME Corporation, Madison Heights, MI
101. Tarahomi, S., *SPE Annual Technical Conference*, **37**, 1761 (1991).
102. Glanvill, A. and Denton, E., *Injection Mold Design Fundamentals* , Machinery Publishing Company, Ltd. (1963).
103. Shah, S.,*SPE Annual Technical Conference*, **37**, 1494 (1991).
104. Shah, S. and Hlavaty, D.,*SPE Annual Technical Conference*, **37**, 1479 (1991).
105. Turng, L.,*SPE Annual Technical Conference*, **38**, 452 (1992).
106. Wilder, R., *Modern Plastics*, **67** (2), 67 (1990).
107. Toensmeier, P., *Modern Plastics* , **69** (10), 69 (1992).
108. Moore, S., *Modern Plastics*, **70** (1), 26 (1993).
109. Simon, T., *Annual Structural Plastics Conference* , Society of Plastics Industry, 221 (1992).
110. Tateyama, H., *Annual Structural Plastics Conference* , Society of Plastics Industry, 223 (1992).
111. Medina, P., *Annual Structural Plastics Conference* , Society of Plastics Industry, 124 (1993).
112. Zuber, P.and Gennari, A., *Annual Structural Plastics Conference* , Society of the Plastics Industry, 124 (1993).
113. Turng, L.,*SPE Annual Technical Conference*, **39**, 74 (1993).
114. Okeke, E. and Cosma, L.,*SPE Annual Technical Conference*, **39**, 79 (1993).
115. Rusch, K., *Plastics Engineering*, **45**, (7), 35, (1989).
116. Technical Bulletin SFR-28B, *Engineering Structural Foam* , General Electric Plastics, Pittsfield, MA 01201.
117. Peach, N., *Plastics Design Forum* , **19**, (8), 19, (1976).
118. Anonymous, *Plastics Design Forum* , **1**, (5), 36, (1976).
119. Farrah, M. and Barone, D., *Plastics Design Forum* , **7**, (4), 59, (1982).
120. Turner, N. and Koski, G., *Plastics Design Forum* , **5**, (4), 60, (1980).
121. Malloy, R., Kadkol, P. and Hornberger, L., SPI Structural Plastics Conference, 191 (1992).
122. Johnson, R., *Plastics Design Forum* , **10**, (4), 94, (1985).
123. Anonymous, *Plastics Design Forum* , **7**, (4), 73, (1982).
124. Technical Bulletin ESF-30, *Conterpressure Processing* , General Electric Pastics, Pittsfield, MA 01201 (1987).
125. Ysseldyke, D., Nimmer, R., and Stokes, V., Annual SPI Structural Foam Conference, 133 (1986).
126. Smoluk, G., and Daruas, R., *Modern Plastics* , **41**, (10), 125, (1964).
127. Semerdjiev, S., *Introduction to Structural Foam* , Society of Plastics Engineers, Brookfield, CT (1982).
128. Theberge, J., *Plastics Engineering* , **47**, (2), 27, (1991).
129. Anonymous, *Plastics Design Forum* , **6**, (4), 61, (1981).
130. McRoskey, J., Annual SPI Structural Plastics Conference, 120, (1992).
131. Rasch, S., Annual SPI Structural Plastics Conference, 107, (1992).
132. Klepek, G., *Kunststoffe* , **77**, (11), 13 (1987).
133. Masui, S., Hara, T., Matsumoto, M., Annual SPI Structural Plastics Conference, 112, (1992).
134. Himasekhar, K., et. al., *Advances in Polymer Technology*, **12**, (3), 233 (1993).
135. Himasekhar, K., et. al., *ASME Journal of Engineering for Industry*, **114**, 213 (1992).
136. Santhanam, N., et. al., *Advances in Polymer Technology*, **11**, (2), 77 (1992).

3 The Design Process and Material Selection

3.1 Introduction

Injection molding is a high production process that can be used to produce plastic parts of very complex geometry. The process can be used with both thermosetting and thermoplastic materials to produce products that meet a variety of end-use requirements. When designing plastic parts, designers must consider a number of esthetic, functional, and manufacturing related issues. The final part design must satisfy requirements in each of these separate areas, which in many cases are in conflict with one another. There are a number of different approaches that can be taken when developing a new product. Historically, new parts or products were developed using a sequential engineering or "over-the-wall" approach to design as depicted in Figure 3.1.

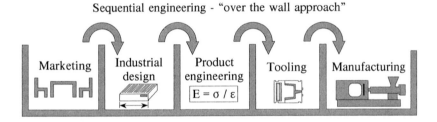

Sequential engineering - "over the wall approach"

| Marketing | Industrial design | Product engineering $E = \sigma / \varepsilon$ | Tooling | Manufacturing |

Figure 3.1. "Sequential Engineering" or the "over-the-wall" approach to product design.

The over-the-wall design process begins with a new product idea generated by marketing groups that have established the need and specify the end-use requirements for the product. This first group then passes the project over-the-wall for the next stage of development, typically done by the industrial design team. The industrial designers specify the overall shape, look and feel of the product, and are most concerned with the ergonomics and esthetics of the design as opposed to manufacturability. Once they have developed the initial models, they pass the design along to product engineering. The project engineering group is generally responsible for selecting the materials and processes that will ultimately be used to manufacture the part, and to ensure that the product will meet all of the end-use requirements. For example, the industrial designer may specify the outward appearance of the computer housing shown in Figure 3.1, but the product engineering group must determine the overall wall thickness and number of ribs that will be required to support the load associated with the monitor sitting in the housing. The product engineers rely on both theoretical analyses and prototype testing. Once the product engineering group is finished with its task, it passes the design on to the tooling engineers who are responsible for both tool design and tool fabrication. It is possible that the plastic part geometries passed on to the tooling engineers are difficult or even impossible to mold, and the designs must be altered at this point in the design process. These design changes must then be approved by the other product design groups (e.g. product engineering, industrial designers, etc.). This approval process can take a great deal of time since other associated design changes may then be required. Eventually, the redesigned product reaches the manufacturing stage.

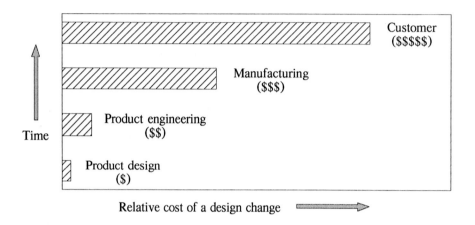

Figure 3.2. The costs and time associated with design changes increase dramatically once a part reaches the manufacturing stage.

While this approach to product development does work, it may not result in an optimum design, and will no doubt take more time and money than would be required using a more concurrent engineering approach. The main problems with the over-the-wall approach to design is the cost and time associated with downstream design changes. For example, industrial designers may not recognize the impact that "zero draft" or "reverse injection" can have on the costs and complexity of injection tooling, since there is little interaction between tooling engineers and industrial designers when the over-the-wall design process is used. The cost of a design change increases dramatically once hard tool building begins.

In recent years, the over-the-wall approach to product design has to a large extent been replaced with a parallel or concurrent engineering approach [1-3]. The concept of concurrent engineering can be illustrated by rotating Figure 3.1 by 90°, and removing the walls to produce Figure 3.4. Perhaps the most important aspect of concurrent engineering is that the development process is team oriented with improved communications between the different marketing, design engineering , and manufacturing groups. It is very common for all of the groups to have an input into each of the design decisions. For example, process engineers who normally are responsible for manufacturing may offer important input on design decisions such as gate location, gate type or material grade selections (from a processing point of view). This would not be the case with the over-the-wall approach, where manufacturing problems are not realized until molded prototypes (or production parts) are produced.

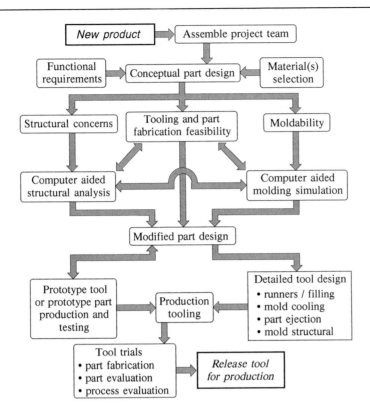

Figure 3.3. When concurrent engineering practices are followed, time to market can be reduced and quality enhanced. This is accomplished by having a number of interconnected, parallel development and engineering streams.

An additional advantage of concurrent engineering is the ability to have design and engineering groups working in parallel. While there is no way tooling or manufacturing can begin before the part has been designed, there are a number of planning and engineering activities that can take place. For example, once the overall sizes and shapes of the parts have been determined, the tooling engineers (who communicate through meetings and CAD integration) can begin ordering steel and components for the production tooling. Likewise manufacturing engineers can ensure that suitable manufacturing equipment will be available when it is needed. Figure 3.3 shows that it is possible to have a number of parallel development side streams that are interconnected [1]. For example, once the conceptual design has been established, different engineering groups can determine the moldability (e.g. using computer aided molding simulations) and structural reliability (e.g. using a computer aided structural analysis packages) concurrently. The advantage here is that significant time savings can be realized compared with the conventional series approach. Concurrent product engineering begins with the assembly of the project team and leader, who communicate regularly throughout the development processes. Improved communication and parallel design streams speed the development process and improve the overall product quality.

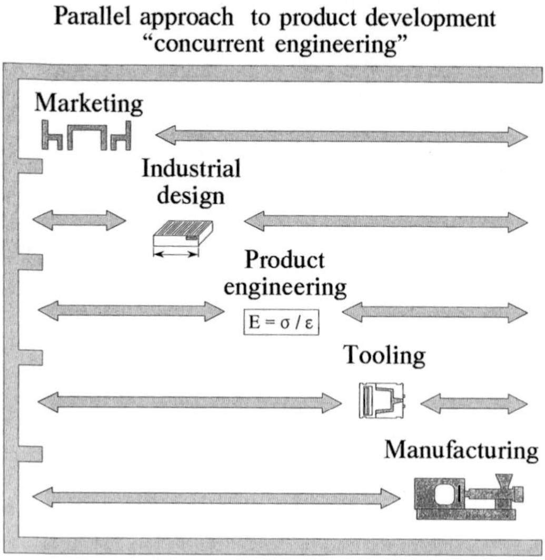

Parallel approach to product development
"concurrent engineering"

Figure 3.4. "Parallel" or "Concurrent Engineering" approaches to product design reduce development time, improves quality, and minimizes the potential for unanticipated production or performance problems.

3.2   The Plastic Part Design Process

While the plastic part design process is best accomplished using concurrent engineering practices, there are a series of steps (some with parallel overlap) that are associated with plastic part design and fabrication. For illustration purposes, it is convenient to consider the following basic stages of part design.

Step 1:   Defining end-use requirements
Step 2:   Create preliminary concept sketch
Step 3:   Initial materials selection
Step 4:   Design part in accordance with material properties
Step 5:   Final materials selection
Step 6:   Modify design for manufacturing
Step 7:   Prototyping
Step 8:   Tooling
Step 9:   Production

Many of the design and development activities in each of these areas occur in parallel, however for discussion purposes, we will look at each phase of the design process individually.

Step 1 - Defining End-Use Requirements

The entire product development process begins with a complete and thorough definition of the product specifications and end-use requirements. Because this is the first stage of development, it is perhaps the most important because designers and engineers will develop a product based on these specifications. If the specifications are incomplete or incorrect, the product will not be suitable for the application. Specifications are the foundation on which designers build. It is important that the end-use requirements of the product be described in "quantitative" rather than "qualitative" terms. Terms such as *strong* or *transparent* leave too much room for misinterpretation. It would be better to say that the product must be capable of withstanding a one meter drop onto concrete at -20°C or the transparency must remain greater than 88% for a period of five years, than to simply indicate that the product needs to be strong or transparent. Unfortunately, it can be difficult to anticipate and quantify all of the end-use requirements for a product, particularly when the potential for misuse is considered. In replacement applications (e.g. metal conversions), there is a product history to draw on, however, this does not exist when entirely new products are being developed. It can be difficult to anticipate all of the end-use product requirements in these new applications. Prototypes (or models) are often used at this stage of design simply to assist in establishing a more complete understanding of the end-use requirements. It is typical to consider factors such as structural loading, environmental conditions, dimensional requirements, standards requirements, and market related issues.

Anticipated Structural / Loading Considerations: The types of loading, rate of loading, duration of loading, frequency of loading etc. must be considered and specified. The loads that can occur during assembly, shipping, storage and end-use must all be considered. Packaging developments, to protect the product during shipping and storage, typically run in parallel with the plastic part design process itself. Part designers must consider both the average case (typical loading conditions) and the worst case scenarios. Perhaps the most difficult decisions here are those which balance the worst case loading scenario vs. the statistical potential for this load vs. the consequences / liabilities of catastrophic failure. Products that are designed to meet unreasonable levels of misuse are more likely to be very expensive, while those that do not consider misuse are likely to experience high failure rates in service. The designer must pay a great deal of attention to the subject of reliability, particularly when product failure can result in personal injury.

Anticipated Environmental Conditions: Because plastic material properties are very sensitive to environmental conditions, it is important to specify the temperatures, relative humidities, chemical environments and radiation exposure that are associated with the end-use application. The environmental conditions that are associated with assembly and storage must also be considered (paint cure ovens, cleaning solvents, adhesives, etc.). High operating temperatures are indicative of creep and possible oxidative degradation problems, while low temperatures indicate a potential for impact problems. The types of chemicals (even household cleaners, etc.) must be clearly specified, along with the potential for ultraviolet radiation exposure (e.g. outdoor use). The problem once again is to anticipate misuse and specify the worst case scenario.

Dimensional Requirements: The dimensions of a plastic part are important in most applications, particularly when a plastic part will be used as a component of a larger assembly. Critical dimensions, surface finishes, flatness and the like must be specified along with realistic tolerances. It is always important to remember that tooling and manufacturing costs are greatly influenced by the tightness of the dimensional tolerance requirements.

Regulations / Standard Compliance: Many plastic products are used in applications that are covered by one or more regulatory agencies. The agencies can be industry / trade groups or government organizations. The important step here is to determine which of these standards organizations have jurisdiction over the product being developed. Once this has been established, it is a matter of obtaining the published standards from these organizations and complying with its requirements. Standards range from material sanctions (e.g. food grades, flammability, etc.) to dimensional standards (e.g. plumbing fittings, fastener dimensions, etc.) to end-use performance standard (e.g. EMI shielding capabilities, etc.). In many cases, pre-production or prototype products are required for evaluation by the standard agency.

Marketing Restrictions: There are also a variety of marketing or industrial design related requirements that must be specified during the initial stage of development. Items such as the anticipated production quantities, service life (replacement interval) and maximum product cost must be specified. Given all of this information, the product development team must develop the best possible design / product for the application at the lowest possible cost (i.e. the most efficient design). Other market related restrictions that are related to esthetic considerations such as color, size, or shape must also be clearly specified as quantitatively as possible. Models (non-functional prototypes) can be extremely useful as a medium for communication here since it can be very difficult to quantify esthetic variables.

Step 2 - Preliminary Concept Sketch

Once the end-use requirements for the product have been specified, the product development team will work with industrial designers to develop initial concept sketches of the product. These sketches are typically 3D renderings rather than CAD drawings. Areas of the part that are of particular concern are highlighted and detailed. At this point, it is best to specify which functions and dimensions of the part are fixed and which are variable. Fixed functions are those in which there is no flexibility from a design point of view (e.g. dimensions which are specified by standards, etc.) while variable functions are those which have not been specified in the initial stage of design. As an example, consider the garden hose nozzles shown in Figure 3.5.

The design task at hand is to design an all plastic hose nozzle. If 10 designers are given equivalent product specifications and are asked independently to design the all plastic hose nozzle, it is likely that 10 different designs will be created. However, certain aspects of each design will be equivalent. For example, the inside dimensions in the areas of the inlet thread will be equivalent because these dimensions are governed by standards, and there is no room for variation or creativity. However, other aspects, such as the product's overall shape or the method used to valve the water flow, may vary from design to design. One of the plastic nozzles shown in Figure 3.5 is very similar in appearance to the die cast metal nozzle. It is very likely that the designer of the plastic part was greatly influenced by the existing metal design. On the other hand, the other plastic hose nozzle in Figure 3.5 performs the same basic function, but does this using different methods. This product has a totally different look.

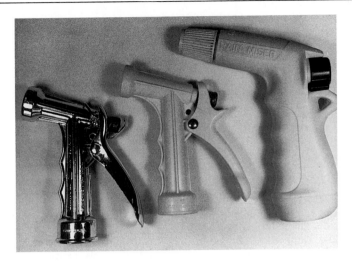

Figure 3.5. Plastic materials are commonly used in material replacement applications. The plastic part in the middle is very similar in form to the metal part on the left, while the plastic hose nozzle on the right has been developed with little influence from the metal product.

In fact, in situations such as this metal replacement application, it is best to work only with the product specifications rather than with the existing metal part alone. Once a designer sees and evaluates the functionality of the metal part, it will be very difficult to avoid the tendency to simply copy the existing design. If the designer is thinking of the existing design, creativity and innovation which could lead to significant quality improvements and component / cost reductions are less likely. In addition, the potential for infringing on patented designs is obviously more likely when existing competitive products are studied prior to the conceptual design process.

Step 3 - Initial Materials Selection

Once the end-use requirements for a part have been specified, designers can begin searching for plastic materials that are suitable for the application. The material selection or screening process is accomplished by comparing material properties with a "property profile" derived from the end-use product requirements. Because there are literally thousands of plastic material grades available commercially, it is very likely that a designer will be able to find at least one material candidate that is suitable for the application. It is generally best to select several potentially suitable material candidates (perhaps 3 to 6 specific material formulations / grades) during the initial material selection process.

Due to the shear number of materials grades that are available, the material screening process can be extremely difficult. It is best to begin the material selection process by considering material properties that *cannot* be enhanced by design. Properties such as coefficient of thermal expansion, transparency, chemical resistance, softening temperature, and agency approval are properties that cannot be enhanced by design. For example, high density polyethylene cannot be used for glazing applications because it is translucent or opaque, while polycarbonate is not suitable for gasoline containers due to its limited resistance to hydrocarbons. Altering the part design will not help in either case. Using these types of properties, it is relatively easy to eliminate entire families of materials, thereby reducing the number of potential plastic material candidates. Factors that complicate the materials selection process here are coatings, additives, and co-injection technologies. In many cases, coatings are used to alter the chemical resistance, abrasion resistance, ultraviolet resistance, and general appearance of a part. When coatings are used, it may be possible to use a material that would otherwise not be suitable for the application. Additives can also complicate the material selection process. It is possible to selectively alter virtually any property of a plastic material by melt blending or compounding.

Unlike the properties listed above, most of the mechanical properties of a polymer can in fact be enhanced by design, within the temperature limitations associated with the application. For example, when designing a metal replacement application, designers generally consider the material modulus to be one of the most important properties when screening material candidates. One problem here is that metals such as steel are both rigid and tough, while many rigid plastic material are relatively brittle (e.g. many glass reinforced grades are rigid but brittle). In many cases, superior performance is achieve when more lightly reinforced or unreinforced grades of engineering polymers are selected. Even though these materials have lower moduli values (and may creep at a greater rate), they are tougher, and the part geometry can be altered (by the addition of deeper ribs, etc.) to compensate for the reduction in modulus.

Step 4 - Design Part In Accordance with Materials Selected

At this point in the design process, it is beneficial to have several candidate materials in mind for the application. Because there are differences in the properties of the individual material grades, there will also be differences in the product geometries associated with each of the different materials. For example, a designer is considering high density polyethylene, polypropylene, and nylon 6/6 for an application involving static loads and organic solvent exposure. The designer feels that each of the three materials has it own merits. It is impossible to make a final choice (based on economic considerations) until each part has been designed, because the material consumption and manufacturing cycle time will be different in each case. The nylon 6/6 is a more costly material per unit weight or volume, but the wall thickness and cycle time reductions may offset the higher raw material cost.

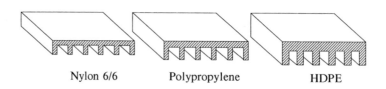

Nylon 6/6   Polypropylene   HDPE

Figure 3.6. Once several material candidates have been selected, the parts can be designed in accordance with the individual plastic material properties. For example, wall thicknesses will be influenced by both the flow properties and rigidity of the material.

The part geometries shown in Figure 3.6 have equivalent stiffness values because the section modulus or moment of inertia values have been adjusted to compensate for the different modulus values of the individual materials. While this is a simple example, in practice, many other geometric features associated with either end-use performance or assembly would vary according to the specific material properties.

Step 5 - Final Material Selection

At this stage of the design process, the designer must commit to one primary material for the product, while keeping the remaining candidate materials in reserve in the event that an unanticipated problem is detected at a later stage of development (e.g. during prototyping or production). It is unlikely that any of the candidate materials are perfectly suited for the application. Each particular material candidate will have its own advantages and limitations. The designer may have a preference for one of the candidate materials based on past experience. While it is an advantage to work with familiar materials, the other candidate materials may be better suited for the application. On the other hand, decisions based solely on material and manufacturing costs do not take performance or processing advantages into account. At this point it is best to consider the overall characteristics of each candidate material in terms of manufacturing cost, end-use performance properties, and processability (both primary and secondary processing characteristics). By rating each of these characteristics, designers can make an essentially unbiased selection of the best candidate material on balance. Properties or characteristics that are particularly important can be given a weighted rating. Consider the three materials, polypropylene, high density polyethylene, and nylon 6/6 that are slated for the chemical / static load application described in the previous section.

Property or characteristic	Rating*		
	HDPE	PP	Nylon 6/6
Overall processability	9	8	6
Creep resistance	2	4	7
Chemical resistance	10	9	10
Manufacturing cost per part **	7	9	8
. . .	. . .	. . .	. . .
Elevated temp performance	3	5	9
Average rating	6.3	7.1	8.0

* 10 = highest rating (best)   0 = lowest rating (worst)

** Considers both material consumption (based on part volume) and manufacturing cycle time.

Figure 3.7. Semi-quantitative materials selection procedures can take some of the bias out of the materials selection process.

While the individual numerical ratings associated with a given property can be somewhat arbitrary, they are hopefully based on actual numerical property data. The technique provides a semi-quantitative method for selecting the best material candidates on balance if *all* of the important characteristics have been considered.

Step 6 - Modify Part Design for Manufacturing

Once the material and initial design have been established, the design must be altered for manufacturing. Input from tooling and process engineers is extremely valuable. The part geometry that has been developed must be moldable. Designers must consider the impact that the various phases of the injection molding process can have on the part design. Each stage of the injection molding process, namely mold filling, packing, holding, cooling and ejection, has its own special requirements as described in Chapter 2.

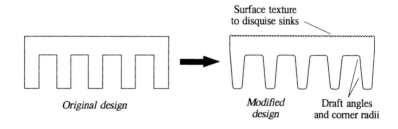

Figure 3.8. The part design must be modified for primary and secondary manufacturing concerns (shrinkage, draft angles, flow leaders, etc.) The effect of these changes on the end-use performance of the part should be evaluated.

Consider the part shown in Figure 3.8. The part has been designed with ribs to support the service loads. In practice, the part must be modified with radii to assist in flow (and reduce stress concentrations), draft angles to assist with part ejection, and surface texturing to improve the visual appearance of the sink marks (due to material shrinkage) on the wall opposite the ribs. These are but a few of the possible design modifications that are required from a manufacturing point of view. The effect of these modifications on the end-use performance of the part should be evaluated after they are made, since design changes such as the addition of draft angles to ribs can have a significant influence on the maximum deflections and stresses that occur due to service loading. Part design checklists, such as the one shown in Figure 3.9, can be useful during planning stages or as final checks to ensure that all aspects of manufacturing and assembly have been considered.

Step 7 - Prototyping

The final part design, modified for manufacturing is generally prototyped at this point in an effort to evaluate both the manufacturability and performance capabilities of the part. Prototyping is required since all process (e.g. molding simulations) and performance design work (e.g. structural analysis) done up to this point in time have been "theoretical"

Part Design Checklist
for injection molded engineering thermoplastics

Material Selection Requirements

☐ LOADS — Magnitude — Duration — Impact — Fatigue — Wear
☐ ENVIRONMENT — Temperature — Chemicals — Humidity — Cleaning agents — Lubricants — U.V. light
☐ SPECIAL — Transparency — Paintability — Warpage/Shrinkage — Plateability — Flammability — Cost — Agency test

Part Details Review

☐ RADII — Sharp corners — Ribs — Bosses — Lettering
☐ WALL THICKNESS
 • Material — Strength — Electrical — Flammability
 • Flow — Flow length — Too thin — Thin to thick — Picture framing — Orientation — Abrupt changes — Thick areas — Thin areas — Height — Spacing
 • Uniformity — Radii — Draft
☐ RIBS — Base thickness
☐ BOSSES — Radii — Draft — Inside diameter/outside diameter — Base thickness — Length/diameter
☐ WELD LINES — Proximity to load — Strength vs. load — Visual area
☐ DRAFT — Draw polish — Texture depth — ½ degree (minimum)
☐ TOLERANCE — Part geometry — Material — Tool design (across parting line, slides)

Assembly Considerations

☐ PRESS FIT — Tolerances — Long-term retention — Hoop stress
☐ SNAP FIT — Allowable strain — Assembly force — Tapered beam — Multiple assembly
☐ SCREWS — Thread-cutting vs. forming — Avoid countersinks
☐ MOLDED THREAD — Avoid feather-edges, sharp corners and pipe threads
☐ ULTRASONICS — Energy director — Shear joint interference — Wall thickness — Hermetic seal
☐ ADHESIVE & SOLVENT BONDS — Shear vs. butt joint — Trapped vapors — Compatibility
☐ GENERAL — Interfit tolerances — Stack tolerances — Thermal expansion — Care with rivets and molded-in inserts — Component compatibility

Mold Concerns

☐ WARPAGE — Cooling (corners) — Ejector placement
☐ GATES — Type — Size — Location
☐ RUNNERS — Size and shape — Sprue size — Balanced flow — Cold slug well — Sharp corners
☐ GENERAL — Draft — Part ejection — Avoid thin/long cores

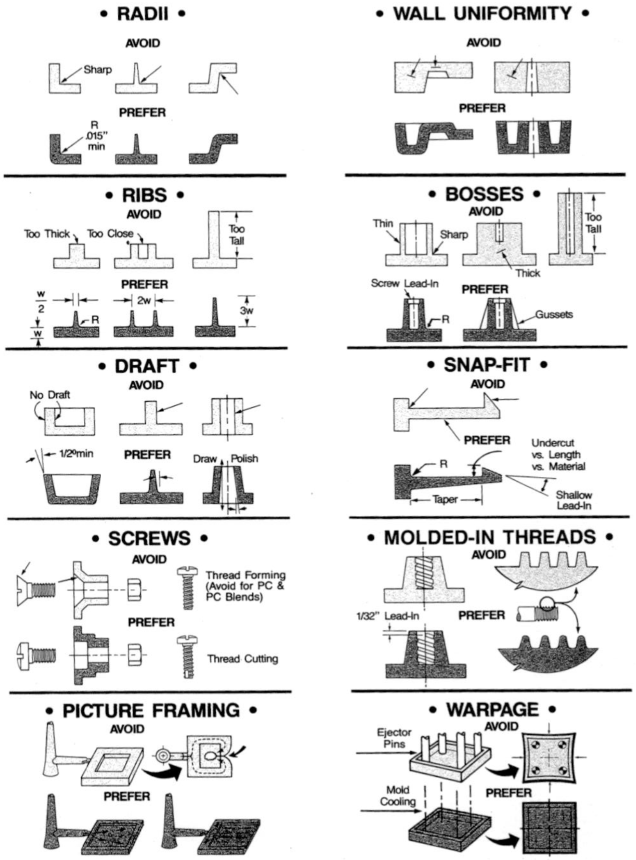

• WALL UNIFORMITY • • RADII • • BOSSES • • RIBS • • SNAP-FIT • • DRAFT • • MOLDED-IN THREADS • • SCREWS • • WARPAGE • • PICTURE FRAMING •

Figure 3.9. Material manufacturers provide aids such as this design checklist to ensure that all factors, including manufacturability, have been considered. (Courtesy Miles Corporation, Pittsburgh, PA)

and must be verified. This is particularly important for molded plastic parts because there are a number of manufacturing related problems that are difficult to predict in advance (weld line appearance and strength, warpage, sink marks, etc.). In order to obtain realistic results, it is necessary to mold prototype parts using the intended production material. This typically involves building a single (unit) cavity tool for smaller parts or soft (often simplified) tools for larger parts. The prototyping process can take a great deal of time and money, however, it is best to detect manufacturing or end-use performance problems with a unit cavity or soft tool, rather than a multi-cavity, hard production tool. Steel safe practices should be followed to minimize the cost of tool rework. While molded prototypes provide the type of information that is required to verify engineering functions and manufacturing, other more easily fabricated prototypes (rapid prototypes etc.) can be produced very quickly (hours or days) and provide invaluable hands-on models for communication and limited functionality long before the prototype tool is built.

Step 8 - Tooling and Step 9 - Manufacturing

Once the prototype tools and parts have been evaluated, and modified as necessary, pre-production or production tools are built. In order to save time, it is common to begin the more basic work on the production tools long before this point in time. Once the tools are built and debugged, the part goes into the initial stage of manufacturing.

3.3   Test Standards for Design Related Plastic Material Properties

Much of the material property data that is generated by material suppliers is generated using either American Society of Testing and Materials (ASTM) or International Standards Organization (ISO) standard test methods. Many of these testing standard tests are associated with single data point property values at ambient temperature (e.g. ASTM D638), and by their very nature, have only limited applications for engineering design. Other test standards describe procedures for generating more detailed design data (e.g. ASTM D2990). It should also be noted that for some properties, there are no applicable ASTM or ISO standards in existence today (e.g. test standards pressure - volume - temperature data). In addition, much of the engineering data used for product design is generated using non-standard (e.g. in-house) testing practices.

3.4   Mechanical Behavior of Plastic Materials

3.4.1   Introduction

There are very few applications where the structural integrity of a plastic part is not important. Most plastic parts are subject to some type of mechanical loading during assembly, or in the end-use application. Parts can be designed to withstand loads, stresses and strains associated with the application if (i) the loading conditions associated with the application (including the potential for misuse) can be identified, and (ii) the mechanical behavior of the plastic material can be described accurately. Unfortunately, the mechanical performance of a plastic material is influenced by a wide variety of environmental and manufacturing related factors. It should be noted here that a material's mechanical properties are actually molded part properties rather than inherent material properties, and are therefore influenced by test specimen processing conditions.

Factors such as time of loading, rate of loading, temperature, chemical environment, U.V. exposure, orientation level, internal (processing related) stress, weld lines and the like all have an effect on the mechanical performance of the material or part. Designers should obtain mechanical property data which correlates most closely with the end-use application (to avoid the use of very large safety factors). Due to the large number of variables involved with mechanical testing, it is effectively impossible for material suppliers to fully characterize the mechanical performance of each given material grade (under all possible conditions). They can, however, provide mechanical property data to describe the general mechanical performance of the material (over a limited range of test conditions) for materials selection and initial design purposes. When mechanical performance is critical to the end-use application, additional information must be obtained or generated in order to make a more accurate and complete performance prediction. Prototype testing of the structural reliability of the end product is still required in the final analysis due to the large number of manufacturing related considerations.

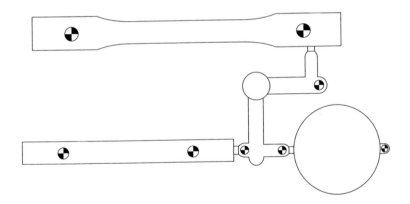

Figure 3.10. Typical test specimen geometries used to evaluate the properties of molded plastic materials. It is important to note that most tests, such as mechanical property tests, measure molded part properties rather than the true material properties.

3.4.2   Short Term Stress-Strain Behavior

Short term stress-strain data (or curves) are relatively easy to generate, and are available for essentially all plastic materials. As the name implies, short term tests take place over a limited time period (typically minutes) and are usually done under ideal laboratory conditions. Short term (data sheet) material property values do not represent an accurate description of the mechanical performance / capabilities of a material, however, they do provide a basis for initial materials screening and selection. The short term stress-strain data presented by material suppliers is typically generated using standard testing procedures and testing conditions (typically using a constant rate of crosshead travel in a universal testing machine). Most short term stress-strain data is generated at the standard conditions of room temperature / 50% relative humidity. Due to the temperature sensitivity of most plastic materials, a more complete performance profile can be established if tests are run over a wider range of ambient conditions.

Plastic materials are also viscoelastic, and therefore exhibit time dependent behavior. Plastic materials are partially elastic, having the ability to store energy, and are partially viscous, dissipating energy as frictional heat, resulting in non-linear behavior and permanent deformation. The rate of deformation associated with the test procedure will affect the viscous behavior and therefore the test results. Most short term stress-strain curves are generated at relatively low rates of deformation. At higher rates of deformation (such as impact loading), plastic materials appear to be more rigid and brittle, while at lower rates of deformation, they appear to be more flexible and ductile. Higher rates of deformation are analogous to lower temperatures, while lower rates are analogous to higher temperatures.

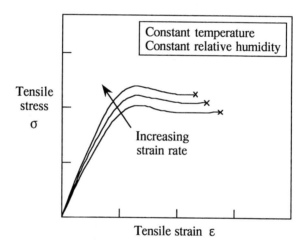

Figure 3.11. The mechanical behaviors of plastic materials are influenced by environmental factors such as temperature and relative humidity, and factors such as the rate of loading.

Relative humidity is also an important factor for hygroscopic materials such as nylon since water acts as a plasticizer, and tends to make the polymer more ductile. It is important that test data used for materials screening / comparison purposes is generated at the same test conditions (i.e. same strain rate, temperature, etc.) so that an accurate comparison can be made. The data reported by material manufacturers is typically generated using ASTM or ISO standards which specify most of the important variables. Short term stress-strain data is used primarily for initial materials selection, however, the data can be useful for design *provided* the temperatures and loading (or strain) rates associated with the testing procedure are equivalent to those of the end-use application.

Even then, however, the effects of processing, aging and chemicals on the mechanical properties of the material must be given special consideration.

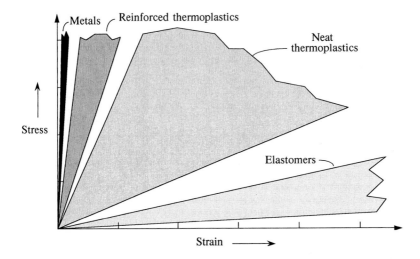

Figure 3.12. Plastic materials are available with a wide range of stress-strain behaviors. Compared to metals, plastic materials have significantly lower modulus values, especially at elevated temperatures.

Compared to most metals or woods, plastic materials are less rigid (i.e. quantitatively they have lower modulus values). For example, an unfilled polycarbonate is only about 1/85th as rigid as carbon steel, and about 1/28th as rigid as aluminum [5]. However, unlike metals or woods, plastic material grades are available having an extremely wide range of rigidities, ranging from flexible elastomers, to very rigid, stiff fiber reinforced polymer grades. Plastic material grades are typically categorized in terms of their short term stress-strain behavior, and are described as being either elastomeric (soft & flexible, highly extensible), ductile (tough materials of medium rigidity) or rigid / glassy (materials with stiff, linear behavior showing little or no yield before failure, and low failure strain). Stress-strain curves provide a quantitative measure of a material's mechanical behavior at the particular temperature, humidity, and strain rate associated with the mechanical testing procedure.

Normal stress, σ, is defined as the ratio of the applied load, F, to the original cross sectional area, A, of the test specimen.

$$\sigma = F / A \tag{3.1}$$

Normal Strain, ε, provides a normalized measure of the deformation of the material as a result of the applied load. Strain is defined as the change in length, ΔL, divided by the original length, L_o.

$$\varepsilon = \Delta L / L_o \tag{3.2}$$

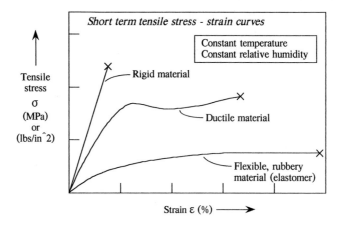

Figure 3.13. Short term stress-strain curves are commonly used for initial screening purposes. The curves can be used for design if the strain rates are similar to those associated with the end-use application. Plastic materials are typically categorized as being rigid, ductile or elastomeric in terms of their stress-strain behavior.

When working with metals, strain is typically given in units of 10^{-6} inch / inch or cm / cm (microstrain units). Because most plastic materials exhibit higher yield and ultimate elongation values, strain is typically expressed directly (without scientific notation), or as a percentage elongation (i.e. strain x 100%). The following strain representations are equivalent.

$$1000 \ \mu\varepsilon = 1000 \times 10^{-6} \ \text{cm/cm} = 0.001 \text{cm/cm} = 0.1\%$$

There are various characteristic features or points on a stress-strain curve that are of particular interest to a designer. A number of related terms are defined below and illustrated in Figure 3.14 [5-7].

• *Proportional Limit*: The proportional limit (for a material exhibiting both elastic and viscous behavior) is the maximum load (stress) the material is capable of sustaining without deviation from the proportionality (linearity) of stress to strain. Some materials maintain this proportionality to relatively high values of stress or strain, while others show little or no proportionality.

• *Elastic Limit*: The point on the stress-strain curve which marks the maximum stress a material can withstand and still recover (with no permanent deformation) to its original dimensions when the stress is released. With plastic materials, the recovery may not be immediate, and the elastic limit can occur at stress levels higher than the proportional limit.

• *Yield Stress*: The first stress value on a stress-strain curve where an increase in strain occurs without an increase in stress (i.e. the stress value at the point where the slope of the stress-strain curve becomes zero). Not all plastic materials exhibit a yield point.

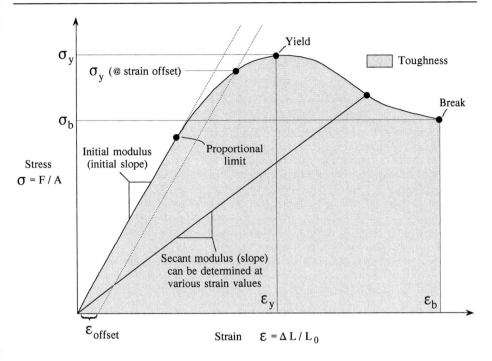

Figure 3.14. Specific points or characteristics of a stress-strain curve are of interest to designers.

• *Yield Strain* : The strain value associated with the yield stress. Often reported as yield elongation in percent (i.e. yield strain x 100).

• *Ultimate (Breaking) Strength:* The maximum stress a material will withstand when subject to an applied load (rupture).

• *Ultimate (Breaking) Strain:* The strain value associated with the breaking strength. Often reported as ultimate elongation in percent (i.e. breaking strain x 100).

• *Proof Stress (offset yield):* Proof stress is sometimes used with plastic materials that yield gradually or exhibit very high yield strains. Proof stress is determined by constructing a line parallel to the linear portion of the stress-strain curve, at a specified strain offset. The stress at the point of intersection of the constructed line and the stress-strain curve is the proof or yield stress at that particular strain offset.

• *True Stress and Strain:* In most cases, stress values are described as "Engineering Stresses" and are determined from the applied load and the initial cross sectional area. When materials are subjected to compressive, shear or tensile loading, their cross-sectional areas will change (particularly at high strains). True stress values are determined by dividing the applied load by the instantaneous cross-sectional area as the test progresses. In almost all cases, engineering stress and strain values are reported and used in practice.

• *Elastic (Young's) Modulus:* The term elastic modulus, E, is defined as the slope of the stress-strain curve for an elastic material (i.e. a material exhibiting linear stress-strain behavior). Since most plastic materials are non-linear, the slope of the stress-strain curve changes with stress or strain level and testing rate. The term elastic modulus cannot strictly speaking be applied to viscoelastic materials because they do not obey Hooke's Law.

• *Initial (Tangent) Modulus:* The slope of the initial (linear) portion of a stress-strain curve is known as the initial modulus. The initial modulus provides a measure of the rigidity of the material at low stresses or strains. For many plastic materials, the linear portion of the stress-strain curve is difficult to identify precisely, and the initial modulus is determined by taking the slope of the line tangent to the initial portion of a stress-strain

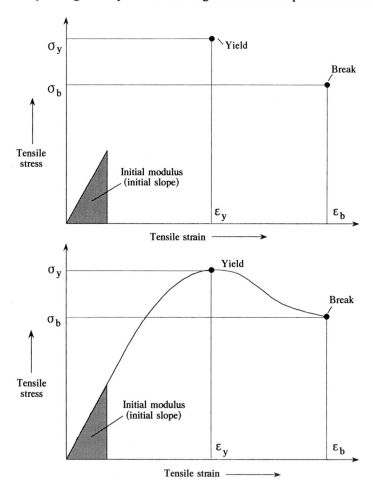

Figure 3.15. When given values of initial modulus, yield and breaking strength, yield and breaking elongation, it is possible to estimate the overall stress-strain behavior of the polymer (at that particular temperature and strain rate).

curve (initial tangent modulus). When the initial portion of the stress-strain curve is non-linear, an alternative method of reporting modulus is to report a secant modulus (typically at 1% strain) as a more representative measure of the rigidity of the material. It can be difficult to compare short term test modulus numbers between different material grades / suppliers (especially for ductile polymers) because the number is very sensitive to the particular method used to calculate the value.

• *Secant Modulus:* The ratio of stress to strain at any point on the stress-strain curve (i.e. the slope of the line from the origin to any other point on the stress-strain curve). Secant modulus values are reported as a function of percent strain and are commonly required when engineering calculations are done for elastomeric or ductile polymers (e.g. in applications involving large deformations).

• *Toughness (Area Under the Stress-Strain Curve:* The area under a stress-strain curve provides an indication of the overall toughness of the material at the particular temperature and rate of loading.

In some cases, designers do not have the actual stress-strain curves, but must work with property data sheets that list key properties such as initial modulus, yield strength, yield elongation, ultimate strength and ultimate elongation. With these values however, it is possible to obtain a rough estimate of the short term stress-strain behavior as indicated in Figure 3.15 (either mentally or by plotting the values).

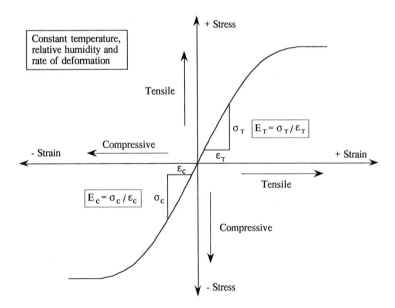

Figure 3.16. The compressive stress-strain behavior of a plastic material can be similar, or in some cases very different, from the tensile stress-strain behavior.

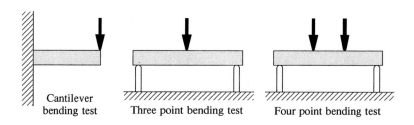

Cantilever
bending test   Three point bending test   Four point bending test

Figure 3.17. A variety of bending tests methods are used to evaluate the flexural properties of plastic materials.

Tensile vs. Compressive Behavior: Short term stress-strain curves are most commonly generated by pulling on test specimens resulting in tensile stresses and strains. For many unfilled plastic materials, compressive properties are similar to the tensile properties, however, for other materials, especially filled and reinforced materials, compressive properties can be very different. It is better to obtain compression property data for compressive applications than to simply assume that the material's compressive behavior is equivalent to that of it's tensile behavior.

Bending Strength and Modulus: It is also very common for material manufacturers to provide short term bending (or flexural) stress-strain data. Bending properties are particularly important since a very large number of plastic parts are subject to bending loads in the end-use application. Compared to tensile and compressive test results, bending test results are even more dependent upon the apparatus and specimen geometry. Bending tests are carried out by subjecting a relatively long, thin, rectangular cross section specimen to either a cantilever (one support, one load), three point (two supports, one load) or four point (two supports, two loads) loading.

During testing, the maximum deflection of a sample is monitored as a function of the applied load. Unlike the uniaxial tension or compression tests, bending test specimens have one surface in compression and the other in tension, with a neutral plane (zero stress or strain) running through the specimen at some point (the neutral plane runs through the midplane only if the compressive and tensile properties are equivalent). Bending stress and strain values must be calculated using the experimental data and engineering formulas for stress and strain. These formulas assume ideal, isotropic elastic material behavior and apply only to small deflections. The bending properties that are typically reported are flexural modulus, from the initial slope of the load deflection curve, and flexural strength. For brittle materials flexural strength refers to the maximum outer fiber tensile or compressive stress (surface stresses) that is associated with the failure of the specimen. For more ductile materials, flexural strength refers to the outer fiber yield stress value (first point where stress no longer increases with strain) or to the outer fiber stress at a certain strain value (typically at 5% outer fiber strain).

Shear Strength and Modulus: The shear modulus, G, of a polymer (also known as modulus of rigidity) is the slope of the initial portion of a shear stress vs. shear strain curve.

$$G = \tau / \gamma \qquad\qquad\qquad (3.3)$$

Values such as shear yield strength, ultimate shear strength, shear yield strain and ultimate shear strain can be obtained directly from the shear stress-shear strain curve, in much the same way that tensile or compressive strength or strain values are determined. If one assumes isotropic, elastic behavior, it is also possible to estimate the shear modulus of a polymer, if the "elastic" modulus and Poisson's ratio are known using elastic theory.

$$G = E / [2(1+\upsilon)] \tag{3.4}$$

Since plastics are viscoelastic, initial tensile, compressive, or flexural moduli values are used for the E term in Equation 3.4 in practice to obtain an approximate shear modulus value.

Poisson's Ratio: When a plastic part (or test specimen) is subject to tensile or compressive stresses, it deforms both along the axis of loading (longitudinal deformation) and perpendicular to the axis of loading (lateral deformation). Poisson's ratio is defined as the ratio of lateral strain to longitudinal strain within the limits of elasticity. The minus sign indicates that the lateral strains are opposite in direction from the longitudinal strains. For example, when a part is stretched in tension longitudinally, the width and thickness (lateral directions) contract.

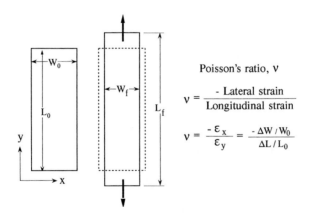

$$\nu = \frac{- \text{Lateral strain}}{\text{Longitudinal strain}}$$

$$\nu = \frac{- \varepsilon_x}{\varepsilon_y} = \frac{- \Delta W / W_0}{\Delta L / L_0}$$

Figure 3.18. Poisson's ratio is a measure of the lateral to longitudinal strain values for a material. The value is used in a variety of design equations and to convert between the materials, shear modulus and tensile / compressive modulus.

Most conventional materials have Poisson's ratio values that lie between 0.0 and 0.5. There are also some unique materials that expand laterally under a tensile stress. A material that has a Poisson's ratio value of 0.0 will exhibit no lateral contraction when strained in tension (or lateral expansion when compressed). A material with a Poisson's ratio of 0.5 will exhibit the amount of lateral contraction (due to a longitudinal tensile stress) that results in constant volume and density. Any material with a Poisson's ratio between 0.0 and 0.5 exhibits volume and density changes when stressed. The Poisson's ratio value for a given material can be determined directly from a uniaxial tension or compression test (using lateral and longitudinal extensometers) or can be calculated if the "elastic" and "shear" moduli values are known.

$$\nu = [E / 2 G] - 1 \tag{3.5}$$

Like the elastic and shear modulus values, Poisson's ratio changes with variables such as temperature, strain or stress level, and strain rate.

Table 3.1. Typical Values of Poisson's Ratio [6]

Material	Range of Poisson's Ratio
Aluminum	0.33
Carbon Steel	0.29
Ideal Rubber	0.50
Neat Thermoplastic	0.20 - 0.40
Reinforced/Filled Thermoplastic	0.10 - 0.40
Structural Foam	0.30 - 0.40

Poisson's ratio values are used to relate elastic and shear moduli values, and are required for many structural design calculations.

3.4.3   Long Term Mechanical Properties; Creep

The mechanical behavior of a polymeric material is influenced by a number of factors including time, stress or strain levels, and environmental factors such as temperature and moisture content (for hygroscopic polymers). The set of short term stress-strain curves given in Figure 3.11 show that at higher loading or strain rates, plastic materials appear to be more rigid and brittle. On the other hand, at lower rates of loading or strain, plastic materials appear to be more flexible or ductile due to viscous effects. These viscous effects are a particular concern in applications where loads are applied for extended periods of time (i.e. static loads). It is not unusual for plastic parts to be subjected to continuous loading (either service loads and / or the part's own weight) or loading for relatively long periods of time (i.e. days, weeks, years). When parts are loaded in this manner, they will exhibit both initial elastic deformation or strain due to the applied load, and will also exhibit a continuous (time dependent) increase in deformation or strain due to viscous or cold flow (i.e. creep). This phenomenon has nothing to due with aging effects (e.g. oxidation, etc.) which must be given separate consideration for longer term applications. The parts shown in Figure 3.19 are all subject to long term loading (or stresses) and as such must be designed with considerations for creep deformation.

In order to design parts that are subject to long term loading, designers must obtain and utilize creep data in an effort to ensure that the parts do not rupture, yield, craze or simply deform excessively over their service life (service life *must* be specified during the initial stage of design since creep deformations are time dependent). The creep data that is used in design must correlate with the type of stress and environmental conditions that the part is subjected to during service. The time and temperature dependent creep modulus, E_c (t,T), of a polymer is given by:

$$E_c (t,T) = \sigma_0 / \varepsilon (t,T) \qquad\qquad (3.6)$$

Where σ_0 is a constant stress and ε (t,T) is the time and temperature dependent strain.

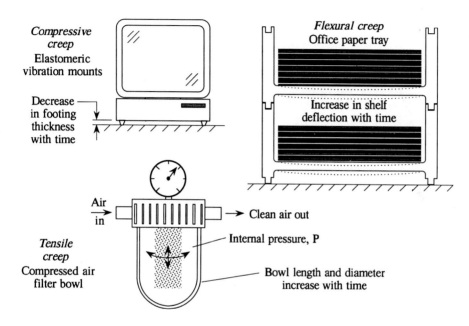

Figure 3.19. Typical applications where molded plastic parts are subject to constant stress for extended periods of time (i.e. creep applications).

Unfortunately, service load magnitudes, durations and environmental conditions can be difficult to predict over the long term, and it may be difficult to find test data which correlates exactly with the end-use application, especially when loads are semi-continuous and recovery must be considered. This can make it difficult to accurately estimate the structural performance of a part subject to creep loading, and it is often best to assume continuous loading at the highest anticipated service temperature for safety.

The creep behavior of a plastic material is often modeled using spring (elastic element) and dashpot (viscous element) analogies. The model shown in Figure 3.20 can be used to describe the general creep behavior of a plastic material subject to a tensile load. The figure shows Voight-Kelvin and Maxwell Models in series with one another to create a four parameter model.

When a tensile load is applied to the spring / dashpot model, elastic element #1 extends instantaneously resulting in an immediate elastic deformation (IED) inversely proportional

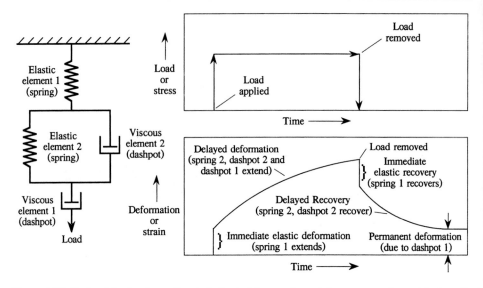

Figure 3.20. Spring (elastic element) and dashpots (viscous elements) are commonly used to describe the mechanical behavior of plastic materials.

to the stiffness of the spring and proportional to the magnitude of the load (this results in stored energy). Elastic element #2 is unable to extend immediately because it is constrained by a viscous dashpot that cannot react instantaneously. The load then causes further deformation with time as dashpot #1, dashpot #2 and spring #2 extend. This represents the time dependent creep or delayed deformation (DD). At some point of extension, spring #2 (hence dashpot #2) will reach equilibrium, but dashpot #1 will continue to extend with time of load application. When the load is ultimately removed, the stored energy in spring #1 will cause an immediate elastic recovery (IER), followed by a delayed recovery (DR) associated with the retraction of spring #2, hindered by dashpot #2. The extension associated with dashpot #1 is irrecoverable and represents the permanent deformation or set (PD). While the actual creep and recovery behavior of most polymeric materials is more complex than this simple analogy, it does provide insight into the general concept of viscoelastic behavior.

In practice, when plastic materials are stressed, an immediate elastic deformation is observed, followed by primary, secondary and tertiary creep [8]. Primary creep is associated with a decreasing creep rate with time, and is at least partially recoverable. Secondary creep occurs at a constant rate with time, while tertiary creep occurs at an increasing creep rate with time just before creep rupture. The rate of creep is material, stress and temperature dependent, as are the creep rupture strain values. It should be noted here that rupture (or yielding) will occur at stresses below the corresponding short term test breaking stress values. Creep rupture occurs at relatively shorter times for higher stresses and relatively longer times for lower stresses.

Creep Testing: Material manufacturers generate creep data by subjecting molded test specimens (prepared by the injection or compression molding process) to different stress

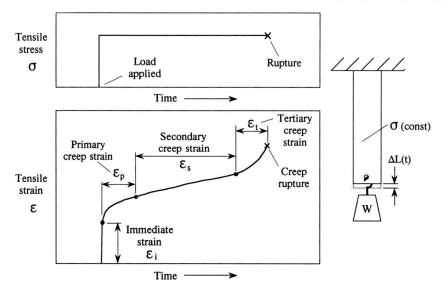

Figure 3.21. The strain response of a plastic material to an imposed stress can involve both elastic strain and creep strain.

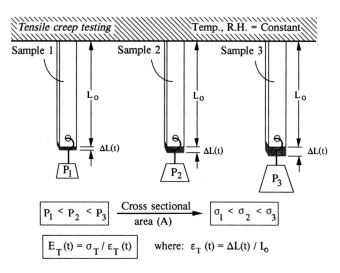

Figure 3.22. Creep data is generated by subjecting molded samples to a series of loads, or stresses and monitoring the change in length, or strain, over time. (tension, compression, bending or shear)

levels (typically four or more different stress values), and monitoring the change in length or strain as a function of time. Tests are commonly conducted at a series of constant temperature environments that are typical use temperatures for the material under consideration. Tests can be conducted in tension, compression, bending or shear. Ideally tests should be run for many years in order to truly quantify the creep and creep rupture behavior of the material; however, due to practical constraints, tests are commonly run for shorter periods of time. It is important for designers to determine whether the creep data they are working with is actual experimental data or extrapolated data (from a shorter term test). It is possible to extrapolate creep and creep rupture curves, however, it should be done with caution, and should generally be limited to one logarithmic decade [9].

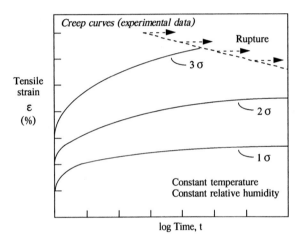

Figure 3.23. The experimental data from a creep test is used to plot strain vs. log time curves at various stress levels (at constant temperature and relative humidity).

The experimental creep data is typically plotted as a graph indicating strain as a function of log time, at constant temperature / relative humidity and various stress levels, to produce a "creep curve". The slope of the creep curve is an indication of the stress related dimensional stability of the plastic material. Higher stress levels cause an increase in creep as do higher temperatures.

The rate of creep for filled and fiber reinforced polymers is significantly lower than that of unfilled materials, provided appropriate coupling agents are used. Figure 3.24 shows that the creep strain values for the glass fiber reinforced nylon are significantly lower than those of the neat nylon 6/6, even when the reinforced material is subjected to higher stress levels. The resistance to creep can be enhanced even further when graphite fiber reinforcements are used as shown in Figure 3.25 [10]. It should be noted here that the effects of weld lines and fiber orientation on creep behavior should be taken into consideration when working with fiber reinforced polymer grades. During creep testing,

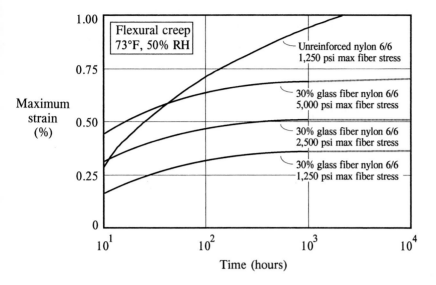

Figure 3.24. The creep resistance of a polymer is improved significantly with the addition of reinforcing fibers.

it is also common to inspect samples for yielding, rupture, stress cracking, crazing and stress whitening. Creep rupture (or yield) test data is typically plotted to produce a set of curves at various temperatures indicating the failure or yield stress as a function of log time as shown in Figure 3.26.

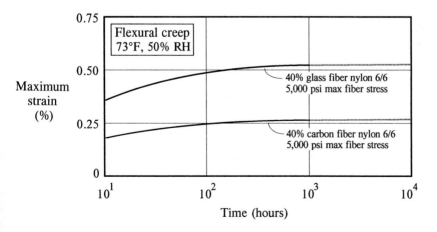

Figure 3.25. Fibers that are commonly used to enhance creep resistance of a polymer include glass and carbon fiber.

Creep rupture can occur by either ductile or brittle failure modes, which are typically distinguished by macroscopic appearance. Ductile fractures involve some type of gross plastic deformation such as yielding, necking, or shear, all of which involve shape changes or distortion. Brittle fractures on the other hand do not involve gross deformation but only very localized plastic deformation [11].

Crazing: In many polymers, crack initiation is proceeded by craze formation. Crazes appear as crack like planar defects, however, they contain an interpenetrating network of voids among highly drawn polymer fibrils bridging the craze faces. Crazing or craze yielding is a cavitation process that is accompanied by a volume increase as shown in Figure 3.27 [11].

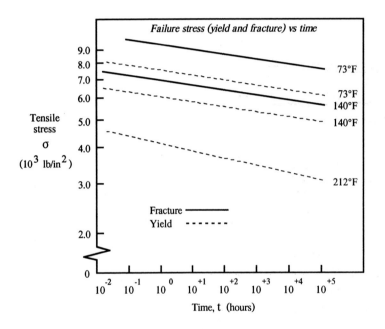

Figure 3.26. The stress at which a plastic part will yield or rupture in creep is dependent on the duration of creep loading and temperature. Creep yield and rupture strength values are shown for a polycarbonate at various temperatures.

Crazes begin with micro void formation under the action of a tensile stress. Once initiated, these voids increase in size and begin to elongate along the direction of the principle tensile stress, forming fibrils that bridge the craze faces. While the appearance of crazes does not in and of itself constitute failure under static loading conditions, crazes can eventually lead to brittle failure or cracks, and are a particular concern in applications where there is the potential for additional impact loading, dynamic loading or aggressive chemical environments.

Crazing is a particular problem for many materials when they are stressed (particularly surface tensile stresses) in the presence of aggressive chemicals. Environmental stress cracking and crazing (ESCC) can occur when plastic parts are stressed (internal / residual molding stresses or externally imposed stress) in a chemical environment, even when the stresses are relatively low. It is the combination of the stress and the chemical that lead to crazing and ultimately to failure (a kind of negative synergy). Even water or mild detergents can have a very negative impact on the mechanical performance of a plastic part (with some materials) subjected to mechanical stress [12].

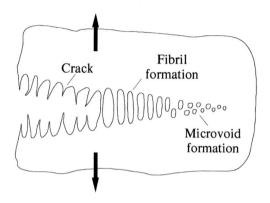

Figure 3.27. Microvoids and crazes can eventually lead to cracking and brittle failure.

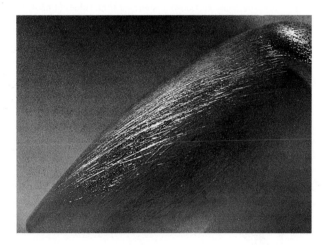

Figure 3.28. Photo showing craze formation on an acrylic part.

Stress Whitening: Stress whitening is a general term that is used to describe phenomena that results in clouding, foggy or whitened appearances in transparent or translucent polymers. The whitening is generally the result of microvoid formation caused by delamination with fillers or fibers, or by localized failure around inclusions such as rubber particles or other impact modifiers [10].

Creep Curves: Creep curves, such as those shown in Figures 3.23 - 3.25, are graphical representations of the experimental data obtained from a creep test. The same creep data can be plotted in other ways that are more convenient to use for design purposes.

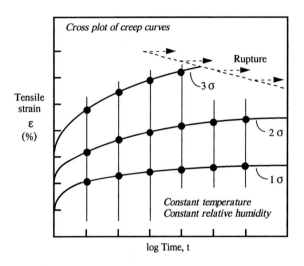

Figure 3.29. Creep curves are commonly sectioned at standard time values (1 hour, 10 hours, 100 hours, 1,000 hours, etc.) to generate data for isochronous stress-strain curves.

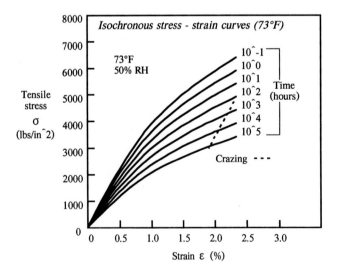

Figure 3.30. Set of isochronous tensile stress-strain curves for a polycarbonate at room temperature / 50% relative humidity.

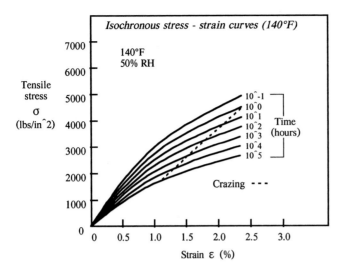

Figure 3.31. Set of isochronous stress-strain curve for a polycarbonate at 140 °F / 50% RH.

Creep curves, such as that shown in Figure 3.29, are commonly sectioned at various constant time values (typically 1 hour, 10 hours, 100 hours, 1000 hours, etc.) to obtain stress-strain data at those specific time intervals. The data is replotted in the form of an isochronous stress-strain curve, as shown in Figure 3.30 [12]. The curves are used in place of short term stress-strain curves when designing for applications involving long term static loading.

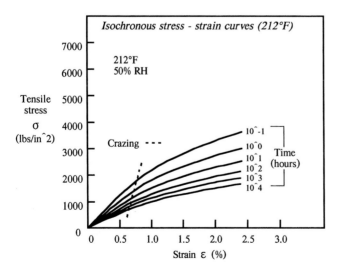

Figure 3.32. Set of isochronous stress-strain curves for a polycarbonate at 212 °F / 50% RH.

Isochronous stress-strain curves are generally available at a series of temperatures so that designers can consider the effects of both time and temperature on the apparent or creep modulus of the polymer. The apparent creep modulus values are commonly used in place of the Young's Modulus value in classical design equations to predict the strains or deflections associated with long term loading. It should be noted that the apparent modulus value varies with time, temperature and stress level. The isochronous stress-strain curves in Figures 3.30 - 3.32 also indicate the craze limits or onset of crazing for the polymer at various temperatures. The stress (or strain) level at the point where the craze limit line (dash line) intersects with an isochronous curve, is the stress (or strain) level associated with the onset of crazing at that particular time. For example, the isochronous stress-strain curve for the polycarbonate at 140 °F / 50% RH shown in Figure 3.31 indicates that crazes will appear in about 10 hours at a stress level of 4,000 psi, while it will take approximately 10,000 hours for the crazes to appear at a stress level of 2,000 psi. While the craze limits are one criteria that a designer can use to determine the upper design stress limit, the information is not always provided on the curves.

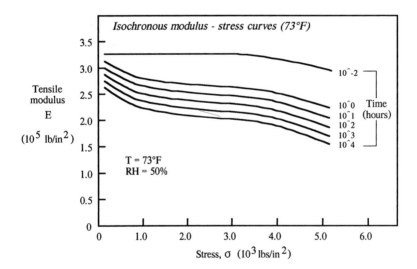

Figure 3.33. Tensile creep modulus vs. stress curves at constant times for a polycarbonate at room temperature / 50% relative humidity.

Creep data can also be plotted in a variety of other ways including modulus vs. stress curves at constant times as indicated in Figure 3.34. The curve clearly shows the importance of considering the effect of stress levels on apparent modulus [12].

Creep data is often provided in a graphical format as plots of apparent modulus as a function of log time at various stress levels. This particular graphical format is convenient because (i) it allows designers to determine the apparent modulus value at non-standard time values, and (ii) the curve is more easily extrapolated to longer time values. However, it should once again be pointed out that extrapolation should be done with caution, and should be limited to one log decade.

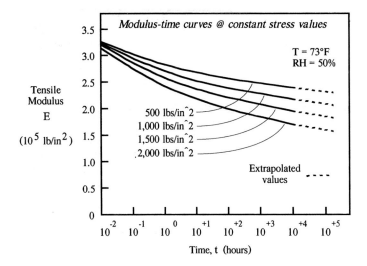

Figure 3.34. Tensile modulus vs. log time curve at various stress levels. Extrapolation of the curve to longer time values should be done with caution and over a limited range of time (within one log decade of time).

3.4.4   Long Term Mechanical Properties; Stress Relaxation

Creep data is used to design plastic parts that are subject to constant loads or stresses for extended periods of time, while stress relaxation data is required for applications where strain levels or deformation remains constant over the long term. When plastic parts are stretched, compressed, bent or sheared to a fixed value of strain or deformation, the stress value associated with that fixed strain continues to decrease with time due to viscous effects (e.g. molecular relaxation). Stress relaxation is analogous to creep in that the relaxation modulus, E_R (t,T), decreases with time according to:

$$E_R (t,T) = \sigma (t,T) / \varepsilon_0 \qquad\qquad (3.7)$$

where the strain value is fixed (constant) and the stress value is a function of both time and temperature. The stress relaxation characteristics of a polymer are important when designing for applications such as those shown in Figure 3.35. Many of these applications involve a degree of interference which has been used to provide some type of friction fit. In the case of the press fit hub, the torque transmission capabilities of the assembly are determined by the area of contact, coefficient of friction, and the normal stress. As the hoop stresses relax, the torsional capabilities of the assembly deteriorate. In the case of the compressed o-ring, normal stresses are required to prevent leakage. As the stresses relax, the potential for leakage increases. The stress relaxation characteristics of a polymer are also important for applications involving assembly preloads or plastic spring components. In order to design parts for these applications, stress relaxation data

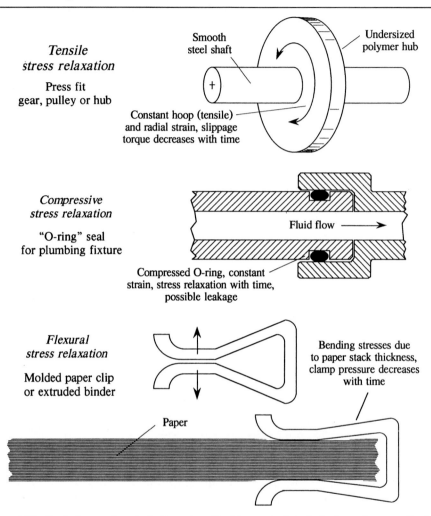

Tensile stress relaxation

Press fit gear, pulley or hub

Smooth steel shaft

Undersized polymer hub

Constant hoop (tensile) and radial strain, slippage torque decreases with time

Compressive stress relaxation

"O-ring" seal for plumbing fixture

Fluid flow ⟶

Compressed O-ring, constant strain, stress relaxation with time, possible leakage

Flexural stress relaxation

Molded paper clip or extruded binder

Bending stresses due to paper stack thickness, clamp pressure decreases with time

Paper

Figure 3.35. Typical examples of plastic parts subject to constant strain in the end-use application. Stress relaxation (rather than creep) data is required for these applications.

generated at the appropriate strain value, temperature, and time must be obtained from material suppliers.

Stress relaxation data is generated by applying a fixed strain to a molded sample, and measuring the gradual decay of stress with time. Tests can be run in tension, compression, shear and bending. The stress relaxation test data can be used to generate isochronous stress-strain curves that are analogous to those generated from creep experiment data [12].

The stress relaxation data can also be provided in a format giving the relaxation modulus as a function of log time at various constant strain values as shown in Figure 3.37 [12].

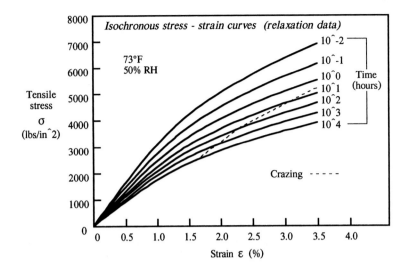

Figure 3.36. Like creep data, stress relaxation test data can be used to construct isochronous stress-strain curves Relaxation data for a polycarbonate at room temperature / 50% relative humidity is shown.

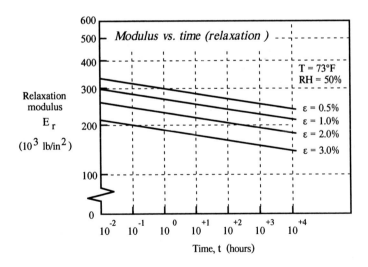

Figure 3.37. Relaxation modulus vs. time and strain for polycarbonate at room temperature 50% RH.

Unfortunately for designers, stress relaxation data is not as widely available as creep data, due in large part to the relative complexity of the stress relaxation testing apparatus in comparison to creep test apparatus. It may be possible to estimate the decay in stress for stress relaxation applications using creep data when stress relaxation data is not available [6,7], however the practice is not recommended. It has been shown that creep and relaxation moduli may be similar at shorter times and low strain levels, however, at longer times and higher strain values, differences in the two modulus values become greater [12]. It is best to use stress relaxation data for constant strain applications whenever possible.

3.5   Impact Resistance of Plastic Materials

Impact strength can be defined as the ability of a material to withstand high rate, impulsive loading [6]. Impact implies a relatively high rate of loading, typically greater than the rates associated with conventional mechanical testing. Impact loading, for example, is encountered when parts are dropped onto a rigid surface or must withstand the effect of a projectile. In either case, the plastic part must be capable of dissipating the energy associated with the impact event. This can be accomplished through both part design (e.g. using large sweeping corner radii, shock mounts, etc.) and proper material selection. Unfortunately, the impact characteristics of plastic materials are highly dependent upon the rate of impact, temperature, type of loading, specimen shape and thickness, and the like. Impact characteristics vary significantly from material to material, however, impact problems are most commonly encountered when plastic materials are used at "low" temperatures (in much the same way that creep and stress relaxation tend to be a problem at elevated temperatures).

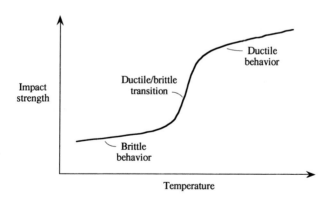

Figure 3.38. The impact strength of most plastic materials increases with increasing temperature.

The standard test methods that are commonly used to evaluate the impact strength of plastic materials do not provide a full impact characterization, and as a result, are not useful analytically. The impact data obtained from these standard impact tests is commonly used to evaluate the "relative" impact resistance and notch sensitivity of a material for initial material selection purposes. Some of the more common impact testing methods that are used in practice are described below [5,6,7,12].

Izod Impact: The most widely used pendulum impact test is the Izod impact test. This test measures the energy associated with failure of a notched cantilever specimen using a pendulum swing from a fixed height. The notch in the specimen acts as a stress concentrator or crack growth site.

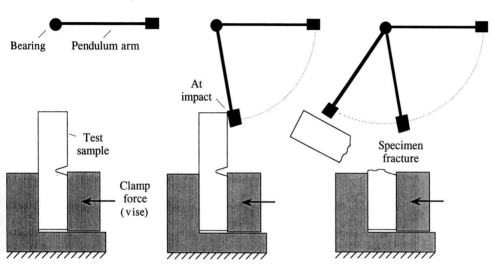

Figure 3.39. The Izod Impact test is a pendulum impact test using a cantilever specimen support.

While the Izod impact test results provide some indication of notch sensitivity, they may have little correlation with the behavior of unnotched parts in actual service (especially at other impact rates and temperatures) [5]. The test is also commonly run without notches, using a reverse notch, or using various notch radius values in an effort to obtain a measure of the notch sensitivity of the material (non-standard test protocols).

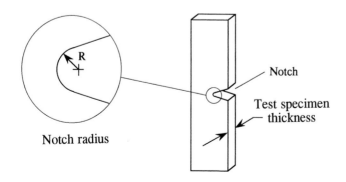

Figure 3.40. The specimen thickness, notch radius and notching procedure are important test variables.

In general, the impact strength of plastic materials increases as temperature and notch radius values increase. It is therefore important to use generous radius values on plastic parts to minimize stress concentration effects (e.g. at wall intersections). However, in practice, radius values are often limited by the appearance of sink marks, voids, or by shrinkage stresses [5,12]. The notch sensitivity of a plastic material must then be balanced against these manufacturing related shrinkage concerns.

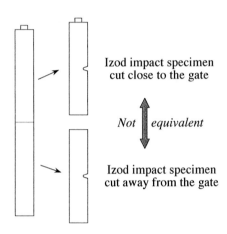

Figure 3.41.   The specimen preparation procedure will have a significant effect on the impact test results.

Izod impact strength values are affected by a very large number of manufacturing related variables associated with both the test specimen molding and notching operations. Notching variables can be eliminated by molding notches directly into the Izod test specimens, however, molded-in notch results are generally higher than machined notch results due to skin effects [13]. The molded-in notch approach does, however, have merit since corners or radii are molded into plastic parts, rather than being machined in. The test specimen thickness is also an important variable for impact testing. For example, test specimen thickness will affect the micro-void content in the sample. In addition, with some materials, impact strength increases with thickness up to a critical thickness where the failure mechanism changes from ductile to brittle failure, and a significant decrease in impact resistance is observed at thicknesses greater than the critical value [5,12].

Charpy Impact: The Charpy impact test is a pendulum impact test method that is similar to the Izod test, however, rather than using cantilevered test specimens, the specimens are simply supported at the two ends, and impacted with the pendulum at the midspan of the test sample [5-7].

Tensile Impact: The tensile impact test is another variation on the pendulum test method, however, unlike the bending test geometries associated with the Izod and Charpy tests, the tensile impact test uses a small dog bone-like specimen that is subjected to uniaxial tensile loading.

Area Under a Stress-Strain Curve: The area under a stress-strain curve is indicative of the toughness of a material at the strain rate associated with the test procedure as shown previously in Figure 3.14. When plastic test samples are tested at high rates (i.e. when they are tested at impact-like strain rates), the area under the stress-strain curve (i.e. toughness) provides a measure of impact resistance. The touhness area value is often reported as either the yield toughness area (i.e. the area under the stress-strain curve up to the yield strain) or as total breaking toughness (i.e. the total area under the stress-strain curve).

Drop Impact Tests: The second most common class of impact tests use a dart or tup that is dropped from a height or shot at a plate-like disc shaped sample (such as that shown in Figure 3.10) mounted in a holder. In some cases, the test is used to evaluate the impact characteristics of finished products. The simplest drop tests use tups with hemispherical heads to evaluate the force or energy required to fracture a specimen from a given height (in that way the initial impact velocity remains consistent).

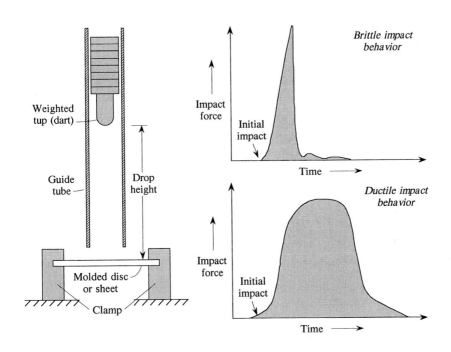

Figure 3.42. Typical instrumented drop impact behavior for both brittle and ductile polymers.

The more sophisticated drop impact tests utilize instrumented tups or darts which are designed to give an indication of the material behavior throughout the impact event. The instrumented drop impact testers utilize both force and displacement sensors, to obtain a measure of the force / displacement data as the tup penetrates the specimen as shown in Figure 3.42 [6].

3.6   Fatigue Properties

The fatigue characteristics of a material are required when designing parts that are subject to repeated or cyclic loading. Parts such as gears, snap members or other components subject to periodic stress (or strain) will fail at stress (or strain) values below those associated with one time loading. Parts subject to fatigue cycle loading for example, can develop micro-cracks or other chemical / physical defects over time that lead to a decrease in overall toughness of the material and eventual failure [5-7,12]. Fatigue tests are generally conducted by subjecting a molded test specimen to an alternating stress between equal positive and negative stress values, or between zero and a maximum positive or negative stress value. Test are typically run in bending, torsion or tension, at a given constant frequency, temperature, and amplitude of loading. The stress at which a material will fail in fatigue decreases with an increase in the number of cycles. With many materials, a fatigue endurance limit is reached, indicating that there is a stress value below which fatigue failure is unlikely, regardless of the number of cycles [6,7] as indicated in the S - N (stress vs. number of cycles) curve shown in Figure 3.43 [10].

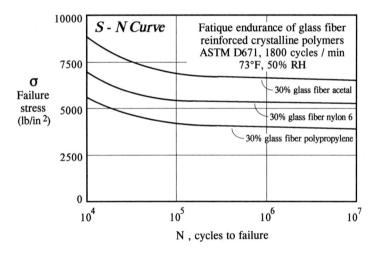

Figure 3.43. Fatigue (S-N) curves for several fiber reinforced polymers.

Because plastic materials are viscoelastic (and very temperature sensitive), the fatigue properties are significantly affected by the test frequency, amplitude, specimen geometry and temperature. At higher frequencies or amplitudes for example, plastic parts tend to run hotter, and fail sooner. Designing with thin walls and fatigue resistant conductive materials is generally recommended for cyclic load type application (see section 4.9.2) to maximize heat transfer. Fatigue test results do provide an "indication" of the relative ability of a plastic material to survive fatigue loading. For design purposes, however, tests should be conducted using injection molded specimens (to account for residual stresses) at conditions (frequency, temperature, etc.) that are representative of those associated with the end-use application [6,7].

3.7   Thermal Properties of Plastic Materials

3.7.1   Thermal Mechanical Behavior

Compared to most metals, plastic material properties tend to be very sensitive to changes in temperature. Changes in temperature can cause significant changes in the dimensions of a plastic part, and significant changes in the mechanical performance of the plastic material. Plastic materials that are said to have good "dimensional stability" are those with a low coefficient of thermal expansion, and good mechanical performance (low creep etc.) over the range of temperatures (and relative humidities) associated with the application. Because most material properties are influenced by temperature, it is important that designers carefully consider both the low and high temperature extremes associated with the application. Most plastic materials become brittle at some specific low temperature range and softer over some range of elevated temperatures. Designers need to obtain (or alternatively generate) mechanical property data over the range of temperatures anticipated during the end-use application.

The thermal mechanical behavior of a polymer is most conveniently described using modulus - temperature curves. Amorphous polymers exhibit modulus - temperature curves similar to that shown in Figure 3.44.

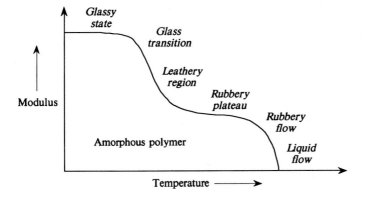

Figure 3.44. Modulus vs. temperature behavior for an amorphous polymer.

Amorphous polymers soften gradually with increasing temperature, and do not have a true melt temperature (since the polymer molecules are randomly dispersed at all temperatures). At low temperatures, amorphous polymers are rigid and glassy. At a critical temperature, or more appropriately over a narrow temperature range, amorphous polymers start to become flexible or leathery. This temperature is known as the glass transition temperature, T_g, and is associated with significant polymer chain segmental movement and mobility. At temperatures above T_g, the polymer becomes rubbery and remains rubbery until the temperature becomes high enough that true liquid like flow is achieved (i.e. processing temperature). The terms "low" and "high" temperature are relative to the Tg. Rigid amorphous polymers such as polystyrene or polycarbonate have Tg values that are higher than room temperature, and as such are rigid at room temperature. Polycarbonate is a more useful material at high temperatures because its Tg is 150 °C compared to 100 - 105 °C for polystyrene [14]. On the other hand, amorphous elastomers (sometimes lightly crosslinked) are flexible at room temperature, and therefore have Tg values that are below room temperature.

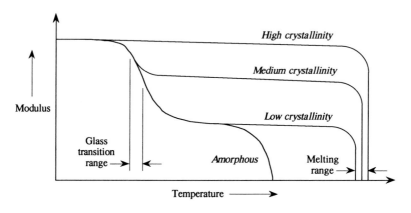

Figure 3.45. Modulus-temperature temperature for amorphous and semi-crystalline polymers.

The modulus-temperature behavior of a semi-crystalline polymer such as a nylon, acetal or polypropylene, is very different than that of an amorphous polymer like polystyrene. Unlike amorphous polymers, semi-crystalline polymers do have a true melting temperature, Tm, (or melt temperature range) associated with the phase change from a solid crystal to an amorphous melt. It should be noted here that semi-crystalline polymers are only partially crystalline, with both amorphous and crystalline regions. The crystalline regions of the polymer remain relatively rigid up to the melting temperature, while the amorphous regions of the polymer remain rigid up to the Tg. Many crystalline polymers have Tg values that are below room temperature, and melt temperatures that are well above room temperature. High density polyethylene for example, has a Tg of less than -60 °C and a Tm of 137 °C. The material remains tough at temperatures above this very low Tg value, giving polyethylene very good low temperature impact properties, but very poor creep resistance at temperatures above Tg. Semi-crystalline polymers that exhibit high degrees of crystallinity remain relatively rigid at temperatures approaching the Tm, and as such remain useful over relatively large temperature ranges. The addition of fillers or reinforcements to a polymer does increase the modulus of the material at a given temperature, but does not change the temperature value associated with thermal transitions (e.g. Tg or Tm).

In many ways the effects of temperature on the mechanical performance of a plastic material are analogous to time. Qualitatively, short times (or high strain rates) correspond with low temperatures, while longer times (low strain rates) correspond with higher temperatures [6,14]. The short term stress-strain curve shown in Figure 3.46 (generated at different temperatures) is similar to the stress-strain curve shown in Figures 3.11 generated at different strain rates. At lower temperatures, or higher strain rates, the polymer appears to be more rigid and brittle, while at lower strain rates or higher temperatures, the polymer appears to be more ductile. This time-temperature relationship can be used quantitatively to estimate the longer term behavior (creep or stress relaxation behavior) of linear amorphous polymers by testing (creep or stress relaxation tests) at elevated temperatures for relatively short periods of time as shown in Figure 3.47 [14,15].

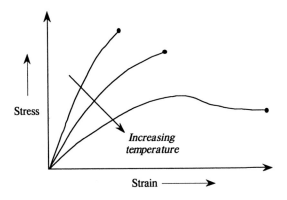

Figure 3.46. Short term stress-strain behavior at different temperatures. At higher temperatures, polymers become softer and more ductile.

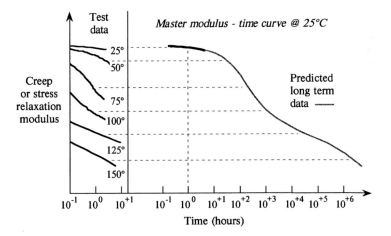

Figure 3.47. The long term mechanical behavior of linear amorphous polymers can be estimated from short term, elevated temperature mechanical property test data using techniques such as time-temperature superposition.

The concept known as the time-temperature superposition principle is used to estimate the longer term mechanical behavior by testing over a relatively short time period (typically hours) at a variety of temperatures. In Figure 3.47, the data generated at 25°C is used as the reference data and temperature. The data generated at the higher (or sometimes lower) temperature is shifted along the time axis to create the master modulus vs. time curve at 25°C. This technique can provide an estimation of the long term behavior of linear amorphous polymers, however, true long term creep or stress relaxation data is of course more reliable.

3.7.2   Deflection Temperature Under Load and the Vicat Temperature

There are several short term, standard tests that are commonly used to indicate the relative high temperature capabilities of plastic materials. The most commonly used test is known as the *Deflection Temperature Under Load (DTUL)* test. The test is often referred to as the *Heat Distortion Temperature (HDT)* test. The DTUL test provides a rough measure of the temperature at which a beam like specimen subject to three-point bending deflects a fixed distance under a specified load (typically an outer fiber stress of 1.82 MPa).

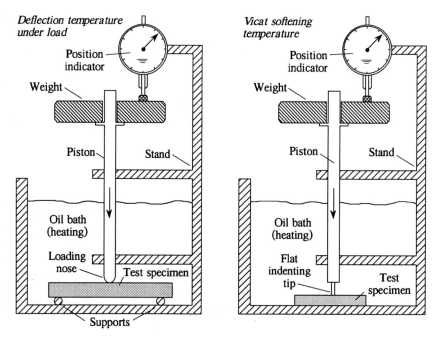

Figure 3.48. Testing configurations and apparatus associated with the Deflection Temperature Under Load (DTUL) and Vicat Softening Temperature tests.

For amorphous materials, the DTUL value is generally close to the glass transition temperature of the polymer. For semi-crystalline polymers, the DTUL value has no relation to glass transition. The DTUL test provides a measure of the temperature at which a polymer achieves a certain flexural modulus value (971 MPa at the 1.82 MPa outer fiber stress), but does not provide any indication as to the shape of the modulus-temperature curve for the polymer (i.e. it is a short term, single point test). As such, the DTUL test is suitable only for initial material screening and should not be used for final material selection and design [5,7].

A variant of the DTUL test is the Vicat Softening Temperature Test. Unlike the bending test configuration associated with the DTUL test, the Vicat temperature test (apparatus shown in Figure 3.48) provides a measure of the temperature for which a lightly loaded flat pin penetrates a fixed distance into a test specimen. The object of the test is to provide a relative indication of the ability of a material to withstand short term contact with a heated object [6,7]. The test is also commonly used for process design purposes (molding simulations) as a measure of the minimum temperature at which an injection molded part can be ejected from a mold. It is likely that ejector pins, sleeves etc. would damage parts if the parts were ejected at temperatures above the Vicat temperature. Both Vicat and DTUL temperature values can also be used as a rough measure of the intrinsic resistance of a thermoplastic to distortion or warpage at elevated temperatures. The values are useful only as a guide since the tendency towards warpage is influenced by factors such as the degree of orientation, residual stress, loads, and part geometry [6].

3.7.3   Coefficient of Linear Thermal Expansion

Like most other materials, plastic materials expand when they are heated and contract when they are cooled (i.e. they have positive coefficients of thermal expansion). Compared to many other materials, plastic materials have relatively high thermal expansion coefficients, however, the values vary significantly from polymer to polymer. The volumetric change associated with a given change in temperature (or pressure) can be characterized using pressure - volume - temperature curves such as those shown in Figures 2.60 a & b. However, for part design purposes, it is the *Coefficient of Linear Thermal Expansion* (CLTE) that is most useful. CLTE values are more commonly measured directly (rather than extracted from pressure - volume - temperature data) because injection molded plastic parts may not exhibit isotropic behavior. The CLTE is defined as the ratio of the change in linear dimension to the original dimension per unit degree change in temperature. The CLTE has units of $1/°C$ ($1/°F$) or $cm/cm°C$ ($in/in/°F$). The latter units are preferred because they implicitly indicate that the value is the linear CTE rather than area or volume CTE. The CLTE value for molded polymeric materials can vary significantly between the flow and cross flow directions, especially for fiber reinforced polymer grades. Oriented fibers restrict the dimensional changes (glass fibers for example have very low CLTE values) in the flow direction, while cross flow CLTE values can become greater since a certain volume change must take place. In addition, CLTE values do change with temperature and can be considered constants only over a small temperature range. Significant changes (increases) in the CLTE value occur when temperatures approach thermal transitions such as Tg or Tm. This is a particular concern for semi-crystalline polymers that are commonly used at temperatures that span their glass transition temperature.

Typical Coefficient of Linear Thermal Expansion values are given for a variety of materials in Table 3.2 [6,7]. When designing parts that must assemble with another, it is best to use materials that have similar CLTE values (i.e. avoid a CLTE mismatch). This can be difficult when parts contain both metal and plastic components, since plastic material CLTE can be an order of magnitude greater than that of steel. In many cases, fasteners themselves present problems since they are commonly produced from steel. The part designs developed for applications involving CLTE mismatches must incorporate features such as clearance holes or slots to accommodate the changes in dimensions over the entire range of temperature associated with the end-use application.

Table 3.2. Typical Linear Coefficient of Thermal Expansion Values [7]

Material type	Typical CTE (10^{-5} cm/cm/°C)	Material type	Typical CTE (10^{-5} cm/cm/°C)
LCP (GFR)*	0.6	ABS (GFR)*	3.1
Glass	0.3 - 0.7	Polypropylene (GFR)*	3.2
Steel	1.1	Polyphenylene sulfide	3.6
Concrete	1.4	Acetal (GFR)*	4.0
Copper	1.6	Epoxy	5.4
Bronze	1.8	Polyetherimide	5.6
Brass	1.8	Polycarbonate	6.5
Aluminum	2.2	Acrylic	6.8
Polyetherimide (GFR)*	1.5 - 3.2	ABS	7.2
Nylon (GFR)*	2.3	Nylon	8.1
TP Polyester (GFR)*	2.5 - 7.5**	Acetal	8.5
Magnesium	2.5	Polypropylene	8.6
Polycarbonate (GFR)	2.0 - 4.0	TP polyester	12.4
Zinc	3.1	Polyethylene	13 - 17

* Typical glass fiber reinforced grade.
** Highest CTE value for cross flow direction.

3.7.4   Aging at Elevated Temperatures

Many plastic materials become brittle or discolored when exposed to high temperatures for extended periods of times. The changes in material properties that occur over time at elevated temperatures can be due to physical effects such as the loss of additives (e.g. plasticizer migration) or chemical changes such as oxidation. The thermal stability of a polymer is typically evaluated by placing a series of molded specimens in an oven held at a specific temperature (typically a high temperature to accelerate the test) for an extended period of time. The samples are removed periodically for evaluation. Once a sample is removed from the oven, it is observed and tested for the desired physical, mechanical, electrical, optical, chemical, etc. property. The test results are then presented as a plot of property (or property retention) as a function of time at the particular aging temperature. This type of test provides a measure of thermal stability at the particular environmental conditions associated with the test.

3.7.5   Flammability

Flammability relates to the burning characteristics of a material after ignition has occurred. Designers must recognize that flammability is not only important in electrical applications, but also in applications where the plastic material is used in a confined space such as a room in a dwelling where flame and heat sources can be present. Some of the more recognized test methods measure combustibility, smoke generation and ignition temperatures [6]. Many material manufacturers offer ignition resistant material grades that are inherently ignition resistant, or contain additives to resist combustion. However, even ignition resistant grades will burn rapidly under the right conditions of heat and oxygen feed [5].

The UL 94 test is commonly used to classify or rate materials in terms of their combustion characteristics. Depending on the test results, materials are given a flammability class rating of V-0, V-1, V-2, 5V, or HB. The test subjects specimens to specific flame exposure criteria. The relative ability of the specimen to maintain combustion after the flame is removed forms the basis for a classification system. In general, materials which extinguish rapidly and do not drip flaming particles receive the higher ratings. In addition, ratings are given based on a defined material thickness (i.e. 1.6 mm or 3.2 mm) which may provide some design assistance with respect to component wall thickness specification [6], however, other results can be encountered for different part geometries, even when wall thicknesses are equivalent. A "V-0" rating indicates the most ignition resistant grade and "HB" rating indicates the least resistant. The rating from a second test of "5V" is added to the first rating if the material passes the second test. The combination of V-0 and 5V is the highest UL 94 rating, while HB is the lowest [5]. Because UL flammability ratings are based on small scale tests, they may not accurately reflect the behavior of the material under actual fire conditions [5]. Other common combustibility test include (i) the *Limiting Oxygen Index Test* which determines the minimum amount of oxygen, expressed as a volume percent, in a mixture of oxygen and nitrogen that will support flaming combustion of a material initially at room temperature, and (ii) *Smoke Generation* tests that determine the smoke density associated with combustion [5].

3.8   Melt Flow Properties

The flow properties of a polymer are influenced by process or test related variables such as temperature, pressure and shear rate, and by material variables such as molecular weight, molecular weight distribution, structure and additives. A variety of tests are used to measure the bulk flow properties of a polymer, with the *Melt Flow Rate Test* (or Melt Index in the case of polyethylene) being the most common. The test is particularly important because most plastic material grades are specified, at least in part, according to their Melt Flow Rate (MFR) value. The melt flow rate test results provide a rough indication of the average molecular weight of a polymer (within a particular family). MFRs are inversely related to average molecular weight. High melt flow rate values indicate low molecular weight averages while low melt flow rate numbers indicate high molecular weight [5]. The melt flow rate value itself is determined using an extrusion plastometer. After loading the plastic pellets, and preheating for a specific period of time,

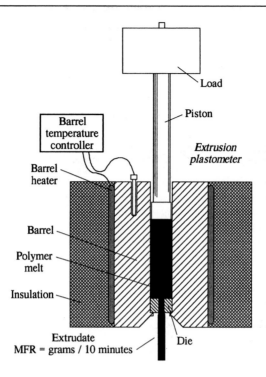

Figure 3.49. An extrusion plastometer is used to evaluate the melt flow rate (MFR) of a plastic melt.

the flow rate (in units of grams/10 minutes) is measured at specific conditions of temperature and load. Polymers that have low MFR values tend to be tougher, offer improved heat resistance, and overall have better properties than higher MFR (i.e. lower average molecular weight) grades. However, higher MFR grades are generally easier to process, and have properties that are less adversely affected by fabrication. Moldings produced with higher MFR grade polymers tend to be more isotropic (due to less orientation, etc.) than those produced using more viscous grades. This is often a complicating factor for material grade selection.

While MFR does provide a rough indication of the processability of a polymer, it is a single point test (for the standard method) and as such, does not describe the complete viscous flow behavior of the polymers. In fact, the flow rates (or shear rates) associated with the MFR test are orders of magnitude lower than those associated with mold filling. Consider a material with a MFR of 6.0 g/10 minutes. During the test, a total of 6.0 grams of material flow through an orifice that has a geometry that is similar to an injection mold gate (e.g. a pin gate on a three plate mold). During injection molding, it is likely that a similar volume of material will pass through the gate in seconds (rather than minutes). This discrepancy in time scales is very significant because most plastic melts are highly pseudoplastic (i.e. they exhibit a decrease in viscosity with increasing shear rate). It is possible that two polymer grades have similar MFR values, but very different melt viscosities at the shear rates associated with injection molding.

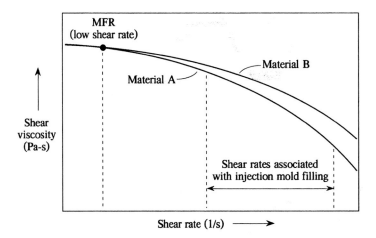

Figure 3.50. Melt flow rate does not adequately define the flow properties of a polymer because it is a single point, low shear rate test.

In order to fully describe the shear flow behavior of a polymer melt, tests must be run at a variety of shear rates, temperatures and pressures. This is most easily and commonly accomplished using a capillary rheometer as described in Section 2.2.2.

3.9   Sources of Plastic Material Property Data

When selecting a plastic material for a given end-use application, a designer must compare the performance requirements of the end-use application (both properties and processing requirements) with those of the "property profiles" of the various plastic materials that are available on the market. In many ways, the designer of a plastic product is fortunate in that there are more than 15,000 commercial plastic material grades from which to choose [16]. It is likely that the designer will be able to identify one or more material candidates (grades) that have property profiles which correlate closely with the performance requirements. The material that is ultimately selected should offer the best performance / cost balance. There are times when no commercially available material will meet the performance requirements associated with the application (or perhaps at the right price). In such a case, the designer has the option of (i) redesigning the product in an effort to minimize the performance requirements, (ii) relaxing the performance standards or cost restrictions, or (iii) working with a material supplier / custom compounder on the development of a "new" material grade (by polymer blending or using additives).

While designers have many materials to choose from, materials selection can be an overwhelming task. Due to the shear number of material grades available, it is difficult to obtain and catalog the vast array of material supplier data sheets and brochures. It is difficult to keep such a library up to date with respect to new material grades, those that are no longer available, as well as material cost. Even if a designer had a complete library of data, the time required to sort through all of the data sheets manually would be excessively long (unless the field of candidates had been narrowed significantly). Time aside, it is also unlikely that the reviewer of the product literature would happen upon the best material for a given application simply by reviewing a limited file of product literature.

It is at this stage of the design process (materials selection) that designers typically begin to consult with material supplier representatives (ideally several). Alternatively, designers can utilize various types of material databases to assist with material selections [16-22]. Databases are available as hard copy publications or on computer format (disc format or on-line). Computer based databases are easier to update and offer the very significant advantage of rapid, automated searching, based on a window of specific property requirements entered by the user. The databases themselves typically fall into one of three major categories:

- Material manufacturer databases (house databases)
- Universal material databases (third party)
- Specific property databases (when specific performance areas such as chemical resistance are critical, third party)

When a designer consults with a material supplier, or uses a material supplier database, he / she is most likely limited to the group of material grades offered by that particular supplier. It is common for designers to work with material distributors that offer a wider range of materials to choose from. While the number of grades are limited, the quality and quantity of data available directly from the material supplier is excellent (this data also serves as the source of the data for universal data bases, which often report only a portion of the data which can be obtained directly from the supplier). House data bases can also provide additional information with regard to processing and design. It is generally best to work with several material suppliers (or use several house databases) to cover a broader range of materials. However, because material suppliers tend to use unique data formats, and testing procedures / specimen preparation methods tend to be inconsistent, direct comparison of data obtained from separate suppliers is often inappropriate. It should also be noted here that material suppliers property data tables will often have a disclaimer indicating that the property data listed are "typical property values, not to be construed as specifications", [5] or "approximate values and are not part of the product specifications" [12], since processing related factors are so significant, and are beyond their control.

Universal plastic material databases provide an alternative to supplier or house databases for initial material selection. These universal databases compile existing data from a variety of different material suppliers. Computerized databases are capable of searching for a suitable material from as many as 10,000 candidate material entries. This format also tends to simplify comparison of competitive materials supplied by different manufacturers [17]. As mentioned previously, direct unqualified comparisons of property data from different material suppliers (or between databases) is not always possible due to a lack of data uniformity and standardization. In fact, the properties listed in the database are not material properties, but are more appropriately described as molded part properties [18].

Table 3.3.   A Listing of Some Plastic Material Databases

Company	Product	Materials	Data Types	Formats
ASM International Materials Park, OH	Mat.DB	Over 8,000 plastics, also other materials	Properties	PC and publication
BASF Corp. Parsippany, NJ	CAMPUS	BASF materials	Properties, ratings, chemical resistance.	PC
D.A.T.A. Business Publishing Englewood,CO	D.A.T.A. Plastics Digest	Over 10,000 thermo-plastics, thermosets, elastomers	Properties, ratings	Publication
Dow Plastics Midland,MI	591Ways to Succeed	Dow materials	Properties, ratings, chemical resistance	PC and publication
GE Plastics Pittsfield, MA	Engineering Design Database (EDD)	GE thermoplastics and foams	Properties, ratings, design data	Online
Hoechst Celanese Corp. Chatham, NJ	Fast Focus	Hoechst materials and equivalents	Properties, ratings, chemical resistance	PC
IDES, Inc. Laramie, WY	Prospector	Over 10,000 thermo-plastics, thermosets, elastomers, films	Properties, ratings, design data, chem-ical resistance	PC and Macintosh
Information Indexing Inc. Garden Grove, CA	CenBase Materials	Over 10,000 plastics, also other materials	Properties, design data, and chemical resistance	PC, work-station, and publication
LNP Engineering Plastics Exton, PA	EPOS	LNP materials	Properties, ratings, design data, chem-ical resistance	PC
McGraw Hill Inc./ Polydata New York, NY	DataPlas	7,000 engineering thermoplastics	Properties, ratings, chemical resistance	PC
Miles Pittsburgh, PA	CAMPUS	Miles materials	Properties, ratings, chemical resistance	PC
Plaspec Yardley, PA	Plaspec	Over 10,000 thermo-plastics, thermosets, elastomers	Properties, ratings, chemical resistance	Online
Plastics Design Library New York, NY	Chemical Compat-ibility and ESCR	More than 60 families of plastics	Chemical resistance	Publication
Prime Alliance Des Moines, Iowa	Prime Alliance Database	Over 700: BASF, Miles, Mobil, Monsanto, Rexene	Properties, ratings	PC
Rapra Technology Ltd. Shropshire, England	Plascams	Contains generic materials	Properties	PC and publication

While the testing procedures used to generate the test data are reasonably well standardized (for a given test), the variables associated with test specimen preparation are not. For example, specimens prepared by the compression molding process will yield different results than samples produced by the injection molding process. Processing variables such as melt temperature, residence time, moisture content, tool temperature, injection velocity, packing pressure, and the like can all have a significant impact on the properties of the molded test specimens. Other test specimen variables such as sample thickness, gate type / location, and runner geometry are equally important. Since in most cases, the standard testing procedures do not fully specify these variables, the test samples can have different degrees of molecular / fiber orientation, cooling stress distributions, and zones of crystallinity (for semi-crystalline polymers). Therefore, the property data sets (property profiles) obtained with different sets of test samples are not necessarily comparable.

Material supplier databases generally list 30 to 40 different material properties (most based on standard ASTM or ISO test methods) and grade descriptions (major additives, agency approval, processing characteristics etc.), however, the various databases tend to list different sets of properties for different materials. As an example, it is estimated that there are more than 30 different methods for obtaining the impact strength of a plastic material [18]. The data profiles are sometimes based upon inconsistent test methods and as a result, the material property values are not directly comparable. In some cases, the data profiles for a given material are also incomplete.

While some databases have extensive listings of properties, many list only short term, single point (typically room temperature / 50% relative humidity) properties such as initial modulus, tensile yield strength (or breaking strength), Izod impact strength, Rockwell hardness, DTUL (HDT) and the like. The single point properties are most easily reviewed / compared manually or by the computer. The single point properties are useful for initial material screening, but do not accurately represent the performance capabilities of the material. More quantitative functional data that describes the effects of variables such as time and temperature on the properties of a material are required for final material selection and part design. Some house databases offer functional property information of this type, but the problems of procedure and format standardization between suppliers are still at issue. Recognizing this, European material suppliers have worked together on the development of a standardized set of basic data catalog property values and database format. A standardized database format was introduced in 1988 under the name Computer Aided Material Preselection by Uniform Standards (CAMPUS) [16,18,20]. The CAMPUS database format provides an internationally uniform system of testing and data presentation format. The database uses more vigorous International Standard Organization (ISO) test methods that must be adhered to by each of the material manufacturers that use CAMPUS as the house database format. While there is still some flexibility in terms of test specimen manufacturing conditions, the data sets are standardized to the point where direct comparisons between suppliers are more appropriate.

The original version of the CAMPUS computer database program (CAMPUS version 1) was based upon a set of 30 Standardized Single Point Basic Data Catalog values that enable a designer to automatically screen material based on mechanical, thermal and electrical properties. While the standardized program was good for initial screening, it did not provide the functional data required for final material selection and design. The current version of the software, CAMPUS version 2, includes (i) single point data for initial screening, (ii) functional time / temperature dependent mechanical data, (iii) rheological data, and (iv) mold filling software data, for use in both process and product design. The development of the CAMPUS database is the first step towards international standardization among material suppliers. While the database does not provide a complete listing of all of the material properties that a designer would like to see, it does provide for a more sound basis on which to make material selection and screening decision.   The functional data given in CAMPUS version 2 computer data base format includes:

- Isothermal tensile stress vs. tensile strain curves over a wide temperature range, for the evaluation of short term mechanical behavior (up to the yield region).
- Secant tensile modulus vs. tensile strain curves derived from the isothermal stress vs. strain curves.
- Isochronous tensile stress vs. tensile strain curves for as many as six different temperatures (typically at 23, 60, and 100°C) for evaluations of the long term mechanical performance.
- Creep tensile modulus vs. time curves derived from the isochronous stress vs. strain curve.
- Shear modulus vs. temperature curves over a very wide temperature range as an indication of the rigidity as a function of temperature.
- Shear viscosity vs shear rate curves over a range of processing temperatures as a measure of the rheological properties of the polymer (with options for different curve fits).

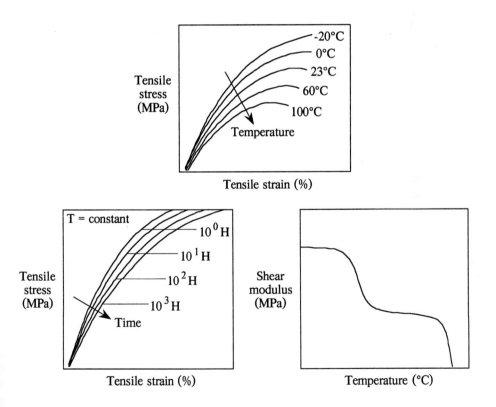

Figure 3.51. Some of the data provided by the CAMPUS version 2 database format.

Once a material has been selected, additional, more detailed design data can be obtained from the material manufacturers as needed. Future versions of CAMPUS are expected to include data on chemical resistance, U.V. light resistance and weathering characteristics, heat aging and pressure-volume-temperature behavior of the various polymers [16,20].

3.10   Materials Evaluation Using Molded Samples

In most cases, designers screen candidate materials for a given application by evaluating numerical property data. Once the field of candidates has been narrowed, it is good practice to request molded samples (such as test specimens) from the material supplier, to gain a hands-on feel for the materials. This is particularly important when working with new and unfamiliar materials. One manufacturer [23] has taken this concept a step further; and has developed a so called universal prototype that can be used for resin comparisons, assembly comparisons and gating comparisons. The Evaluator® is a two piece injection molded unit that is available in many of the more widely used neat and reinforced engineering thermoplastics.

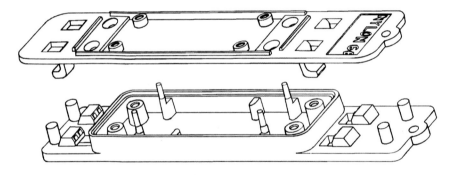

Figure 3.52. The Evaluator® is a universal prototype that can be used to evaluate both resin properties and assembly characteristics.

The Evaluator® can assist the plastic part designer in several ways. As mentioned, the parts can give a designer a hands-on feel for the rigidity, strength and appearance of the various thermoplastics. The evaluator can also provide insight into the shrinkage and warpage characteristics of the different materials (the actual tool dimensions are provided with the samples). The parts themselves have a variable wall thickness and are available in both center and end gated versions (for comparison of gating considerations). Lastly, the two parts that make up the Evaluator® incorporate a variety of assembly features including screw bosses, cantilever snaps and stakes that allow the parts to be assembled / bonded in six different ways. This unique sample provides a great deal of information at a relatively low cost. The Evaluator® is described as a universal prototype that can be used for resin evaluation, assembly comparison and gating comparison. The parts are available in a variety of engineering thermoplastics.

3.11   Standardized Plastic Material Designations

Once a plastic material has been selected by a designer for a particular application, it is generally specified according to the specific material grade as manufactured by a specific material supplier. In most cases, material suppliers specify plastic materials according to:

- *Tradename:* Describing the generic material type

- *Grade:* Particular structure, molecular weight, molecular weight distribution and additive package

- *Lot:* For each particular production batch (not generally specified for design purposes)

In most cases, the tradename and grade designations of the material supplier do not explicitly indicate the material's chemical makeup, additives or physical properties (although a limited number of property values such as melt flow rate are commonly encoded into the grade number designation). By definition, the tradenames are unique to each material supplier, and the grade designation has no resemblance to those of another supplier (i.e. there is no standardization between suppliers).

However, there are standards such as ASTM D4000, "Standard Classification System for Specifying Plastic Materials", that attempt to provide a classification system for tabulating the properties of unfilled, filled and reinforced plastic materials [24]. The classification system and subsequent line callout (material specifications) is intended to provide a universal means of identifying plastic materials used in the fabrication of end products, in much the same way that steel is specified (e.g. 1030 steel is a generic indication of a steel grade that can be obtained from a number of suppliers). The classification system is based on the premise that plastic materials can be arranged into broad generic families based on chemical family and basic material properties.

ASTM D 4000 Line Call-Out

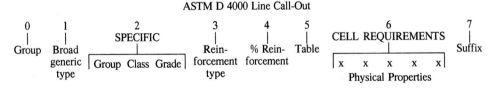

0 = One digit for expanded group, as needed.
1 = Two or more letters identify the material family based on abbreviations given in D 1600.
2 = Three digits identify the specific chemical group, the modification or use class, and the grade by viscosity or level of modification. A basic property table will provide property values.
3 = One letter indicates reinforcement type.
4 = Two digits indicate percent reinforcement.
5 = One letter refers to cell table listing of physical specifications and test methods.
6 = Five digits refer to the specific physical parameters listed in the cell table.
7 = Suffix codes indicate special requirements based on the application, and identify special tests.

Figure 3.53. Line callout format for ASTM D4000 materials classification / specification system.

This clasification system provides a means of identifying plastic materials using standardized line callout designations. This more complete material description may make it easier for a designer to locate alternate materials for a given application from competitive material suppliers. The classification system is based on generic material families, sub-groups within generic families, fillers / reinforcements, and physical properties.

An example of a reinforced plastic material identified according to the standard classification system is as follows:

Material: D4000 PA120G33A53380

Specifications:

PA120 = Nylon 66 heat stabilized from Table PA of specification D 4066
G33   = Glass reinforced with 33% glass, nominal
A   = Table A (D 4066) for property requirements
5   = Tensile strength, 175 MPa min
3   = Flexural modulus, 7500 MPa min
3   = Izod impact, 75 J/m min
8   = Deflection temperature, 235°C min
0   = Unspecified

While the classification system is by no means perfect, it does provide a more standardized format for materials identification. For example, the standard cannot quantify the subtle difference associated with competitive material grades (e.g. in terms of processability or shrinkage characteristics). While the standard is not widely used at this time, it is likely that line callout systems of this type will become more popular as materials databases and testing / specimen preparation procedures become more standardized.

3.12   References

1. Nagarsheth, P., SPE Annual Technical Conference, **35**, 220 (1989).
2. Woodruff, D., *Business Week* , April 30, 110 (1990).
3. Kelley, D., *Plastic Design Forum* , **12**, (1), 80, (1987).
4. Technical Bulletin, "Material Properties Needed for Engineering Design", The Dow Chemical, Midland, MI.
5. Technical Bulletin, "Basic Design Manual, Polycarbonate", The Dow Chemical, Midland, MI.
6. Technical Bulletin, "Engineering Materials Design Guide", General Electric Plastics, Pittsfield, MA.
7. Technical Bulletin, "Designing with Plastics", Hoechst Celanese, Chatham, NJ (1989).
8. Rietveld, J., "Viscoelasticity", Engineered Materials Handbook, Vol. 2, Engineering Plastics, ASM, 412, (1988).
9. Throne, J., and Progelhof, R., "Creep and Stress Relaxation", Engineered Materials Handbook, Vol. 2, Engineering Plastics, ASM, 658, (1988).
10. Newby, G. and Theberge, J., *Machine Design* , March 8 (1984).

11. So, Pa, "Fractography", Engineered Materials Handbook, Volume 2, Engineering Plastics, American Society of Metals, 805, (1988).
12. Technical Bulletin, "Polycarbonate Design Manual", Miles Corporation, Pittsburg, PA.
13. Rucinski, P.,"An Evaluation of Molded-in and Machined-in Notches for Izod Impact Testing", MS Thesis, Department of Plastics Engineering, University of Massachusetts Lowell (1993).
14. Deanin, R., "Polymer Structure, Properties and Applications", Cahners, Boston, MA (1972).
15. Aklonis, J., MacKnight, W., and Shen, M., "Introduction to Polymer Viscoelasticity", Wiley Interscience, NY (1972).
16. LeVerne, L., *Plastic Design Forum*, **18**, (1), 36, (1993).
17. Dieckmann, D., *Plastics Engineering*, **45**, (11), 29, (1989).
18. Mehta, K. and Oberbach, Society of Plastics Engineers RETEC, Rochester, **51**, (1991).
19. Klein, A., *Plastics Design Forum*, **14**, (2), 39, (1989).
20. Kennedy, J., Bornschlegl, E., and Tullman, R., SPE Annual Technical Conference, **36**, 1736, (1990).
21. Friedman, M., *Plastics Design Forum*, **11**, (4), 61, (1986).
22. MacDermott, C., "Selecting Thermoplastics for Engineering Applications", Marcel Dekker, Inc., NY (1984).
23. Technical Bulletin, The Evaluator®, The Corr Company, Windsor, VT 05089.
24. ASTM D4000, "Standard Classification System for Specifying Plastic Materials", Annual Book of ASTM Standards, **8.0**, (1990).

4 Structural Design Considerations

4.1 Introduction

The design of a molded plastic part or component is influenced by factors such as esthetic requirements, manufacturability, and various end-use performance considerations. In many cases, the functional requirements of the product include dimensional stability and the ability to withstand externally induced service stresses or strains. The stresses or strains encountered during product manufacturing and assembly operations can also be a significant concern. As a result, it is necessary to evaluate the structural reliability of a proposed design to ensure that the product will perform adequately during assembly and service. The objective of the structural design process is to generate a part design that will be able to withstand the loads or imposed deflections that are likely to be encountered during service. This must be done within the constraints dictated by the material and manufacturing operations that have been selected for the application. Since it is not always possible to quantify the loading conditions for a particular part with great certainty, a series of structural design calculations are usually performed at loading conditions that are representative of those anticipated during normal service conditions, and under conditions that are thought to represent the worst case scenario. The concept of structural design can be summed up using the *Limit States Principle* [1]:

The purpose of structural design is the achievement of an acceptable probability that the structure being designed will not become unfit for the use for which it is required, i.e., that it will not reach a Limit State.

While this philosophy is clearly the goal of the structural design engineer, it can be difficult to predict the probability of failure for a given plastic part design since the properties of plastic materials are a strong function of both the service environment and manufacturing conditions, two factors that to a large extent are beyond the complete control of the product designer. For example, parts that have been designed correctly, but processed / molded incorrectly, may fail due to factors such as material degradation, excessive orientation, residual stress, poor weld strength or other processing related problems.

4.2 Design Methodology

A plastic product designer can approach structural design problems in one or more of the following ways. The designer can:

- Base the design on past experiences (make an educated guess or use *rules of thumb*)
- Take an experimental approach, developing a reliable design using prototype analysis
- Use an analytical approach, using engineering relations for stress and strain.

All of these approaches have their own relative advantages and limitations, and in most cases, the product design process involves combined elements of each approach.

4.2.1   Design by Experience

There is of course no substitute for design experience, however, the dynamic evolution of the plastics industry has resulted in a shortage of experienced plastic product designers. Historically, plastic part designs have been based on past experience or general *rules of thumb*. This design approach has been widely used for the design of plastic products, especially for parts slated for use in non-structural or very light structural applications. Using this approach, the designer's decisions are based upon past experiences, both good and bad. Highly experienced designers, working with familiar materials and routine design geometries may in fact be quite successful using this approach. However, when the designer is faced with a product having a significantly different shape, or a product that will be manufactured using a new or unfamiliar plastic material, his/her previous experience may be of little or no use.

It is likely that a large number of products designed using this approach will be "under-designed", leading to premature product failure during service, or possibly during product assembly. On the other hand, a part that is "over-designed" may function well in service, but may not be an efficient design. The performance of this over-designed part would be viewed as a good experience by the product designer, and would influence future product design decisions. The over-designed part might not fail in service, however, it may (i) be more complicated than necessary, (ii) use more material than required, (iii) have overly thick wall sections resulting in production cycle / quality problems, and (iv) in general, the part may be more expensive to produce than another more suitable design option. While there is no substitute for experience, there is little chance of hitting upon the optimum structural design using only rules of thumb.

4.2.2   Design by Experimental Approach

A part designer may also choose to evaluate the design concepts for a plastic part based purely on experimental testing performed on prototype plastic parts. This approach has significant merit, and would probably constitute the most conservative route to part design. Structural design based solely on prototype analysis and iterative redesign would most likely lead to a reliable design, provided (i), the prototype quality is representative of the production part quality, and (ii), the anticipated service conditions can be simulated and evaluated. However, this approach is expensive and perhaps more importantly, can take an excessive period of time, especially if long term effects such as creep behavior or environmental stability are evaluated. True to life prototype parts, in terms of structural, dimensional and environmental performance, can only be generated if the production material system (containing all additives) is processed using the actual production manufacturing technique as described in Chapter 5. The prototype tooling required to produce these realistic prototype parts is relatively expensive and can take weeks or even months to fabricate. When molded prototype parts are used, the costs and time associated with several design iterations (tooling modifications) can be excessive. Machined prototypes, cast prototypes, or solid object manufacturing prototypes (rapid prototypes) can be used for initial testing, however the structural performance of parts produced using these techniques will not be truly representative of the performance of the molded production part. Product development based purely on this experimental approach is not generally practical, and could be considered poor engineering practice since many of the basic and early design iterations can be predicted in advance using appropriate engineering analyses.

It is important to note that the prototype stage of plastic product development cannot be avoided altogether, since experimental verification of an engineering design is always recommended (or may be required by certain regulatory agencies). However, the cost and time associated with prototype part or tooling development can be significantly reduced by incorporating a structural engineering analysis into the early stages of the plastic product design process as shown in Figure 3.4.

4.2.3   Design Using an Analytical Approach

Structural engineering relations allow a designer to *estimate* the stresses or strains that occur when a product is subject to a mechanical load or imposed deformation. The results of such a theoretical structural analysis provide a sound basis on which design decisions can be made, many of which are not instinctively obvious. An engineering analysis generates only an estimate of how the product can be expected to behave under load, since a number of assumptions as the material's properties, regularity of form, and boundary conditions, all of which are simplifications, must be made. In addition, the theoretical relationships are derived by mathematical procedures that often involve further assumptions [2].

Classical Formulas for Stress and Strain: The simplest of these structural analyses utilize engineering formulas that have been derived assuming isotropic, homogeneous, elastic material behavior. Even though most plastic materials do not exhibit linear elastic, isotropic behavior, computation is feasible for uniaxial and multiaxial stress applications if the appropriate viscoelastic or time dependent stress-strain relationships are used. Crate [3] summarizes the point well when he states that "the use of engineering formulas to design parts out of engineering plastics is a logical approach, but should be done with care". The results can usually be generated within a relatively short period of time at a minimal cost. The designer must review the resulting stresses and strains obtained from the structural analysis, and carefully compare those stresses and strains with allowable stresses and strains for the plastic material being used to manufacture the product.

Finite Element Analysis: The use of computer aided linear and non-linear structural analysis techniques has improved both the accuracy, interpretation, and the speed at which structural design evaluations can be accomplished. Computers are commonly used to analyze structural design problems using numerical or finite element techniques. In a Finite Element Analysis (FEA) or a Boundary Element Analysis (BEA), a complex problem is broken down into a series of interrelated sub-problems that are solved with the aid of a computer. These powerful techniques were developed decades ago for metallic structures, and are now commonly used to analyze the structural and thermal behavior of plastic parts. Linear FEA techniques are used to solve for stresses and strains in situations where the loads and deflections are relatively small. The finite element techniques can also take factors such as non-linear stress-strain behavior, time / temperature dependent stress-strain behavior, anisotropy and hysteresis into account. The output from a finite element analysis can alert a designer to areas of potentially high stress, and allow the designer to optimize variables such as corner radii, part wall thickness or fastener locations. FEA does not eliminate the need for prototype testing, but rather compliments the prototyping procedure by providing an early indication of problem areas that can be targeted for prototype testing. The use of FEA is likely to minimize the number of physical prototyping iterations required during product development.

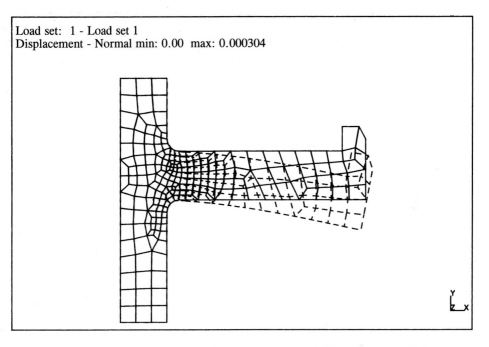

Load set: 1 - Load set 1
Displacement - Normal min: 0.00 max: 0.000304

Figure 4.1. A finite element analysis is used to predict stresses and deflection for a molded cantilever snap assembly beam subjected to a concentrated load at the free end.

Consider the example of a snap beam assembly. The structural design of snap fit assemblies is a design problem encountered on many plastic parts. Snap beams molded directly into plastic parts are deflected briefly or momentarily during product assembly, and then catch in an undercut in the mating part. The cantilever snap beam molded into the automotive wheel cover shown in Figure 4.2 is deflected as the wheel cover is pushed onto the rigid metal tire rim. The stresses and strains associated with this assembly operation can be estimated using classical engineering formulas that have been derived for beams subject to bending (a cantilever beam in this case). The formulas are derived using assumptions such as the beam length is significantly greater than the beam depth, and therefore bending stresses predominate. The formulas may then be reasonably accurate for beams having a relatively large L/h ratio, however, the results could be misleading and lead to significant error when the classical formulas are applied to relatively short beams, i.e. beams having a relatively low L / h ratio. One finite element study has shown that errors associated with the classical bending theory increase as the beam aspect ratio decreases, as shown in Figure 4.3 [4].

Figure 4.2. A cantilever snap assembly beam is molded into an automotive wheel cover.

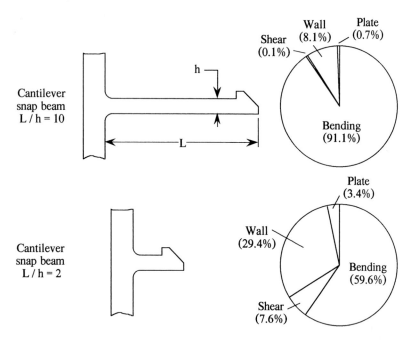

Figure 4.3. Classical bending formulas work well for long slender beams, but are not appropriate for short beams where shear and wall deflections becomes significant.

The FEA techniques can be used in place of the classical approach here to obtain a more accurate description of the stresses and strains associated with the deflection of the cantilever beam or snap. The geometry of the entire plastic part, or section of the part, is modeled using Computer Aided Design (CAD) software, and a finite element mesh made up of a series of simple elements interconnected at the vertices or nodes, is superimposed on this geometry [4-6]. The number of elements, or mesh density, used in the analysis is dependent on factors such as the rate of change in strain at that particular area of the part, and on computer capacity. Mesh densities can be increased in problem areas such as corners where stress concentrations are high. Boundary or restraint conditions / loads are then imposed on the network of elements or computer model, and the response in terms of stress, strain and deflection are generated as the computer solves hundreds of equations simultaneously. Ideally, an FEA for plastic parts should include effects due to non-linear stress-strain behavior for high strain applications such as snap fits [5]. These computer based structural analysis techniques are capable of handling more complicated geometries and loading conditions, or in general, situations where the use of classical formulas is not appropriate. The FEA analysis techniques are especially useful for dynamic applications since both heat transfer and stress strain behavior can be considered.

Regardless of the analytical technique used by the designer, the accuracy of the results obtained (i.e. their correlation to actual product performance) is directly related to the ability of the designer to *quantify* the design problem correctly. The designer must obtain a vast array of information, and simplify the information to a degree that is appropriate for the analysis being used. For example, initial screening analysis can be done using simplified geometries, while more realistic (and more complicated) geometries and computer based structural analyses would be used for final and more critical design calculations. A detailed description of the finite element approach is beyond the scope of this introductory text. The intent here is to review the fundamental procedures and concepts associated with applying classical engineering theory to the design of plastic products.

4.3   Quantifying the Design Problem

In order to evaluate the structural characteristics of a plastic part or component, the designer must first define the structural design problem(s) clearly, and put things in a form that can be evaluated analytically. The designer will need to assess and specify a number of factors before beginning any type of structural calculations. These factors include:

- Part geometry
- Type of support or restraint
- Loading conditions
- Environmental conditions
- Material behavior / mechanical properties
- Safety factors

Once these items have been quantified, the designer can perform a series of design calculations, examine the results, alter the design, recalculate and iterate on the design details until the desired results are obtained.

4.3.1   Simplification of Part Geometry

Plastic parts vary in geometric complexity, however, it is common for injection molded plastic parts to have fairly complex geometries since one of the major advantages of plastic materials is their ability to be molded into complex shapes. In order to predict the stresses, strains or deflections that result from an anticipated service loading, it may be necessary to simplify the geometry of the part to a degree dependent upon the analysis technique being used.

Classical formulas for stress and strain have been derived, and are given in handbooks [2], for most regular geometries. These geometries include: straight, tapered or curved beams, columns, plates, or shells of revolution. Plastic part geometries can often be approximated using one or more of these basic geometric forms. Consider the part shown in Figure 4.4, which consists of a flat surface with integral supports running along the two short sides. An undersized hollow boss extrudes up from the nominal part wall and is designed to receive a pushed-in (press fit), internally threaded metal insert.

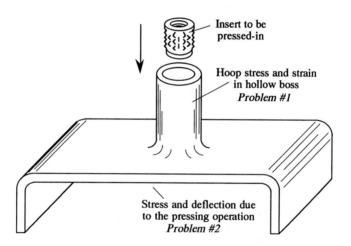

Insert to be
pressed-in

Hoop stress and strain
in hollow boss
Problem #1

Stress and deflection due
to the pressing operation
Problem #2

Figure 4.4. More complex part geometries can be broken down into a series of regular geometries for an approximate analysis.

A structural analysis of this product would involve several separate calculations. For example, one calculation would focus on the hoop stresses and strains in the hollow boss wall associated with pressing an oversized metal insert into the receiving hole. The hollow boss geometry can be described as a cylindrical shell having certain inner and outer radius values. The stresses and strains (for example hoop stresses) associated with pressing the metal insert into the hollow boss can be calculated using appropriate formulas for cylindrical shells. A designer could also determine the force associated with the pressing operation. The forces associated with pressing the insert into the boss would cause deflection (and stresses) along the horizontal product surface. This second structural design problem could be evaluated using a beam or plate analysis. The reaction forces from the boss problem are used as the loading conditions for the beam or plate deflection problem. It is common practice to divide parts with complicated geometries up into a series of sub-parts having regular geometries, and evaluating the stresses and strains in each of these sub-parts individually (as in the example of the cantilever beam, where the beam is treated as a separate entity). The results of the independent analyses should be considered as approximations, since the sub-parts are not truly independent entities. In this case, we assume the boss geometry has no effect on the rigidity or stress distributions for the beam, and that the beam does not influence the behavior of the hollow boss. This approach does introduce an error having a magnitude that is related to the degree of interaction between the different geometries. Some part geometries lend themselves to a simple analysis of the type described above, while other more complicated part geometries cannot be simplified without introducing very significant errors. In such cases, FEA structural analysis techniques are recommended.

4.3.2   Stress Concentration

One area that deserves special attention when considering part geometry is that of stress concentration effects. Stress distributions in parts are influenced by the presence of features such as corners, holes or any discontinuity in the design geometry. Stresses tend to concentrate at these discontinuities, leading to local stress values that can be significantly higher than those in areas adjacent to the discontinuity. Therefore stresses and strains predicted using an analysis that assumes simple geometry will be in error. The knurled surfaces on the insert shown in Figure 4.4 act as stress raisers and would generate local stress values that are higher than those predicted using the classical formulas for stress and strain. The maximum intensity of such stress raisers can be difficult to determine theoretically, and as a result, the importance of experimental stress analysis on prototypes (or pre-production) parts cannot be overemphasized.

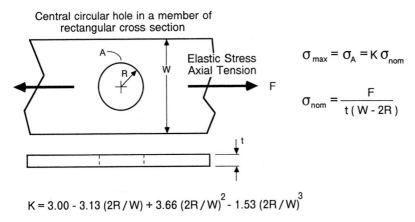

Central circular hole in a member of rectangular cross section

Elastic Stress
Axial Tension

$$\sigma_{max} = \sigma_A = K\,\sigma_{nom}$$

$$\sigma_{nom} = \frac{F}{t\,(W - 2R)}$$

$$K = 3.00 - 3.13\,(2R/W) + 3.66\,(2R/W)^2 - 1.53\,(2R/W)^3$$

Figure 4.5. Tensile stress concentration factor, K, for a rectangular section, with a central circular hole.

A stress concentration (or intensity) factor, K, is defined as the ratio of the true maximum stress (the peak stress at the discontinuity) to the stress anticipated or determined using classical formulas of mechanics (for regular geometries) for the net section, ignoring the more complex stress distribution. Stress concentration factors can be calculated for the various stress raiser geometries for elastic materials, however, equivalent values may not be applicable for more ductile (or viscoelastic) materials [2,7,8].

Figure 4.5 gives an equation which relates the stress concentration factor, K, for rectangular cross sections having a central circular hole, that are subject to uniaxial tension. Using these relationships, one can estimate the local stress at location A, along the circumference of the hole. As an example, a part having a width of 0.500 inches (12.7 mm) and a 0.125 inch (3.2 mm) diameter central hole, would have a K factor of 2.44. In other words, the stress at location A is 2.44 times greater than the nominal (calculated) value determined by dividing the tensile force by the minimum part cross section. Similar relationships are available for various other stress riser geometries [2].

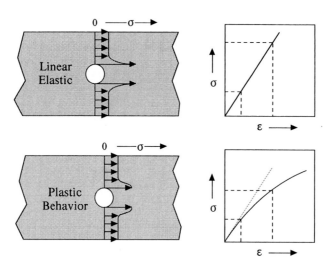

Figure 4.6. Tensile stress concentration at the edge of a hole for materials with linear and non-linear stress-strain behavior.

The actual value of the stress concentration factor is dependent upon both the part geometry and the stress-strain behavior of the material. The ductile behavior of many plastic materials results in a non-linear relationship between stress and strain at higher strain levels. For these ductile polymers, the increase in local stress is less than proportional to the increase in local strain [8].

Stress concentration factors are sometimes provided in graphical format. The stress concentration at the wall intersection for a cantilever snap beam is often described using a graph such as that shown in Figure 4.7 [9]. The figure indicates that an increase in the value of the radius at the wall intersection reduces the stress concentration factor. Figures of this type should be used with care, however, since an excessively large radius value could lead to sink mark formation, void formation, and shrinkage / cooling stresses due to the local increase in wall thickness [10]. Excessive radii can also increase stress levels for very short cantilever beams due to their effect on the overall thickness of the beam

[5]. Many sources indicate that radii values should be equal to or greater than 0.20 to 0.40 times the base wall thickness, as a compromise between uniform stress distribution and uniform wall thickness.

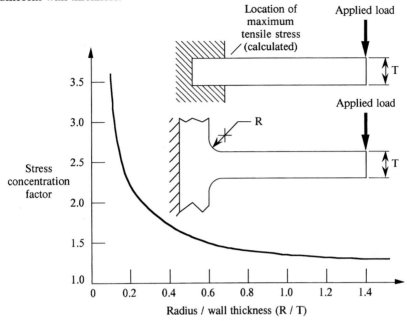

Figure 4.7. Stress concentration factor vs. R/T for a cantilevered beam.

Flow Analogy: Potential areas of stress concentration on a part can also be visualized in a qualitative manner using a fluid flow-streamline analogy. Using this approach, the part or part section is treated as a conduit through which an ideal incompressible fluid is flowing. The theoretical streamlines that form are parallel to one another and evenly spaced in areas that are under uniform stress. Areas of stress concentration are characterized as line spacings that change rapidly over a short distance. Closely spaced lines indicate faster flow and higher stress. The concept is demonstrated using the example of a notched bar subject to tensile loading [11].

The notched bar shown in Figure 4.8a has streamlines that are closely spaced at the notch area, indicating an area of high stress. The streamlines also converge rapidly over a relatively short distance, described as a transition zone. This short transition is also an indication of stress concentration. Increasing the notch radius in Figure 4.8b does not change the spacing between the lines, but does increase the length of the transition zone, indicating a reduction in the stress concentration. The example shows that removing material from certain areas of the part may actually make the part stronger. The addition of material to the back side of the molding increases both the spacing between the streamlines and the length of the transition zone, and therefore the strength of the part as shown in Figure 4.8c. The design is refined further by increasing the radius at the top of the notch, which results in more uniform spacing of the streamlines, and a more uniform part wall thickness.

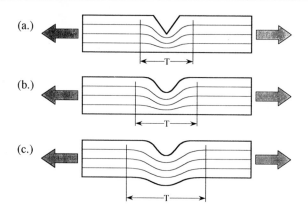

Figure 4.8. Streamlines can be used to obtain a qualitative indication of stress concentration. Rapid convergence and close spacing indicate high stress concentration.

While it is clear that stress concentration effects are significant under static loading conditions, they are even more important in dynamic loading applications. Small imperfections, notches or defects will lower the endurance limits of plastic products subject to dynamic loading. The magnitude of the stress concentration is influenced by the imperfection geometry, location, loading level, and by the notch sensitivity of the material. Ductile materials which may not be significantly affected under static conditions may show greater notch sensitivity under dynamic loading conditions. The notch sensitivity of a particular material / product is not easily predicted. Parts that will be subject to dynamic or fatigue loading should be prototyped in the production material, and evaluated under the anticipated loading conditions [2].

4.3.3   Type of Support

The ends or various points along the length of a part must be supported in one way or another for that part to support the applied load(s). In order for the loaded part to remain in equilibrium (i.e. $\sum F = 0$), the balancing forces are the reaction forces at the supports. Classical formulas for stress and deflection of beams, plates, and the like have been derived using idealized support conditions. Most real life products have support conditions that differ from these idealized cases to some degree. It is therefore necessary to compare the part support with these ideal cases, and select formulas that have been derived based on conditions that approximate the actual support condition. If a product exhibits characteristics of more than one idealized support condition, several sets of stress / deflection calculations would be recommended, including those expected to represent *the worst case* scenario.

Some idealized supports or constraints for beams (or at the edge of a plate or shell) are represented and defined as follows [2,12]:

Guided: A condition of support at the end(s) of a beam or column that prevents rotation of the edge of the neutral surface but permits longitudinal and transverse displacement.

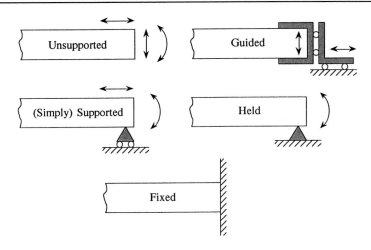

Figure 4.9. Some idealized conditions of end or edge support for beams or plates.

Free or Unsupported: A support condition where the edge of a beam is totally free to translate or rotate in any direction. The right end of the cantilever beam in Figure 4.10 is unsupported.

Held: A support condition at the end(s) of a beam or column that prevents longitudinal and transverse displacement of the edge of the neutral surface, but permits rotation in the plane of bending.

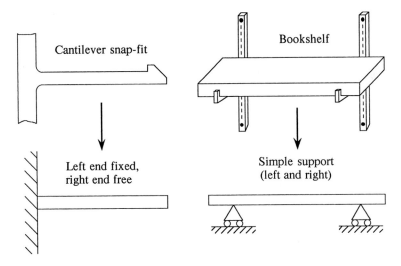

Figure 4.10. The cantilever snap member can be described as cantilever beam (left end fixed - right end free) while the bookshelf is a beam that is simply supported (left and right ends).

(Simply) Supported: A condition of support at the end(s) of a beam or column that prevents transverse displacement of the edge of the neutral surface, but permits rotation and longitudinal displacement. The bookshelf shown in Figure 4.10 could be described as simply supported.

Fixed (clamped, built-in): A support condition at the end(s) of a beam or column that prevents rotation and transverse displacement of the edge of the neutral surface but permits longitudinal displacement. The "molded-in" support end of the cantilever snap shown in Figure 4.10 could be described as a fixed support, however, some deformation of the adjacent wall (depending on the relative rigidity of the wall section) may occur as the beam is deflected.

4.3.4   Loading Conditions

Introduction: Once the part geometry and support conditions have been established, the load(s) (or imposed deflections) acting on the product must be defined and transformed or quantified into a form that is suitable for a stress or deflection calculation. The "anticipated" structural loading conditions, the environmental exposure, and the load / time relationships should have been assessed during the early stages of product development as indicated in Figure 3.2. In some cases, these values are determined using prototype parts, or the values may be determined based on past experience with similar products.

Most plastic products are required to function or perform under a variety of different end-use loading conditions. It is best to evaluate the stresses and deflections associated with each of these anticipated loading conditions. At a minimum, the performance of the product under loading conditions that are expected to represent the "worst case loading conditions" should be evaluated for safety. External loads associated with product service are usually of primary concern to the designer, however, the designer should not overlook loads, stresses or deflections resulting from assembly, shipping, thermal expansion mismatches, or those due to the weight of the product itself. In addition, most molded parts have a certain amount of frozen-in or molded-in stress associated with the product manufacturing operation. Parts may fail in service due to the combined effects of service, assembly, and molding related stresses [10]. While the internal or residual stress levels associated with processing are not easily predicted, their magnitude can be minimized with proper tool design, and by following design practices such as maintaining a uniform wall thickness [10]. Computer aided process simulation packages can also provide a great deal of insight in this area, enabling one to minimize residual stresses by altering the gating scheme, the injection mold design and optimizing processing conditions. In most cases, however, the processing conditions (e.g. mold temperature, injection rate, etc.) are beyond the direct control of the designer. The designer can make recommendations, which may, or may not be followed on the production floor.

Static or Intermittent Loads: In order to evaluate the structural characteristic of a plastic part, both the location, magnitude, and type of loading must be quantified. The designer must decide what type(s) of ideal load most closely approximates the real life situation. The load type can be described as concentrated at a point, line, or boundary, or distributed over a large area (either uniformly or as a load gradient). The magnitude and direction of the load must also be specified.

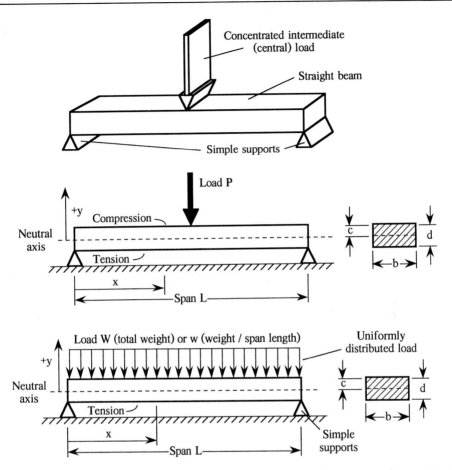

Figures 4.11. Representation of simply supported rectangular beams with concentrated and uniformly distributed loads.

As an example, the bookshelf in Figure 4.10 has the potential to be loaded with books across its entire width, or perhaps loaded with a heavy object at the mid-span. The latter case would be treated as a concentrated central load, while the former would constitute a uniformly loaded beam. In both of these cases, the load is likely to be applied for an extended period of time. The magnitude of the forces or loads for this application is determined by the weight of the objects to be supported, along with the weight of the product itself. Both normal and / or worst case loading conditions are typically defined. A problem of this type would therefore involve a series of design calculations to describe the shelf behavior under a number of possible loading scenarios. In this case, the additional stresses and deflections due to the weight of the shelf itself should also be taken into consideration, with the final result determined by superposition (i.e. the total stress or deflection is due to the sum of that associated with the external load and the shelf weight).

Boundary values: Concentrated intermediate load, left end free, right end fixed (cantilevered)

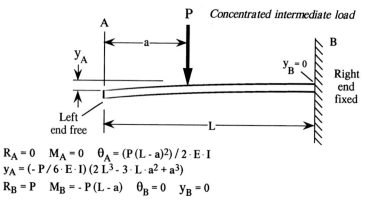

$R_A = 0$ $M_A = 0$ $\theta_A = (P(L - a)^2) / 2 \cdot E \cdot I$

$y_A = (- P / 6 \cdot E \cdot I)(2 L^3 - 3 \cdot L \cdot a^2 + a^3)$

$R_B = P$ $M_B = - P(L - a)$ $\theta_B = 0$ $y_B = 0$

Boundary values: Partially distributed load, left end free, right end fixed (cantilevered)

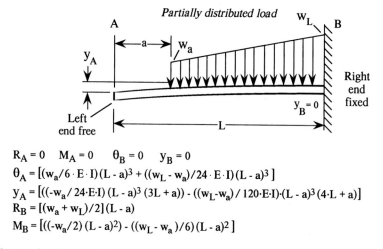

$R_A = 0$ $M_A = 0$ $\theta_B = 0$ $y_B = 0$

$\theta_A = [(w_a/6 \cdot E \cdot I)(L - a)^3 + ((w_L - w_a)/24 \cdot E \cdot I)(L - a)^3]$

$y_A = [((-w_a / 24 \cdot E \cdot I)(L - a)^3 (3L + a)) - ((w_L - w_a) / 120 \cdot E \cdot I) \cdot (L - a)^3 (4 \cdot L + a)]$

$R_B = [(w_a + w_L)/2](L - a)$

$M_B = [((-w_a/2)(L - a)^2) - ((w_L - w_a)/6)(L - a)^2]$

Figure 4.12. Representation of a cantilever beam with a concentrated, intermediate load (top) and a partially distributed load (bottom).

Multiple Static or Intermittent Loads: When a series of loads are acting on the product, the total stress or deflection can be found by superposition. For an elastic system, the stress, strain or deflection resulting from any final state of loading is the same whether the forces that constitute that loading are applied simultaneously, or in any sequence. The result is equivalent to the effect that the individual forces would produce if they were added separately. It is then possible to break a complex problem down into a number of simpler problems (i.e. those involving individual loads), which can be solved separately for stresses and deflections, and then algebraically added to produce the final solution

[2]. It should be noted here that while the stresses and deflections due to static or intermittent loading may be found by simple superposition, the same approach is probably not applicable for dynamic loading applications, or those applications involving stress concentrations.

The Boltzmann superposition principle can be used to predict stresses and deflections for viscoelastic materials subject to multiple static loads, provided (i) the creep or stress relaxation characteristics of the plastic material are known (recovery characteristics must also be known for situations where the loads are removed), and (ii) the loading history (load-time relationships) can be defined.

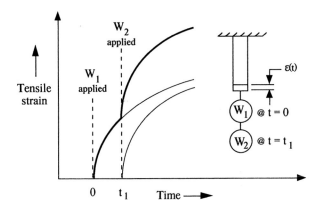

Figure 4.13. Tensile creep strain due to loads W_1 applied to t_0 and W_2 applied at t_1.

The tensile strain at any time due to an initial constant stress applied at time, t_0, is:

$$\varepsilon_0(t) = \sigma_0 / E(t) \qquad (4.1)$$

where $E(t)$ is the tensile creep modulus - time relationship. The tensile strain due to an an additional stress applied at time, t_1, is given by:

$$\varepsilon_1(t) = \sigma_1 / E(t) \qquad (4.2)$$

The total tensile strain, $\varepsilon_T(t)$, due to the combined effects of stresses σ_0 and σ_1 is then:

$$\varepsilon_T(t) = \sigma_0 / E(t) + \sigma_1 / E(t - t_1) \qquad (4.3)$$

The Boltzmann technique allows the designer to predict both deflection and recovery, if the materials creep and recovery characteristics, and the loading time period(s) and magnitudes can all be defined [13].

4.3.5   Plastic Material Properties

Introduction: The stress-strain behavior of a plastic material must also be quantified before any structural design calculations can be carried out. Material properties such as modulus are used in design equations to evaluate the strains and deflections associated with product loading. In addition, these maximum strain or stress estimates must then be compared to the material's stress-strain behavior to determine if these values remain within acceptable limits for the material that will be used to manufacture the product. Unfortunately the mechanical behavior of a plastic material is fairly complex and difficult to fully characterize. Unlike many other materials, plastic materials do not generally exhibit elastic behavior. These materials may respond to short term loading, micro or millisecond time frame, in an elastic manner [14]. However, in most cases, service loads occur over longer time spans, and the plastic material behavior is described as viscoelastic since it exhibits both viscous and elastic behavior. A great deal of testing is required in order to truly quantify the complex mechanical behavior of a plastic material. In many cases, material manufacturers are unable to supply all of the necessary data, and in-house testing may be required. The effects of tool design and processing conditions on the stress-strain behavior of a plastic material must also be taken into consideration since it is unlikely that the test data generated under ideal laboratory conditions will be exactly equivalent to the material behavior observed for more complex part geometries. In short, the mechanical properties of a polymer are influenced by factors such as those listed in Table 4.1.

Table 4.1. Considerations in Selecting Mechanical Property Data for Plastic Materials

End use environment	Conditions of loading	Processing considerations
Temperature	Duration of loading	Crystallinity / morphology
Relative Humidity	Frequency of loading	Molecular orientation
Chemical exposure	Constant stress (creep)	Reinforcement orientation
Ultraviolet exposure	Constant strain (S/R)	Level of degradation
Oxidation	Magnitude of the load	Weld quality
Time of exposure	State of stress:	Voids / sinks
	compression, tension	Packing conditions
	shear or bending	Internal stress level

A very important concept in structural design is to use material property data that has been generated under test conditions that most closely approximate the conditions associated with the end-use application. The degree of correlation will have a significant impact on the accuracy of the design calculations. Even the most advanced finite element analysis techniques will be in significant error if factors such as creep, orientation or weld strength are not taken into account, since these factors can have a very significant effect on mechanical properties of the material and the performance of the final part.

There are so many variables associated with materials testing that it is essentially impossible to characterize a material's mechanical behavior for universal application. For example, some weld strength data may be available for a particular polymeric material, however, the strength of a weld can be influenced by dozens of injection mold design and

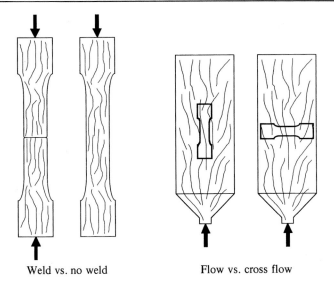

Weld vs. no weld   Flow vs. cross flow

Figure 4.14. The mechanical behavior of a plastic part is influenced by factors such as the presence of weld lines and molecular or fiber orientation.

injection molding process variables. Weld strength data generated at one set of process conditions, in one mold, is not likely to be representative of the weld quality for a mold having longer flow lengths that is run at different process conditions. Similar problems are encountered when a designer takes factors such as processing induced orientation or degradation into account.

Short Term Properties: The cantilever snaps on the molded wheel cover shown in Figure 4.2 are deflected momentarily and fairly rapidly when the wheel cover is installed or removed. In this application, the designer would be interested in evaluating the forces associated with deflecting the beams (to obtain assembly forces), and in the maximum tensile stress or strain levels associated with this imposed short term deflection. In order to evaluate the assembly related stresses, the designer could use short term stress-strain data generated on a universal testing machine (as opposed to longer term creep data). Stresses, strains and deflections would be evaluated at the extreme environmental conditions (i.e. the high and low temperatures anticipated in the application). It is important that the mechanical property data used in the calculations is generated at temperatures and humidities that are equivalent to those encountered in the end-use application. In addition, the rates of testing must correlate closely with the strain rate (inch/inch/s, m/m/s or %/s) or range of strain rates associated with the end-use application, since the properties such as modulus and yield / breaking strength of a plastic material vary with rate of loading as illustrated in Figure 4.15.

It is also important to consider the type of stress associated with the application. The cantilever snap shown in Figure 4.1 is a beam like protrusion that "bends" during assembly / disassembly. Portions of the cantilever snap are subject to compressive stresses, while other sections are subject to tensile stresses (and shear stresses that depend on the span to depth ratio). In a more complex analysis, both the compressive and the tensile behavior of the material is used in the design calculations. As an alternative for this bending application, the polymer's flexural properties, generated at the appropriate test conditions, can be used in engineering calculations that require a single modulus value. The bulk flexural modulus of a polymer is influenced by both the tensile and compressive modulus of the polymer. It should be emphasized here, however, that the non-linear behavior of most plastic materials indicates that properties such as modulus or breaking strength are by no means constant values. These material properties change with variables such as those listed in Table 4.1.

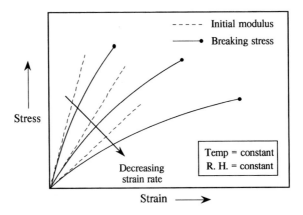

Figure 4.15. The stress-strain characteristics of plastic materials are influenced by strain rate, temperature, and relative humidity.

Long Term Properties (Creep): In other applications, such as the bookshelf shown in Figure 4.10, plastic parts are loaded for extended periods of time (i.e. time spans ranging from hours to years). Short term stress-strain curves can be used to predict the deflections and stresses associated with the initial loading, however, the increase in deflection (or changes in stress for stress relaxation applications) can only be predicted if the longer term, creep characteristics of the polymer are known. Creep properties are determined by loading sets of identical test specimens for extended periods of time. In creep testing, test specimens, held at a given temperature and relative humidity, are subject to constant stress while deflections or elongations are measured over an extended time period. The time dependent elongation values are used to calculate strains as a function of time. The concept of tensile creep testing is depicted in Figure 3.22, where tensile test samples are subjected to various loads (creating uniaxial tensile stresses in this case) and the extensions (or tensile strains) are measured over the long term.

Creep data is available for most plastic materials, however, the time spans associated with creep testing vary, and are often short relative to the service life of the product. It is important for a designer to determine if the creep data being used is truly experimental creep data, or data that has been extrapolated from creep tests conducted over a relatively shorter time span. It is also important that the designer considers the type of stress that results from the loading of the part during service. Creep data is commonly measured in a state of uniaxial tension, however, creep data can also be generated in compression, bending, and shear. The creep data used by the designer in the design calculations should have been generated in a state of stress that is equivalent to that experienced by the product.

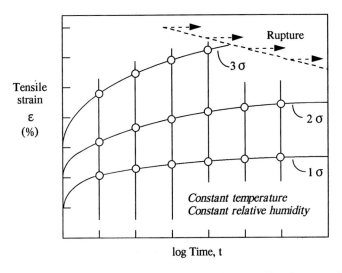

Figure 4.16. Typical tensile creep curve (tensile strain as a function of log time, at various tensile stress levels). The data can be replotted to produce sets of isochronous stress-strain curves.

The experimental creep data, extension or strain as a function of time and stress, is typically plotted to produce a graph such as that shown in Figure 4.16. The figure shows the immediate elastic deformation which occurs during initial loading, and the increase in strain over time (i.e the tensile creep or delayed deformation). The creep problem becomes more significant as the stress level increases, as indicated by the increase in slope of the curve with increasing stress level. The figure also shows that the time to failure (rupture), decreases with increasing stress level. While creep rupture will occur at relatively short times for very high stress levels (i.e. stress levels approaching the short term strength), rupture can take many years at relatively lower stress levels. As a result, a full description of the creep rupture envelope is rarely available due to the practical limitations of testing time. This is a significant problem since the time to ultimate failure at the lower stress values, which are typically used in long term design to minimize creep effects, can only be estimated. Parts designed using extrapolated creep data should be designed with extra margins of safety due to the uncertainties associated with using extrapolated data. A general recommendation is that creep data should not be extrapolated for more than one log decade on the time axis [14].

The creep curve (experimental data) shown in Figure 4.16 [15] is typically replotted to produce a set of isochronous stress-strain curves (cross plots at constant time) as shown in Figure 4.17.

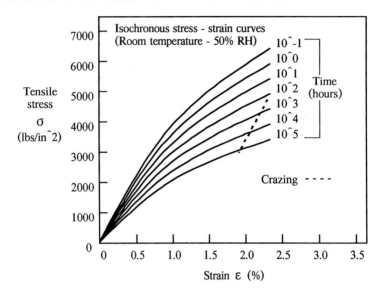

Figures 4.17. A set of isochronous stress-strain curves for polycarbonate at standard conditions.

The slopes of these curves can be used to obtain apparent modulus values for the polymer at various times of loading and tensile stress levels (for a particular test environment). All of these variables can have a significant influence on the rigidity or modulus of a plastic material. The creep data can also be replotted to produce sets of modulus-time (or log time) curves at various stress levels, as shown in Figure 4.18. This is a convenient creep data format when limited extrapolation to longer times of loading is required. The modulus data derived from the curve can be used in design equations, to predict how the deflections due to service loading will increase with the time of loading, provided the stress level and ambient conditions associated with the application are equivalent to those of the test data. When designing for minimum deflection, it is common for the designer to use test data that is representative of the maximum time of loading (i.e. service life for parts subject to continuous loading), and the highest service temperature / relative humidity for safety. This would represent the worst case scenario from a minimum deflection point of view.

Long Term Properties (Variation in Load / Temperature / Relative Humidity): Deflection predictions for parts subject to intermittent loading or temperature cycling are generally more difficult than those associated with constant loading. Predicting deflection and stress changes due to loading and unloading, or day / night / seasonal temperature changes are difficult since (i) the recovery properties of polymers are not widely available (compared to creep properties), and (ii) load / temperature / relative humidity prediction over the long term is often a crude estimate. In applications of this type, superposition is used if the loading / temperature conditions for the application are known and the material properties (including recovery characteristics) are fully characterized. Otherwise, it is safest to assume continuous loading at the highest anticipated temperature / relative humidity (i.e. the worst case scenario).

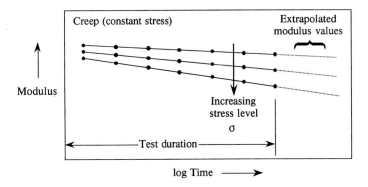

Figure 4.18. Creep modulus values at various stress levels can be plotted against log time and curve fit to provide a means of estimating longer term behavior by extrapolation.

Long Term Properties (Crazing):   In some cases, the isochronous stress-strain curves obtained from a material supplier indicate craze boundaries or limits. The dashed lines shown in Figure 4.17 indicate the relationship between craze initiation, stress level, and time. Crazes, in and of themselves, may not constitute part failure, however, their presence becomes a particular concern for applications where impact loading, fatigue loading, or chemical attack is possible. At the least, crazes represent a visual imperfection. A designer should avoid designing at stress levels above the craze limits. Figure 4.17 (isochronous stress-strain data at 73°F / 50% RH) shows that it would take approximately 1,000 hours for crazes to appear on a part subject to a tensile stress of 4,000 lb/in^2 (27.6 MPa), while at a stress level of 2,800 lb/in^2 (19.3 MPa), the time associated with craze appearance is 100,000 hours. The figure emphasizes the importance of carefully evaluating and limiting the design stress values. Unfortunately, crazes must be detected by visual inspection during the creep testing procedure, and as a result, data of this type is not always provided. However, designers should recognize the fact that crazing can occur, particularly in the presence of chemicals, even though the craze boundaries may not be indicated on the isochronous stress-strain curves.

Long Term Properties (Stress Relaxation):   In certain applications, parts are subject to constant or fixed deflections or strains (rather than constant stress) for extended periods of time. Press fit bearing races or hubs are examples of constant strain applications. In these applications, the stress relaxation characteristics (decay in stress level with time at constant strain) of the polymer must be known in order for a designer to predict the product's performance. Isochronous stress-strain curves, such as those shown in Figure 4.17 (generated from creep experiments) may not accurately represent the material's behavior for stress relaxation applications. Stress relaxation data is more appropriately generated in a set of stress relaxation experiments. Unfortunately, the equipment required for stress relaxation testing is somewhat more complicated and expensive than that required for creep testing. In stress relaxation tests, the test specimens must be deformed and held in the deformed state, while the loads associated with the fixed deformation are measured as a function of time, strain level, temperature, and relative humidity. The stress relaxation test data can be replotted to produce sets of modulus-time curves at various strains (isometric modulus-time curves) as shown in Figure 4.19. This data format is especially convenient when limited extrapolation to longer times is required.

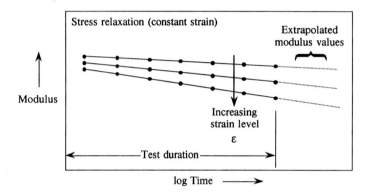

Figures 4.19. Modulus data determined in stress relaxation tests at various constant strain levels is plotted against log time.

Stations for stress relaxation testing are generally more expensive than creep test stations, which is one of the reasons why creep test data is more widely available than stress relaxation data. Unfortunately, material property values derived from creep tests may not be suitable for stress relaxation applications [15]. This lack of material property data can represent a major problem for plastic part designers. Consider the following example. A designer is faced with the task of designing a part for a constant tensile strain design application (tensile stress relaxation data is required). Tensile creep data (constant stress) is available for the plastic material, however, stress relaxation data (constant strain) is not. In this situation, the designer has several options. The designer could (i) design the part using the creep data and apply an additional safety factor (since creep and stress relaxation data are not necessarily equivalent), or (ii) develop a testing program where the stress relaxation data is generated. From an engineering point of view, the latter approach is preferred, however, the costs and time associated with stress relaxation testing can be significant. The time required to conduct the tests could be reduced by generating data for only a relatively short testing time period and extrapolating the data to longer times. However, this cannot be done with a high level of confidence. The stress relaxation data extrapolated to much longer times (i.e. times equivalent to the service life of the product) may not be as useful or realistic as the longer term creep data that is available. A third option available to the designer is to conduct an accelerated testing program by running stress relaxation test at higher temperatures, and establishing a relationship between time and temperature.

4.3.6   Safety Factors

There are no well established rules when it comes to selecting safety factors for plastic materials, and there are a large number of uncertainties associated with the plastic part design and manufacturing processes [12]. The term "safety factor" is somewhat ambiguous, and may have different meanings to different designers. Several terms are considered. The term "factor of safety", commonly used with metals, is defined as the ratio of the load that would cause failure of a member or structure, to the load that is imposed upon that structure in service [2]. The term loses some of its meaning when applied to plastic materials if creep or stress relaxation effects are significant, since crazing, yielding, excessive creep, or excessive stress relaxation, rather than rupture, may constitute product failure.

The term "acceptable working stress" (or strain) may have more significance with plastic materials, and is usually a stress value (tensile, compressive or shear) that has been deemed acceptable for use in a given application by the material manufacturer [12,15,16]. A related term, "partial safety factor for the material" (or capacity reduction factor) is a measure of safety with respect to material properties based on the fact that material properties in the product may not be equivalent to those determined using test specimens developed under ideal laboratory conditions [1]. The term may also be used to account for differences in material properties associated with lot variation or processing effects. The properties of plastic materials are influenced by processing or fabrication conditions, because these conditions have an impact on molecular / fiber orientation, percent crystallinity, degradation level, residual stress, weld quality and the like. In addition, the effect of end-use parameters such as temperature, relative humidity, rate of loading and frequency of loading, on the properties of a plastic material are not always known with certainty.

An additional safety factor designated "partial safety factor for loads" (load factor) is used to account for possible increases in load, stress, or strain beyond the anticipated value due to factors such as inaccurate calculations (as a result of over-simplification of geometry, stress concentrations, etc.) or uncertainties associated with anticipated loading conditions or product abuse. It is common to utilize one *Overall Safety Factor* for design purposes that lumps both the material and load safety factors under one heading [1].

The safety factor that a designer uses is determined by both the product application, consequences of failure (e.g. critical vs. non-critical) and the quality of the design procedures utilized during product development. The consequences of failure deserve careful consideration. The risk of injury resulting from part failure is always a major concern. When the probability of injury is high, relatively large margins of safety are used. For example, catastrophic failure of a transparent molded plastic household water filter cartridge housing (perhaps due to a water pressure spike) could result in both personal injury and a great deal of water damage to household items. In other cases, such as a press fit volume control knob for a portable radio, the consequences of part failure are not as critical, since the product should continue to function and the knob itself is relatively inexpensive and can be easily replaced.

The level of engineering associated with product development will also have an influence on the magnitude of the safety factors used in a particular application. For example, the use of FEA techniques should provide a better estimate as to the maximum stress levels associated with the service loading of the part compared to classical formulas for stress and strain. Safety factors would be less of a concern for products where stress concentration factors have been taken into account as part of the stress analysis. A designer would also have more confidence working at higher stress values / longer times if the product in question has undergone extensive prototype testing under conditions anticipated in service, compared to a product for which no such experimental testing was performed. Prototyping and experimental analysis are perhaps the best methods of obtaining maximum utilization of the plastic material (unfortunately at the expense of development time and engineering costs). Computer aided process simulation packages are also invaluable tools as they allow the designer to locate weld lines in non-critical areas, optimize gate(s) position, optimize the tool design, and estimate molded-in / residual stress levels. All of these aspects of design influence the magnitude of safety used in each application.

The type and quality of the material data that is available for designing the product is also an important factor in determining the magnitude of the safety factor. A designer will have more confidence in products designed using creep or stress relaxation data (at the appropriate temperature and relative humidity) than products designed using short term (materials screening) data. In fact, it should be noted that the practice of deriving a maximum design stress value by dividing the short term stress-strain yield or breaking strength by a safety factor is not appropriate for most applications [14]. Such a practice may be acceptable for shorter term loading applications, provided the stress-strain data is representative, in terms of temperature, relative humidity, and strain rate, of the end-use application.

When parts are loaded for extended periods of time under a predetermined load (or imposed deformation), they must also have a predetermined design life specified. In these applications, the safety factors must be applied to the creep or stress relaxation data. The safety factor can be applied to either the stress (or strain), or to the time to rupture values. In longer term loding applications, the time to failure (i.e. creep rupture) is a critical concern. For example, a part being designed for two continuous years of loading could be designed at a maximum stress level that would provide for eight years of operation before rupture (safety factor of 4 in terms of time). Short term data is no substitute for creep or stress relaxation data. If short term stress-strain data must be used for design (i.e. if longer term data is not available), the uncertainties associated with the design calculations are very large, and large safety factors must be used.

The safety factor issue is by no means straightforward. For example, creep may be less of a problem for glass reinforced polymers, however, the weld line strengths for these reinforced materials is not easily predicted and can be very low (as a percentage of the published strength value). A reduction in component strength at the weld location should be anticipated. Additional complications arise since the flow and cross flow strength values for reinforced materials can be very different. These strength reductions must be quantified as part of the structural design process. If they are not, additional safety margins must be used. Various of rules of thumb are given by material manufacturers for initial design work, however, most manufacturers recommend prototype product testing under the anticipated structural and environmental conditions before production tool dimensions are finalized.

A variety of approaches are used to select the magnitude of the safety factor in practice. One approach suggests that the appropriate yield strength value for a material (at the anticipated service temperature, strain rate etc.) be multiplied by a *percentage utilization factor* in order to obtain working stress values [12]. As mentioned earlier, this approach may be suitable for parts subject to short term or intermittent loading, however, this simplified approach is not recommended for continuous load applications where it is more appropriate to use creep / stress relaxation data.

Table 4.2. Typical Guidelines for Percentage Utilization Factors [12]

Type of loading	Failure not critical	Failure critical
Intermittent (non-fatigue) loading	25 - 50% x σ_y	10 - 25% x σ_y
Continuous loading	10 - 25% x σ_y	5 - 10% x σ_y

The effects of stress concentration should not be over looked when evaluating the stress level. Permissible design stress levels for plastic parts subject to static load can be determined by combining the material percentage utilization factor, S_T, and the geometry / material dependent stress concentration factors, K [8].

$$\sigma_D \leq (S_T \times \sigma_y) / K \qquad (4.4)$$

where the yield stress is the first maximum of a stress-strain curve, measured at the appropriate rate, temperature, relative humidity and strain rate. Creep strengths should be used when the products are subject to loading for extended periods of time. The stress concentration factors are added to account for geometry related discontinuities such as holes or fillets. A K value of 2.0 to 4.0 is commonly used for geometries with adequate fillets, however, a K value as high as 6.0 is used for sharper corners (poor fillets). The material percentage utilization factor, S_T, (the reciprocal of safety factor) can be determined in a number of ways. One method is given below [8].

$$S_T = S_1 \times S_2 \times S_3 \times S_4 \qquad (4.5)$$

where: S_1 = *Risk of Injury to People in the Event of Failure*
             No risk of injury= 1.0
             Possible injury   = 0.7
             Probable injury = 0.5

          S_2 = *Processing Factor (guidelines)*
             Neat polymer = 1.0
             Fibers oriented in the direction of maximum stress = 0.8
             Fibers oriented perpendicular to the direction of maximum stress = 0.5
             Random fiber orientation = 0.7
             Unknown fiber orientation = 0.5 (safe side)

          S_3 = *Stress Calculation Accuracy*
             Accurate FEA model = 1.0
             Use of classical formulae = 0.75
             Estimates = 0.5

          S_4 = *Material Degradation*
             Values are material specific $\leq$ 1.0

In some cases, material manufacturers recommend working stress levels directly in their material design literature. The material manufacturers effectively apply percentage utilization factors to yield strength values, generating information such as that shown in Table 4.3. for an unfilled polycarbonate. As a reference, the short term tensile yield strength for the polycarbonate is listed as 9,000 lbs/in^2 (62 MPa) at room temperature [16].

Table 4.3. Recommended Working Tensile Stress for a General Purpose Polycarbonate

Temperature (°C)	Working stress: continuous load*		Working stress: intermittent load**	
	lbs/in^2	(MPa)	lbs/in^2	(MPa)
-54	4200	(29.0)	5200	(35.9)
-18	2300	(15.9)	4200	(29.0)
23	2000	(13.8)	4000	(27.6)
54	1600	(11.0)	3500	(24.1)
71	1000	(6.9)	3200	(22.1)
93	500	(3.4)	3000	(20.7)
121	0	(0)	2500	(17.2)

In this case, continuous loading* is defined as loading for a period of time more than 6 hours, while intermittent loads** are defined as those loads that are applied for less than 6 hours, with an equal recovery time period. The material manufacturer also recommends that the results be scaled downward for lower viscosity (i.e. lower average molecular weight) grades of polycarbonate. Lower molecular weight grades may have similar short term yield strengths, however, they tend to have reduced impact and creep resistance.

The safety factors used in design can cover a range from about 2 (i.e. the estimated design stress is equal to 50% of the material's yield stress) to more than 20 (i.e. design stress is less than 5% of the material's yield stress) for static loads due to the various uncertainties associated with material properties and part manufacturing conditions. Safety factors (in terms of stress, or time to rupture for creep applications) are more appropriately applied to creep or stress relaxation data for long term structural applications. Products subject to cyclic or fatigue loading are of even greater concern, and the safety factors are applied to fatigue endurance material data. In practice, designers can achieve maximum material utilization (i.e. lowest safety factors) by obtaining the appropriate material data (including data on such factors as weld strength, anisotropic behavior, etc.), applying a rigorous engineering analysis, and verifying product behavior by conducting a realistic experimental evaluation of prototype part performance.

4.4   Beams

4.4.1   Introduction

A structural member designed to support loads applied at various points along the member is known as a beam [17]. Beams are generally long, straight prismatic bars with a cross section designed to provide the most effective resistance to shear and bending produced by the applied loads. The classical engineering formulas used to calculate stresses and deflections in straight beams are based on many assumptions including [2]:

- The beam material is homogeneous with the same modulus (of elasticity) in tension and compression.
- The beam is straight or has a curvature in the plane of bending with a radius of curvature at least 10 times the beam depth.
- The cross section of the beam is uniform.
- The beam has at least one longitudinal plane of symmetry.
- All loads (and reactions) are perpendicular to the axis of the beam, and lie in the same plane, which is the longitudinal axis of symmetry.
- The beam is long in proportion to its depth. Note that the Standard Test Method for "Flexural Properties of Plastics and Electrical Insulating Materials" (ASTM D790) states a general rule: ... *support span to depth ratios of 16:1 are satisfactory when the ratio of the tensile to shear strength of the material is less than 8:1*
- The beam is not disproportionately wide.
- The maximum stress does not exceed the proportional limit.

The engineering formulas given for beams will be in error if any of the assumptions stated are not realistic. This will generally be the case for plastic materials, since the materials exhibit viscoelastic rather than elastic behavior. However, the formulas are useful for providing an "estimate" of the performance that can be expected in many applications. The bookshelf and the cantilever snap arm (sub-part) shown in Figure 4.10

Figures 4.20. The touch key pad elements or fingers are cantilever beams subjected to periodic loading.

are both beam-like geometries. Other examples of cantilever beam geometries include the cantilever snap beams on the auto wheel cover shown in Figure 4.2, and the molded cantilever touch key pad elements shown in Figure 4.20.

The behavior of a beam under load is most easily described using an example where the beam is horizontal and the load and reaction are vertical. Once loaded, the beam will deflect or bend, and the fibers (infinitely thin layers of material) on the concave side will shorten (i.e. these layers are in compression), while fibers on the convex side will lengthen (i.e. these layers are in tension). The neutral surface or plane of the beam is normal to the plane of the loads and is also the horizontal central axis. If shear effects are considered to be negligible, the fiber stresses and strains are proportional to the distance from the neutral surface (i.e. the plane or layer where the stress and strain are zero) and the beam deflection is due only to bending.

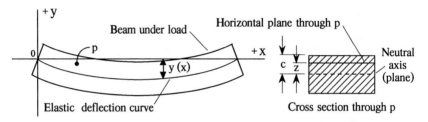

Figure 4.21. Schematic of a simply supported, elastic beam subjected to a bending load.

The fiber stress, σ, at any point, p, within the boundaries of the beam can be given by:

$$\sigma = M \cdot y / I \tag{4.6}$$

where M is the bending moment at the cross section containing p, I is the second moment of area (moment of inertia) of the beam with respect to the neutral axis, and y is the distance between the neutral axis and p. The fiber stress can be positive or negative. The maximum fiber stresses (i.e. outer surface compression or tensile stresses) at any section, occur at the points / planes furthest from the neutral axis (i.e. where y = ± c).

$$\sigma_m = M_m \cdot y_m / I = M_m \cdot c / I \tag{4.7}$$

The term c is defined as the distance from the neutral plane to the outer fibers. Using the neutral axis as a reference, there is both a positive and a negative c value. The maximum fiber stresses for the beam occur at the beam surfaces, and at the cross section having the greatest bending moment M_m. This maximum outer fiber tensile and compressive stresses will be different if the beam is not symmetrical about the neutral axis, or if the material's tensile and compressive stress-strain behaviors differ. The deflection and bending moment equations for common loading and support configurations for uniform, tapered and curved beams are given in handbooks [1,2] or in the form of computer programs [18].

4.4.2   Properties of a Plane Area (Beam Cross Sections)

Many plastic part (or sub-part) geometries can be simplified to the point where they constitute a beam of constant cross section. In order to design a beam with an effective cross section for a particular loading application, that is, one that will provide the desired resistance to bending for a given load, the loading conditions, support conditions, material properties, and the area properties of the beam cross section must be determined [17]. These area properties include:

Second Moment of Area: The cross sectional geometry of a beam section (for a given material of construction) determines its ability to support a load. Consider the irregular cross section shown in Figure 4.22.

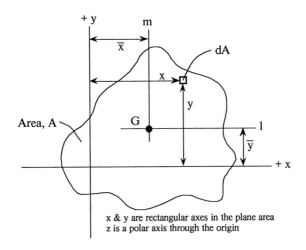

x & y are rectangular axes in the plane area
z is a polar axis through the origin

Figure 4.22. Beam cross section (plane area) showing the location of the centroid and a set of perpendicular centroidal axes.

The *second moment of area* (often called *moment of inertia* in common engineering practice, not to be confused with the term *mass moment of inertia*) with respect to an axis in the plane of the area, say the x axis, is the sum of the products obtained by multiplying each element of area, dA, by the square of its distance, y, from that axis [2,17].

$$I_x = \int dA \cdot y^2 \tag{4.8}$$

$$I_y = \int dA \cdot x^2 \tag{4.9}$$

This commonly used theorem, known as the *parallel axis theorem* can then be expressed with reference to Figure 4.22 [17]. The *parallel axis theorem* can be written in the following ways:

$$I_x = I_1 + A \cdot y^2 \tag{4.10}$$

$$I_y = I_m + A \cdot x^2 \tag{4.11}$$

where l and m are rectangular axis parallel to x and y and intersecting at G, the centroid (geometric center) of the area. The distances x and y are the distances between y and m, and x and l respectively [2]. In general terms, the *parallel axis theorem* is given as:

$$I = I_c + A \cdot d^2 \tag{4.12}$$

where I, the second moment of area with respect to any axis (having units of length to the 4th power), is equal to the second moment of area with respect to the parallel centroidal axis, Ic, plus, the product of the beam cross sectional area, A, times the square of the distance, d, between the two parallel axes. The *parallel axis theorem* is commonly used to determine moment of inertia values for more complicated beam cross sections for which handbook solutions are not readily available.

Centroid and Centroidal Axes: The centroid of an area is defined as the point in the plane of an area about any axis through which the moment of the area is zero. The centroid of an area coincides with the center of gravity of the area for an infinitely thin, homogeneous, uniform plate. A centroidal axis of an area is an axis that passes through the centroid [2]. The axes l and m in Figure 4.22 are centroidal axes lying in the same plane as the area.

Neutral Axis: The neutral axis of a beam that is subject to a bending load is defined as the line of zero stress in any cross section of the member. It is the line formed by the intersection of the neutral surface and the section area [2]. For example, when the straight beam of a uniform cross sectional area, such as that shown in Figure 4.21, is subjected to a perpendicular load, the resulting deflection puts the sections between the neutral axis and the top surface in compression, and the surfaces between the neutral axis and the convex outer surface of the beam in tension. There is a neutral surface within any uniform, homogeneous beam that contains the centroids of all cross sections and is perpendicular to the plane of the load causing the deflections. The neutral axis of a simple, homogeneous beam is coincidental with the horizontal centroidal axis of the beam if one assumes uniform, homogeneous material behavior. Tensile and compressive stress and strain values at the neutral axis are essentially zero [15].

Section Modulus (Z): The section modulus (or section factor) for a symmetrical cross sectional area with respect to either principle axis of a beam is defined as the second moment of area with respect to that axis divided by the distance from that axis to the most remote point of that section area [2]. The section modulus value has units of length to the 3rd power.

Radius of Gyration (r): The radius of gyration of an area with respect to a given axis is the square root of the quantity obtained by dividing the *second moment of area* with respect to that axis, by the area.

$$r_x = (I_x / A)^{1/2} \quad \text{and} \quad r_y = (I_y / A)^{1/2} \tag{4.13}$$

Moments of inertia, centroid locations, and radius of gyration values for some common areas of regular geometry are given in Figure 4.23. More extensive listings can be found in handbooks [2].

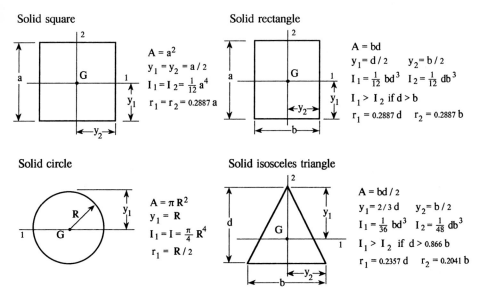

Solid square

$A = a^2$

$y_1 = y_2 = a/2$

$I_1 = I_2 = \frac{1}{12} a^4$

$r_1 = r_2 = 0.2887\, a$

Solid rectangle

$A = bd$

$y_1 = d/2 \quad y_2 = b/2$

$I_1 = \frac{1}{12} bd^3 \quad I_2 = \frac{1}{12} db^3$

$I_1 > I_2$ if $d > b$

$r_1 = 0.2887\, d \quad r_2 = 0.2887\, b$

Solid circle

$A = \pi R^2$

$y_1 = R$

$I_1 = I = \frac{\pi}{4} R^4$

$r_1 = R/2$

Solid isosceles triangle

$A = bd/2$

$y_1 = 2/3\, d \quad y_2 = b/2$

$I_1 = \frac{1}{36} bd^3 \quad I_2 = \frac{1}{48} db^3$

$I_1 > I_2$ if $d > 0.866\, b$

$r_1 = 0.2357\, d \quad r_2 = 0.2041\, b$

Figure 4.23. Area properties of a square, rectangle, circle and triangle.

The area properties for many more complex areas are also given in handbooks, however it is possible to calculate area properties such as moment of inertia provided the more complicated geometries (beam cross sections) can be broken down into *geometrically regular shapes* to produce a *composite area*. It may be necessary to simplify the cross sectional geometry of the part, neglecting small features such as corner radii, in order to obtain an estimate of the cross section's neutral axis moment of inertia value. The following concepts are used for composite areas:

(1) The moment of inertia of a composite area or section (one regarded as made up of regular geometries, rectangles, triangles, etc.) about an axis is equal to the sum of the individual moments of inertia (or the geometries making up the composite area) about the same axis. This can be written:

$$I_x = \sum I_{i,x} \tag{4.14}$$

(2) A void in the cross sectional area can be taken into account by subtracting the moment of inertia of the corresponding void area about the same axis for which the I value is being determined (i.e. the voids have a negative contribution).

(3) The statical moment (first moment of an area), M, about any axis for the entire composite area is equal to the sum of the statical moments of the individual areas that make up the section about that axis. (The statical moment of an area with respect to an axis is the sum of the products obtained by multiplying each element of area, dA, by the first power of its distance from that axis).

$$M_x = \int dA \cdot y \tag{4.15}$$

For a composite area, the total first moment about an axis, x, is given by:

$$M_x = \sum M_{i,x} \tag{4.16}$$

The total area for the composite section is given by:

$$A = \sum A_i \tag{4.17}$$

The values determined in Equation 4.16 and 4.17 can be used to determine the location of the centroidal axis (perpendicular to the applied load) for a beam cross section, with respect to a reference axis or datum. The distance between the reference axis, x, and the centroid axis (or neutral axis) of the composite area can be determined using:

$$y_c = \sum M_{i,x} / \sum A_i \tag{4.18}$$

Equation 4.18 can be used to determine the location of the neutral axis for unsymmetrical beam cross sections where the neutral axis location is not obvious. Once the location of the composite area centroidal axis that is perpendicular to the applied load (i.e. the neutral axis), the areas of the individual geometries, and the moment of inertia values of the individual regular geometries with respect to their own parallel centroidal axes are known, the moment of inertia value for the entire composite section about the composite section's neutral axis can be obtained by combining Equations 4.12 and 4.14.

$$I_T = \sum [I_{c,i} + (A_i \cdot d_i^{\,2})] \tag{4.19}$$

where Ic is the moment of inertia value for each regular geometry about its own centroidal axis, A is the area of each individual section, and d is the distance between the centroidal axis of each individual area and the centroidal (neutral) axis of the entire composite area. It should be noted that the section modulus, Z, (the radius of gyration, r) of a composite area is not equal to the sum of the individual values, and should be determined using the total moment of inertia value for the composite area. Several examples follow.

Example 4.1. Moment of Inertia for Simple Geometries: The beam cross section shown in Figure 4.24 can be described as axisymmetric with respect to both the x and y axes.

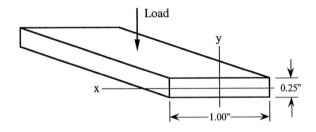

Figure 4.24. Rectangular beam cross section.

If the beam is loaded perpendicular to the x-axis, then the x-axis is an axis of symmetry, then it is also the centroidal axis perpendicular to the applied load (for a material of homogeneous construction). This particular centroidal axis is coincident with the neutral axis for a homogeneous, elastic material. The beam then has a width, b, of 1.00 inch, perpendicular to the applied load, and a depth, h, of 0.25 inch in the direction parallel to the applied load. A designer would need to determine the moment of inertia about the x-axis before stresses or deflections due to the applied load can be determined using the classical formulas for stress and strain. For this example, the I value about the centroidal axis perpendicular to the applied load is determined using Equation 4.10 and the information given in Figure 4.23.

$$I_x = I_1 + A \cdot y^2 \tag{4.10}$$

$$I_x = (b \cdot h^3 / 12) + (b \cdot h \cdot y^2)$$

$$I_x = [(1.0)(0.25)^3/(12)] + [(1.0)(0.25)(0)^2]$$

$$I_x = 0.0013 \text{ inch}^4$$

The I value for the same cross section about the y axis would be of interest only if the beam was to be loaded perpendicular to the y-axis. In that case, the depth of the beam, h, is the 1.0 inch dimension (the dimension parallel to the applied load) and the beam width, b, is 0.25 inch. The y-axis becomes the axis of symmetry, the centroidal axis perpendicular to the applied load, and the neutral axis.

$$I_y = I_m + A \cdot x^2 \tag{4.11}$$

$$I_y = (b \cdot h^3 / 12) + (b \cdot h \cdot x^2)$$

$$I_y = [(0.25)(1.0)^3/(12)] + [(0.25)(1.0)(0)^2]$$

$$I_y = 0.021 \text{ inch}^4$$

Note that the y-axis moment of inertia value is 16 times as great as the x-axis moment of inertia value, indicating that strategic placement of material at a distance away from the neutral axis is an important design consideration in applications where bending stiffness is required. This is clear when looking at Equation 4.10 since the moment of inertia value for a rectangular section is proportional to the depth of the beam, h, to the third power. The deflection of a beam under a given service load is always inversely proportional to its moment of inertia about the neutral axis (i.e. designs with high I values reduce deflection). On the other hand, when large deflections are required (e.g. snap beams etc.), thinner wall sections are used.

Example 4.2 Moment of Inertia for Composite Area (Axisymmetric): A classical example of an efficient beam cross section in terms of minimizing defection is that of the I-beam. The I-beam geometry places large quantities of material far away from the neutral axis of the cross section (to obtain a high I value), yet the beam consists of relatively thin wall sections, minimizing both the weight of the beam and material usage. I-beam geometries have relatively high *stiffness to weight ratios*.

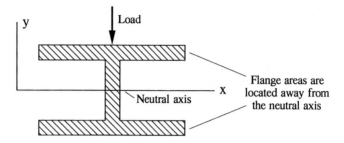

Figure 4.25. I-beam geometries provide stiffness by strategically placing material some distance away from the neutral axis.

Like the solid rectangular area in Example 4.1, the I-beam geometry is symmetric about both the x and y-axes (the beam is usually loaded perpendicular to the x axis). However, the beam is not a regular geometry, and the I value must be calculated by breaking the more complicated cross section up into a series of regular *solid* or *void* cross sectional areas (I-beam moment of inertia values could also be obtained from handbooks). Given that the beam is loaded perpendicular to the x-axis, the I_x value would be the I value of interest to the design engineer (i.e. the I value about the neutral axis). The value can be calculated any number of ways, however, it is good practice to simplify the problem as much as possible. Several approaches are presented, yet the final results are equivalent in each case.

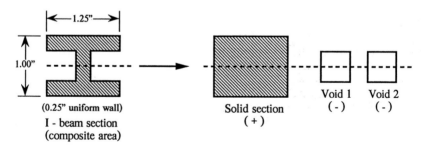

Figure 4.26. The I-beam geometry can be represented as a solid rectangle and two void rectangles for a moment of inertia calculation.

Example 4.2a I-beam Moment of Inertia: The I-beam cross section shown in Figure 4.25 could be represented as a solid rectangular area, less the two smaller void sections. The centroidal axes for each of these three regular rectangular geometries, one solid and two smaller voids, are coincident with the centroidal axis of the entire composite I-beam section.

$$I_T = \sum [I_{c,i} + (A_i \cdot y_i^2)] \tag{4.19}$$

Equation 4.19 reduces to:

$$I_T = \Sigma\, I_{c,i} = I_c \text{ solid} - I_c \text{ void } 1 - I_c \text{ void } 2$$

since the y value for each of the three regular geometries (i.e. the rectangular solid and the voids) is zero in this case. Since the geometry of void 1, is equivalent to the geometry of void 2:

$$I_T = I_c \text{ solid} - [2\,(I_c \text{ void } 1)]$$

$$I_T = [(b_s \cdot h_s{}^3/12)] - [2\,(b_v \cdot h_v{}^3/12)]$$

$$I_T = [(1.0)(1.0)^3/(12)] - [2\,(0.5)(0.5)^3/12)]$$

$$I_T = 0.0938 \text{ inch}^4$$

The I-beam section in Figure 4.25 could also be treated as a large solid rectangular area less one smaller, single void area as shown in Figure 4.27. The moment of inertia value about the x-axis for the c-channel shown is equivalent to that of the I-beam section (the shapes are equivalent in this respect only).

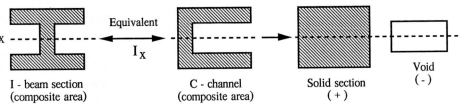

Figure 4.27. The I-beam geometry can also be represented as a solid rectangle and one large combined rectangular void for the moment of inertia calculation.

Example 4.2b I-beam Moment of Inertia: The I-beam cross section shown in Figure 4.25 could also be treated as a series of solid rectangular areas as shown in Figure 4.28. In this case, the location of the centroidal axis perpendicular to the applied load for both the composite area (i.e. the neutral axis), and centroidal axes for the individual rectangular sections that make up the area (sections 1,2, and 3) are easily determined by inspection.

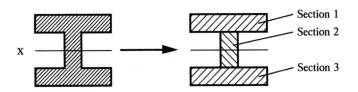

Figure 4.28. The I-beam geometry can also be represented as three solid rectangles for a moment of inertia calculation.

However, the centroidal axes for two of the three rectangular areas (namely areas 1 and 3) are not coincident with the parallel centroidal axis of the entire composite area. As a result, the *parallel axis theorem* must be used in order to calculate the moment of inertia of the composite area about the neutral axis.

$$I_T = \sum [I_{c,i} + (A_i \cdot y_i{}^2)] \tag{4.19}$$

$$I_1 = [(1.25)(0.25)^3 / (12)] + [(1.25)(0.25)(0.375)^2] \qquad \textit{Section 1}$$

$$I_2 = [(0.25)(0.50)^3 / (12)] + [(0.25)(0.50)(0.0)^2] \qquad \textit{Section 2}$$

$$I_3 = [(1.25)(0.25)^3 / (12)] + [(1.25)(0.25)(-0.375)^2] \qquad \textit{Section 3}$$

$$I_T = \sum I_i = I_1 + I_2 + I_3 = 0.0456 + 0.0026 + 0.0456$$

$$I_T = 0.0938 \text{ inch}^4$$

Note that the I value determined using this approach is equivalent to that determined in Example 4.2 a. However, in this case the intermediate results provide additional useful information. These values indicate that it is the upper and lower flanges of the beam that are primarily responsible for the stiffness of the beam. The web does not contribute a great deal in terms of stiffness, but it is necessary to maintain flange separation and transfer the bending stress.

4.4.3   The Use of Reinforcing Ribs to Improve Stiffness

Qualitative Considerations for Reinforcing Ribs: Many plastic parts incorporate rib like geometries in order to increase the stiffness or I value for the section. This is especially true for parts subject to flexural loading in service. Reinforcing ribs provide a relatively efficient means of increasing the rigidity of a section, while maintaining the moldability of the part by eliminating the undercut associated with I-beam type structures.

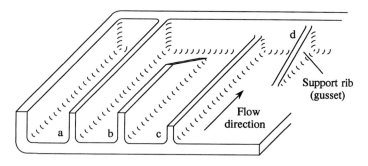

Figure 4.29. Typical rib configurations used to increase the stiffness of plate like injection molded parts. Designers must consider the structural performance of the rib as well as manufacturing concerns such as venting and ejection.

Reinforcing ribs are usually placed on the non-appearance surfaces of a plastic molding. Ribs are generally designed to run along the direction of maximum stress and deflection. The rib placement decisions are also affected by a number of manufacturing related issues associated with mold filling, shrinkage and ejection. The ribs can run the entire length of a part as shown in Figure 4.29a, or can be used as local reinforcements to stiffen selected areas of a part as shown in Figure 4.29b. Ribs that do not intersect with vertical walls should not end abruptly. A gradual transition zone to the surface / nominal wall will reduce the potential for stress concentration, improve melt flow, and improve venting during mold filling, thereby reducing the potential for gas traps, short shots or burn marks. Other rib like structures such as support ribs or gusset plates (Figure 4.29d) are commonly used to support vertical walls.

In their simplest form, reinforcing ribs are rectangular, beam like cross sections attached to the load bearing surface of a part. However, there are several manufacturing, structural, and esthetic concerns that cause the shape and dimensions of this ideal rectangular profile to be modified in practice, as shown in Figure 4.30. Reinforcing ribs are usually tapered (i.e. they have a draft angle) to reduce the forces of ejection and provide immediate release during part ejection. Another modification is that the base of a rib (i.e. where the rib intersects with the nominal wall) usually has a radius or fillet to reduce the potential for local stress concentration and to provide a more gradual wall thickness transition. This fillet at the base of the reinforcing rib also improves the mold filling characteristics and provides a buffer for shrinkage / cooling stresses. The minimum practical width of a rib is limited by mold filling concerns, while the maximum possible rib width is limited by the shrinkage characteristics of the material being used to produce the part, ability to pack the part, and flatness / appearance requirements of the molding.

Ribs that have not been designed for manufacturing

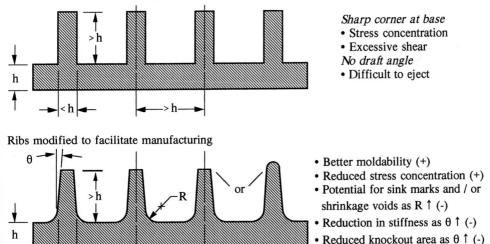

Sharp corner at base
• Stress concentration
• Excessive shear
No draft angle
• Difficult to eject

Ribs modified to facilitate manufacturing

• Better moldability (+)
• Reduced stress concentration (+)
• Potential for sink marks and / or shrinkage voids as R ↑ (-)
• Reduction in stiffness as θ ↑ (-)
• Reduced knockout area as θ ↑ (-)

Figure 4.30. Rectangular ribs must be modified to improve manufacturability.

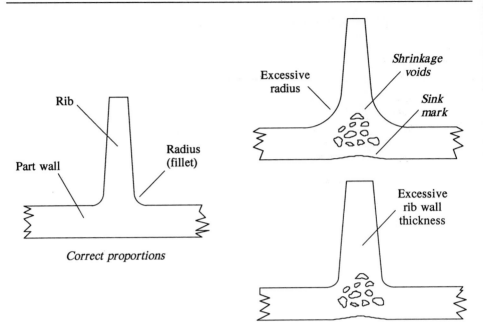

Rib

Part wall

Radius (fillet)

Correct proportions

Excessive radius

Shrinkage voids

Sink mark

Excessive rib wall thickness

Figure 4.31. Ribs with excessive wall thicknesses or fillet radii can result in the formation of shrinkage voids or sink marks due to the local increase in wall thickness.

Reinforcing ribs that have thick walls (relative to the thickness of the wall from which they project) are more likely to result in sink mark or shrinkage void formation. The same problems are likely to occur if excessive radii are used for the fillets at the base of the rib. While the use of larger radii should theoretically reduce the local stress concentration, as shown in Figure 4.7, the thicker wall section associated with the excessive radii may lead to shrinkage stresses and shrinkage voids, which may actually reduce the ultimate strength in the area, since the shrinkage stresses superimpose and the voids act as stress risers or structural discontinuities. Some material manufacturers provide molded test parts / plaques that contain a series of ribs having different geometries. The designer can evaluate the surface appearance of the wall opposite the rib, and determine if the proposed rib design is suitable in terms of surface appearance (i.e. size of the sink mark). The part shown in Figure 4.36 has various rib geometries as well as various surface finishes / surface textures on the surface opposite the ribs [19]. Surface defects such as sink marks (or weld lines) tend to be less obvious when the surface is textured.

There are in fact many *rules of thumb* or guidelines that are used to assist in the design of reinforcing rib geometries [9,12,16,20-29]. However, it is important that the reinforcing ribs are designed with consideration for the specific plastic material being used to produce the plastic part. Material processing variables such as melt viscosity and mold shrinkage have a large impact on rib design from a manufacturing point of view, while the material's creep behavior (usually tensile creep) is an important consideration from a structural point of view.

Figure 4.32. Test part used to evaluate the effect of rib thickness on the surface appearance of the part wall opposite the rib (Allied Signal Inc., Engineered Plastics, Morristown, NJ 07962).

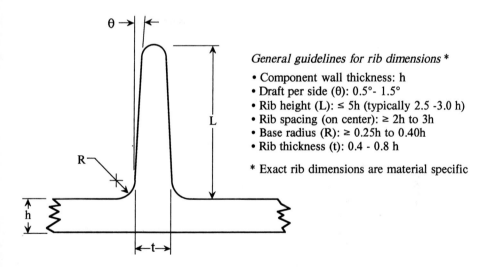

General guidelines for rib dimensions *

- Component wall thickness: h
- Draft per side (θ): 0.5°- 1.5°
- Rib height (L): $\leq$ 5h (typically 2.5 -3.0 h)
- Rib spacing (on center): $\geq$ 2h to 3h
- Base radius (R): $\geq$ 0.25h to 0.40h
- Rib thickness (t): 0.4 - 0.8 h

* Exact rib dimensions are material specific

Figure 4.33. General guidelines for rib dimensions. Material suppliers can provide more specific rib design recommendations for individual material grades.

For example, from a manufacturing point of view, rib heights are limited by the melt flow and part ejection characteristics (i.e. mold shrinkage, coefficients of friction, and rigidity) of the material used to produce the part. Deeper reinforcing ribs can be produced using lower viscosity, lower coefficient of friction, higher shrinkage materials, that have both good melt flow and ejection properties, while the use of more viscous, lower shrinkage materials would limit the permissible rib height. The use of a larger draft angles with deeper ribs does improve ejection characteristics, however, as the rib draft angle increases (for a given base wall thickness), both the stiffness and the surface area available for ejection decrease. The latter problem can be offset by the use of ejector pin pads or more expensive blade ejectors as described section 2.6. Ribs should also be polished in the direction of ejection (draw polished) to improve release characteristics. From the structural point of view, deeper ribs provide improved stiffness without adding a significant amount of weight, however, bending stresses at the extreme edges (or outer fibers) of a rib can be very high and increase with distance from the neutral axis as described by Equation 4.7. The designer should evaluate the proposed design of reinforcing ribs to ensure that the outer fiber stresses (usually tensile stresses) remain within acceptable limits [10]. Optimum rib design must focus on selecting proper rib spacing, rib height, rib wall thickness, draft angle, part wall thickness, and rib fillet radius [25-29].

As a general rule, it is better to use a larger number of thin, shallow ribs, rather than a few wide, deep ribs from both a stress and manufacturing point of view. A mold (especially a prototype mold) for a ribbed part is typically built so that the width (and possibly the depth) of the ribs, as well as the number of ribs, can be increased to provide improved structural capacity if the part does not perform adequately during prototype testing. This concept is commonly known as *steel safe design*, since it is generally easier and less expensive to remove mold steel than it is to add steel by inserting or welding. Reinforcing ribs can also vary in both width and depth in order to match the stress distribution in the part. From a manufacturing point of view, ribs are ideally placed in-line with the direction of flow to assist in both filling and venting. In fact, ribs are often used as internal runners or flow leaders to assist in filling and packing for both conventional and gas assisted injection molding processes. It is also common practice to use orthogonal ribs on the underside of plate like parts that are subject to multi-axial bending stresses. A designer should be especially concerned with gating complicated, ribbed parts, produced in molds having many cores and long flow lengths, since weld lines are likely to be present. When weld lines are likely to form along ribs, the designer should be sure that the maximum outer fiber stresses do not exceed the material's weld line strength value.

Moment of Inertia Calculations for Beams Containing Reinforcing Ribs: Moment of inertia calculations for beam sections (or parts) having reinforcing ribs running along the length of the part (or beam) are somewhat more complicated than those described previously. This is because the reinforcing ribs usually extend up from only one surface of a part (i.e. the underside of the part), and as a result, the area cross section does not exhibit symmetry about the neutral axis. The location of the neutral or centroidal axis for non-symmetrical cross sections is not readily apparent and must be determined using Equation 4.18 prior to the moment of inertia calculations. In addition, the geometry of the reinforcing rib itself can be fairly complicated. As mentioned previously, reinforcing ribs generally have corner radii or fillets to reduce stress concentration effects, improve mold filling, and act as a buffer for shrinkage stresses. The effects of the fillets on the stiffness of the ribs is commonly neglected in bending design calculations, however, it is more appropriate to consider the effects of these radii, and the effects of draft angle whenever possible.

Example 4.3 Moment of Inertia for Non-axisymmetric Areas - Ribbed Structures: This example will illustrate the procedure for moment of inertia calculations (about the neutral axis) for non-axisymmetric beam sections. The beam section shown is loaded perpendicular to the x-axis in service. Because the ribbed cross section is not axisymmetric (with respect to the neutral axis), the location of the cross section's centroidal axis (neutral axis) is not known, and must be determined by dividing the statical moment of the section by the total area of the section as described by Equation 4.18. The location of the datum or reference axis (x-axis) is defined / placed at some convenient location, such as at the top or bottom of the cross section (the latter is selected as the use of negative numbers is avoided).

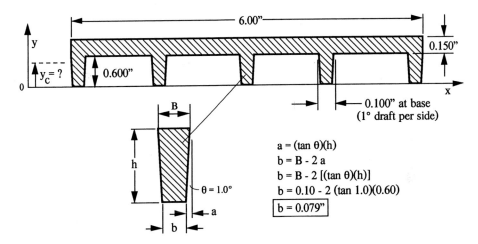

Figure 4.34. Beam cross section incorporates five ribs to increase the moment of inertia or stiffness of the section.

In order to calculate the moment of inertia of the ribbed area (cross section), the cross section or composite geometry must be divided into a series of areas, each having a regular geometry. In this case, the ribbed cross section is divided up into six individual areas or sections.

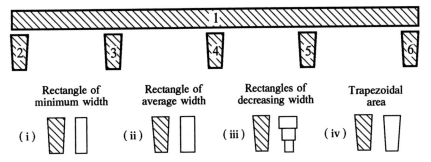

Figure 4.35. The complex beam cross section is represented as a series of six individual cross sections for a moment of inertia calculations.

Section 1 is simply a solid rectangular area, while the reinforcing ribs, areas 2-6, can be described in one of the following ways:

- Rectangular section using the narrow (free end) width - *a conservative approach*
- Rectangular section of average width - *tends to overestimate stiffness*
- An elemental approach - series of rectangular sections - *a good approximation*
- A trapezoidal geometry - *the best approach*

The area properties of a truncated isosceles triangle (or right trapezoid) are given in Figure 4.36 [2].

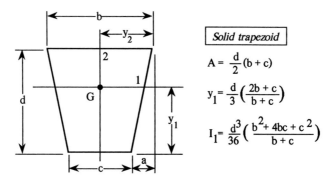

Figure 4.36. Area properties of a trapezoidal are used to describe the area properties of a drafted rib.

The area, A, and the centroidal axis locations (perpendicular to the applied load) , y, for each rib section (sections 2-6) are determined.

$$A_2 = A_3 = A_4 = A_5 = A_6 = (0.6/2)(0.100 + 0.079) = 0.0537 \ inch^2$$

$$y_2 = y_3 = y_4 = y_5 = y_6 = (0.6/3)[((2)(0.1)+(0.079))/((0.1)+(0.079))] = 0.312 \ inch$$

The area, A, of the rectangular section (section 1), and the location of the centroidal axis that is perpendicular to the applied load (relative to the x-axis) for the rectangular section, must also be determined.

$$A_1 = (6.00)(0.150) = 0.900 \ inch^2$$

$$y_1 = (0.600) + (0.150/2) = 0.675 \ inch$$

The centroidal axis location (neutral axis) for the composite area (full cross section) can then be determined using the principle of first moments.

$$M_x = \Sigma M_{i,x} = \Sigma A_i \cdot y_i \qquad\qquad (4.16)$$

$$y_c = \Sigma M_{i,x}/\Sigma A_i = \Sigma (y_i \cdot A_i)/\Sigma A_i \qquad\qquad (4.18)$$

Equation 4.18 is used to determine the distance between the reference axis (the x-axis in Figure 4.34) and the parallel centroidal axis for the composite area (neutral axis), while y is the distance between the reference axis and the centroidal axis of each of the individual sections that make up the total area (sections 1-6).

$$y_c = [((0.675)(0.15)(6.0))+(5\,(0.312)(0.0537))] / [((0.15)(6.0))+((5)(0.0537))]$$

$$y_c = 0.592 \text{ inch}$$

The distance between the reference axis (placed at the bottom of the component as shown in Figure 4.34) and the centroidal axis of the composite area is 0.592 inch.

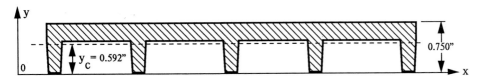

Figure 4.37. Location of the centroidal axis perpendicular to the applied load for the ribbed cross section.

The moment of inertia for the composite area about the centroidal axis perpendicular to the applied load (neutral axis) can be calculated now that the location of the composite section's centroidal axis has been determined.

$$I_T = \sum [I_{1,i} + (A_i \cdot y_i{}^2)] \tag{4.19}$$

$$I_1 = [(6.0)(0.15)^3 / (12)] + [(0.15)(6.0)(0.675 - 0.592)^2] = 0.00789 \text{ inch}^4$$

$$I_2 = (0.6)^3/36 \, [\,(0.267)] + [(0.3)(0.1+0.079)(0.312 - 0.592)^2] = 0.0058 \text{ inch}^4$$

$$I_3 = I_4 = I_5 = I_6 = I_2 = 0.0058 \text{ inch}^4$$

$$I_T = \sum I_i = I_1 + I_2 + I_3 + I_4 + I_5 + I_6 = 0.00789 + [(5)(0.0058)] = 0.0369 \text{ inch}^4$$

The ribbed cross section shown has a moment of inertia value equivalent to a solid rectangular section 6.0 inches wide x 0.42 inches deep (or thick). The example demonstrates that ribs do provide an efficient means of improving product rigidity, while keeping the overall wall thickness to an acceptable value with respect to material consumption, production cooling time, and part surface appearance.

4.4.4   Moment of Inertia for Non-homogeneous Materials / Structures

Certain types of plastic products that have beam like geometries may not consist of a single, homogeneous plastic material. For example, parts that consist of more than one material layer (i.e. layers of different materials having different mechanical properties), moment of inertia calculations based on the true cross section cannot be determined since moment of inertia calculations assume material homogeneity throughout the area cross section.

Examples of non-homogeneous plastic products include:

- Coextruded profiles / coinjection molded parts
- Painted, plated, or metallized products
- Laminated products
- Structural foam parts

If the "elastic moduli" of the various materials that make up the part cross section (or beam) are different, then the centroidal axis of the area (perpendicular to the applied load) will not coincide with the neutral axis for the cross section. This is also true for plastic parts produced with plastic materials that exhibit different properties in tension and compression.

The moment of inertia value for beams (or cross sections) that are constructed of more than one material can be estimated using an equivalent width technique [2]. Using this technique, the non-homogeneous section is transformed into an equivalent homogeneous cross section (i.e. a theoretical cross section of equivalent stiffness produced using only one of the beam materials). The width of each material layer, parallel to the principle axis of bending, is increased or decreased in the same proportion that the modulus of elasticity of that component makes with the modulus of the homogeneous reference material. Any one of the component materials can be selected as the reference material.

Example 4.4 Moment of Inertia for Non-Homogeneous Areas - Multi-layer Structures:
An ABS beam cross section has a width, w, of 6.000 inch, a thickness, h, of 0.125 inch, and is painted with a 0.003 inch thick layer of acrylic enamel. The addition of the paint layer will influence the rigidity of the final structure, and its effect on the beam's stiffness can be approximated using the equivalent width technique, provided the modulus value for both the ABS and paint layer are known, and perfect adhesion is assumed (i.e. complete stress transfer between layers).

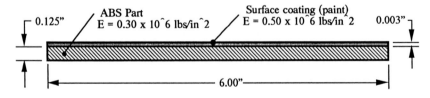

Figure 4.38. Cross section of a rectangular ABS beam coated with a layer of paint, resulting in a non-homogeneous rectangular cross section.

If the ABS is selected as the reference material, its width, w'(ABS), in the equivalent section remains unchanged, while the width of the paint layer, w'(P), will increase (since it has a higher modulus value in this case) in proportion to the ratio determined by the relative modulus values.

$$w'_i = (E_i / E_{Ref})(w_i)$$ (4.20)

$$w'(ABS) = (E_{ABS} / E_{Ref})(w_{ABS})$$

$$w'(ABS) = [(0.30 \times 10^6) / (0.30 \times 10^6)](6.0) = 6.0 \text{ inch (unchanged)}$$

$$w'(P) = (E_P / E_{Ref})(w_P)$$

$$w'(P) = [(0.50 \times 10^6) / (0.30 \times 10^6)](6.0) = 10.0 \text{ inch}$$

The thicknesses of the individual layers that make up the structure do not change using this technique. An equivalent cross section, a cross section of equivalent stiffness, determined using ABS as the homogeneous reference material (produced only of ABS) is shown in Figure 4.39.

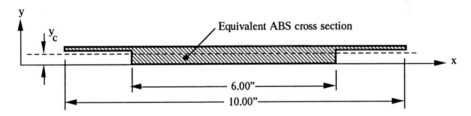

Figure 4.39. Homogeneous ABS cross section having a stiffness that is equivalent to the painted ABS beam. Moment of inertia values can be determined for the equivalent, homogeneous cross section.

The moment of inertia for the equivalent, homogeneous ABS cross section can be determined, once the centroidal axis of the section is located (note that the neutral axis location is not obvious due to a lack of symmetry).

$$M_x = \Sigma M_{i,x} = \Sigma A_i \cdot y_i$$ (4.16)

$$y_c = \Sigma M_{i,x} / \Sigma A_i = \Sigma (y_i \cdot A_i) / \Sigma A_i$$ (4.18)

$$y_c = [(0.003)(10.0)(0.1265) + (6.0)(0.125)(0.0625)] / [(0.003)(10.0) + (6.0)(0.125)]$$

$$y_c = 0.065 \text{ inch}$$

The composite I value for the equivalent geometry about the centroidal (neutral) axis can now be determined by summing the I values for two rectangular geometries that make up the composite area.

$$I_T = \sum [I_i + (A_i \cdot y_i{}^2)] \tag{4.19}$$

$$I_1 = [(10)(0.003)^3/(12)] + [(10.0)(0.003)(0.1265 - 0.065)^2]$$

$$I_2 = [(6.0)(0.125)^3/(12)] + [(6.0)(0.125)(0.0625 - 0.0650)^2]$$

$$I_T = \sum I_i = I_1 + I_2 = 0.0011 \text{ inch}^4$$

The deflection and stresses associated with loading of a multilayer beam can be calculated using this I value, the modulus of the reference material, and appropriate engineering formulas. In this case, neglecting the paint layer would result in 12% underestimation of the stiffness of the beam. The deflections calculated for the equivalent beam would be the same as those of the actual multi-layer beam. The fiber or bending stress values calculated for the equivalent beam, however, need to be converted into true stress values for the actual composite beam by adjusting the equivalent stress values for the width differences. Fiber stress values for the ABS remain unchanged since it is the reference material, and its width does not change. However, fiber stress values calculated for the wider, upper section of the equivalent beam are lower than those for the paint layer of the actual beam, by an amount determined by the width or modulus ratios. The actual paint layer is not as wide as the equivalent paint layer, yet it supports the same load, and therefore the fiber stresses increase.

4.4.5   Sample Beam Analysis

The park bench shown in Figure 4.40 can be used to illustrate the method a designer can use to estimate bending stresses, strains and deflections for a beam like plastic product subject to bending loads. It is common practice to use plastic materials (particularly recycled post consumer plastics waste) for the planking on park type benches, in place of

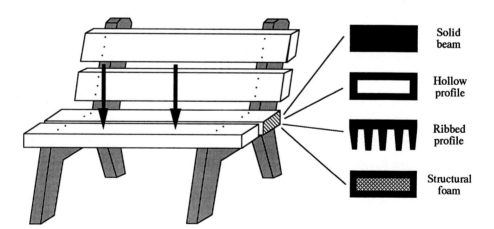

Figure 4.40. The seat members for the park bench are beam like profiles. Several alternative designs are proposed.

more conventional wooden planks. Advantages of the plastic planks include durability, smoothness, through coloring and design flexibility (integral assembly features and details can be incorporated). However, compared to wood, most plastic materials (especially the commodity plastic materials that would most likely be used in such an application) have relatively low modulus values, particularly at elevated temperatures. As a result, in this application, it is important for the product designer to estimate the maximum stresses and deflections for each of the proposed designs, since the loads associated with the application are potentially quite high, and the consequences of failure are likely to involve personal injury. In addition, the designer should be very concerned with creep, since a reasonable service life for such a product (i.e. the replacement interval for the planks) is probably in excess of 10 years. An analysis of each proposed design will give a designer quantitative information on which design decisions can be based.

The planks or seat members used for this product could be produced using any number of melt processing techniques, such as injection molding, gas assisted injection molding, foam molding, extrusion molding, blow molding or continuous extrusion processing. Several possible cross sections for the plastic planking include:

- A solid rectangular profile
- A hollow rectangular profile
- A ribbed profile (ribs on the underside of the part)
- A foam profile (such as a structural foam)

The various beam cross sections evaluated in this example are shown in Figure 4.41. Each of the cross sections has a width of 6.0 inches, and an overall depth of 1.50 inches.

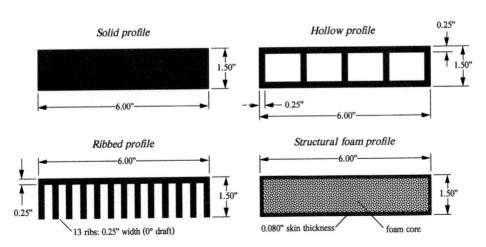

Figure 4.41. Alternative beam profiles for the seat members include a solid profile, a hollow profile, a ribbed profile, and a structural foam profile.

While the solid profile has the simplest shape, it is not the most efficient design since there are large quantities of material close to the neutral axis of the beam, material that is effectively "wasted" since it does not make a significant contribution to the stiffness of the beam. In addition, the solid part would be heavy, would consume relatively large quantities of material, and the production / packing / cooling times for the thick solid product would be extremely long. Each of the three other options makes better use of the material, and in the case of the ribbed or hollow profiles, there would be a very significant reduction in the production cycle time due to a significant reduction in the time required to cool the relatively thinner wall sections.

This example illustrates how the stresses and deflections associated with each of the various bench plank cross sections can be evaluated. The park bench actually consists of a number of components, including the legs / plank supports, the seat planks, the back planks, and the assembly hardware. Each of these components has its own functional and structural requirements. The discussion here is limited to the horizontal seat members. Obvious concerns for the product are the maximum deflections and stresses for the two bench seat members due to the anticipated service loads.

The seat members shown in Figure 4.41 are filled polyolefin profiles of constant cross section (i.e. beams), supported at two locations along their length, and are subject to loading at various points along the unsupported length. Each of the seat members has an overall width of 6.0 inches, a depth of 1.5 inches, and an overall length of 56 inches. The planks are centrally mounted on rigid concrete supports located 48 inches apart. This example problem is concerned with stresses and deflections due to loading of the unsupported distance (span) between the supports. Any effects due to the short cantilever overhang section are neglected in this example.

Before stresses and deflections for the unsupported section of the seat planks can be evaluated, the following factors must be identified and specified:

• Beam support conditions
• Loading conditions
• Service environment
• Material properties

Beam Support Conditions: Each of the two horizontal members or beams resting on the bench supports has an unsupported length (span) of 48 inches. The plank members will be attached to the rigid concrete supports using machine screws. Steel sleeves will be used to limit the local compressive stresses around the fasteners. The actual support conditions at both the right and left sides of the planks are likely to exhibit characteristics of both "simple" support and "fixed" support conditions, depending on the type and number of fasteners that are used. The support approaches the fixed condition (i.e. a condition where the angle between the loaded plank and the horizontal plane at the support is zero degrees) as the rigidity or quality of the joint assembly increases. In actuality, the assembly is likely to represent a condition between the conditions of ideal fixed and ideal simple support.

A plank with simple supports on both the left and right sides is considered for this problem since it represents the worst case scenario in terms of center deflection (maximum possible midspan deflection and midspan stress). However, both simple and fixed support conditions would normally be evaluated by the designer as a more complete and realistic evaluation. Figure 4.42 [9] shows that the deflections and stresses at the midspan are lower for a condition of fixed support, however, the fixed condition must be

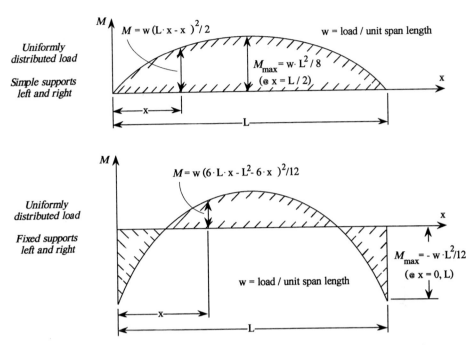

Figure 4.42. Bending moment diagrams for uniformly loaded beams with simple supports (top) and fixed supports (bottom).

evaluated to estimate the maximum stresses (and stress concentrations associated with assembly) at the left and right supports.

Loading Conditions: While it is not possible to specify the loading conditions for this product with complete certainty, a designer can anticipate or forecast a number of possible loading scenarios. The bench is designed to seat several adults across its width. The bench is loaded and unloaded periodically at a frequency that is dependent upon walking traffic in the local area. Loading here is described as intermittent rather than fatigue since the frequency of loading / unloading is very low (perhaps several times per day). The loads are essentially static, however, the dynamic effects associated with the application of the load should also be considered. The bench may be loaded for a period of minutes or hours, however, it is not expected to see continuous use throughout the entire day. The weight of the seat member itself is also of concern here since the product is relatively large, and over the long term (years in this case), plastic materials will creep under their own weight.

In this example, it is assumed that two adults, averaging 220 pounds each, will sit on the bench (between the supports) for a period of 8 hours per day. This load could be treated as a single concentrated (point type) load, a multiple point load, or as a distributed load. The loading condition here is taken as the total weight of the two individuals, distributed over the width of one board only, for a period of 8 hours. The effects of additional intermittent loads could also be evaluated to account for possible misuse / abuse (load safety factor). Full recovery of the deflection associated with the intermittent service loading is assumed to occur overnight (i.e. during the rest period). In addition, the magnitude of the continuous, uniformly distributed load, due to the weight of the seat member itself, must be determined from the beam geometry and the material density. The deflections and stresses resulting from the intermittent external load are superimposed on the continuous uniformly distributed load caused by the weight of the seat member itself.

The combination of support (i.e. simple support left and right) and loading conditions due to both the external load and the weight of the beam (both uniformly distributed loads) lead to the selection of the appropriate design equations [2]. Generalized equations for beams with partially distributed loads and simple support left and right are given in Figure 4.43.

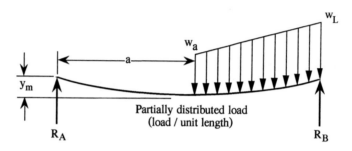

Boundary values: Partially distributed load, left and right end simply supported.

$$R_A = [(w_a / 2 \cdot L)(L - a)^2 + ((w_L - w_a)/6 \cdot L)(L - a)^2] \qquad M_A = 0 \qquad y_A = 0$$

$$\theta_A = [-(w_a / 24 \cdot E \cdot I \cdot L)(L - a)^2 (L^2 + 2 \cdot a \cdot L - a^2)$$
$$- ((w_L - w_a)/360 \, E \cdot I \cdot L)(L - a)^2 (7 \cdot L^2 + 6 \cdot a \cdot L - 3 \cdot a^2)]$$

$$R_B = ((w_a + w_L)/2)(L - a) - R_A \qquad M_B = 0 \qquad y_B = 0$$

$$\theta_B = [(w_a / 24 \cdot E \cdot I \cdot L)(L^2 - a^2)^2 + ((w_L - w_a)/360 \, E \cdot I \cdot L)(L - a)^2 (8 \cdot L^2 + 9 \cdot a \cdot L - 3 \cdot a^2)]$$

If a = 0 and $w_a = w_L = w$ (i.e. a uniform load over the entire span) then;

$$y_{max} = (-5 \cdot w \cdot L^4)/(384 \cdot E \cdot I) \qquad @ \quad x = L/2$$

$$M_{max} = (w \cdot L^2)/(8) \qquad @ \quad x = L/2$$

Figure 4.43. Classical bending equations for a simply supported beam subjected to a partially distributed load.

The terms in Figure 4.43 are defined as follows; M_A and M_B are the bending moments at the left and right supports respectively, θ_A and θ_B are the externally created angular displacements at the supports, the y values are the deflections at the left (A) and right (B) ends of the beam respectively (zero deflection here), L is the unsupported length of the beam (span), the w values are the distributed load values at locations a and L(B) respectively, the R values are the vertical end reactions at the left and right supports, I is the moment inertia about the centroidal axis of the beam cross section perpendicular to the applied load, and E is the modulus of elasticity of the beam material (note that the appropriate time / temperature / stress dependent modulus must be used here). In the case of the part bench seat member, the load has been assumed to be equally distributed across the entire span, therefore w at a = w at L = w, and a = 0. For this special case, the equation for maximum deflection at the midspan (i.e. @ x = L/2) is given by [2]:

$$y_m = (- 5 \cdot w \cdot L^4) / (384 \cdot E \cdot I) \qquad (4.21)$$

The maximum bending moment, M_m , also at the mid-span (i.e. @ x = L/2) is given by:

$$M_m = (w \cdot L^2) / (8) \qquad (4.22)$$

and can be used with Equation 4.7 to evaluate the maximum bending stress values.

Service Environment: The bench is a product that is used outdoors throughout the course of the calendar year. The product has the potential to be used in various climates, and is therefore exposed to various temperatures, relative humidities, and weathering effects. The bench may also come in contact with various cleaners as part of a maintenance program. Like most plastic materials, polyolefins have mechanical properties that are significantly influenced by temperature. Unlike other more polar polymers such as the nylons, the properties of most polyolefins are not a strong function of relative humidity, and temperature is probably the most important environmental factor. For example, the impact characteristics of the bench seat are expected to decrease as temperature decreases. On the other hand, the rigidity of the polymer (and stiffness of the seat boards) is more likely to be a problem at the higher temperatures and longer times. In terms of deflection, the worst case scenario is when the maximum service load is applied at the highest temperature (and highest relative humidity if moisture has a significant influence on the polymer's properties), and for the longest period of time (due to creep). The long term effects of weathering on the properties of a polymer are also important in this exterior, long term application and should also be taken into consideration since the properties of the polymer are likely to change over the 10 year period. For the sample bending calculations in this problem, the maximum continuous service temperature for the product is assumed to be 100°F, while the maximum service life (replacement interval for the boards) is taken to be 10 years.

Material Properties: The formulas that will be used to evaluate the stress and deflection for the beam (Equations 4.7, 4.21 and 4.22) have been derived using the assumption that the material is an elastic, homogeneous, isotropic material having a tensile modulus that is equivalent to its compressive modulus. These assumptions are generally not valid for plastic material applications that exhibit some degree of anisotropy, non-linear stress strain behavior and time dependent mechanical behavior. In this application, the planks are loaded for extended periods of time and creep effects must be taken into account. Since plastic materials are not linear elastic materials, the appropriate creep modulus (at the appropriate temperature / relative humidity / time / stress) is used in place of the elastic modulus value in Equation 4.21. Recovery of the deflection due to the 8 hour loading period each day is assumed to be complete for this problem, however, creep recovery data should ideally be used since any non-recoverable creep (set) will superimpose on the long term deflection due to the beam weight. If complete recovery is not realized during the time period between loadings, the total deflection at any time can only be calculated if the recovery characteristics of the material and the loading cycle are fully characterized. Given no information on recovery, a designer could assume continuous loading, the worst possible case, for safety.

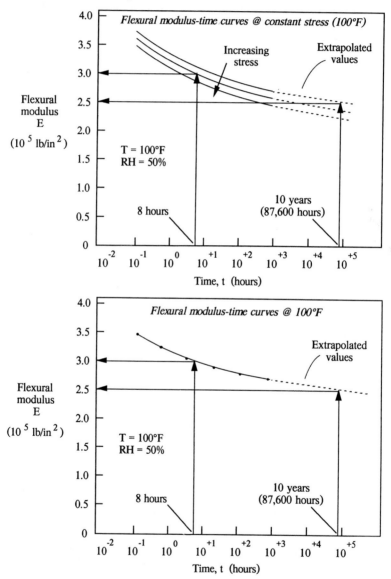

Figure 4.44. Flexural creep modulus vs. log time curve for the polyolefin used to manufacture the bench seat members (a) modulus independent of stress, i.e. linear stress-strain behavior, and (b) modulus is dependent on stress level, i.e. non-linear stress-strain behavior.

The deflection / stress equations have also been derived assuming that the compressive and tensile modulus values for the material are equivalent. The creep characteristics for the polymer in both uniaxial tension and uniaxial compression should be evaluated to determine if there are significant differences. If the values at the appropriate time are significantly different, one could use the lower of the two values as a conservative approach, or use an equivalent width technique to account for the differences. The most practical approach in most bending applications is to utilize flexural creep modulus data.

For this beam problem, the deflection and stress are due to both the beam weight and the external load. The maximum deflections due to the weight of the beam will occur at the longest time, that is at the end of the service life of 10 years (creep). For that deflection calculation, the creep modulus determined at the appropriate stress level, time, and temperature must be used. The extended service life for this product would most likely necessitate the use of an extrapolated modulus value, determined from shorter term tests. As a result, the value is only an approximation, and does not consider the longer term effects of aging and weather, and the potential for creep rupture, once again emphasizing the importance of designing at relatively low stress values for applications subject to long term (creep) loading.

The flexural creep modulus of the plastic material used to produce the board can be determined using the modulus vs. log time curves (at the appropriate temperature) given in Figure 4.44. Using curve 4.44a, the modulus after 8 hours of continuous loading (at $100°F$) is 3.0×10^5 lb/in^2, while the modulus after 10 years of loading is estimated to be 2.5×10^5 lb/in^2. The 8 hour creep modulus value is used to determine the deflection of the seat member due to the external load (at the end of the day), while the 10 year value is used to account for creep due to the beam weight. The creep modulus data in Figure 4.44a is assumed to be independent stress level. In actuality, the stress values associated with each of these loads (i.e. the external load and the beam weight) are in fact very different, and the modulus values at the various times and stresses (at constant temperature) are more appropriately determined using a set of stress dependent creep curves such as that shown in Figure 4.44b.

Example 4.5 Deflection and Stress for the Seat Member Profiles - Beams: The stresses and deflections due to the external load (i.e. people sitting on the bench) and the beam weight, for the 4 proposed designs (cross sections) shown in Figure 4.45 are determined in the following sections.

Neutral Axis Moment of Inertia: The moment of inertia (about the neutral axis) must be calculated for each section. Assuming isotropic, homogeneous material behavior, the solid and hollow profiles shown in Figure 4.41 and 4.45 are both axisymmetric profiles with respect to the neutral axis (i.e. the centroidal axis perpendicular to the applied load). The neutral axis location is readily identified as the axis of symmetry for these two geometries. However, the ribbed profile shown in Figure 4.45 is homogeneous but not axisymmetric, and the location of the neutral axis is not readily identified. As a result, the location of the neutral axis must be determined using Equation 4.18. The 13 individual ribs can be combined into one wider rib for simplicity in this case, since the ribs do not have draft angles.

The structural foam profile shown in Figure 4.45 is axisymmetric, but not homogeneous. Bending calculations for structural foam parts can be done using bulk modulus values determined by testing structural foam specimens of equivalent thickness and bulk density.

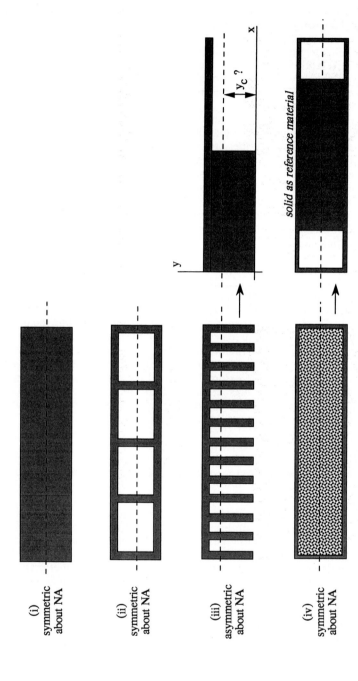

Figure 4.45. Alternative profiles for the seat planks; a solid rectangular section, a ribbed section, a hollow section, and a structural foam profile.

The part is treated as a homogeneous solid for the moment of inertia calculation, and the bulk modulus value is used for deflection calculations. Alternatively, the foam part can be treated as a series of layers (i.e. outer skins and a core). If the mechanical properties and thicknesses of the individual layers are known, the equivalent width technique described in Section 4.4.4 can be used to create a homogeneous, equivalent section for which the moment of inertia can be determined. This latter procedure is used for the structural foam calculations here to illustrate the concept of stress distribution in a multilayer structure.

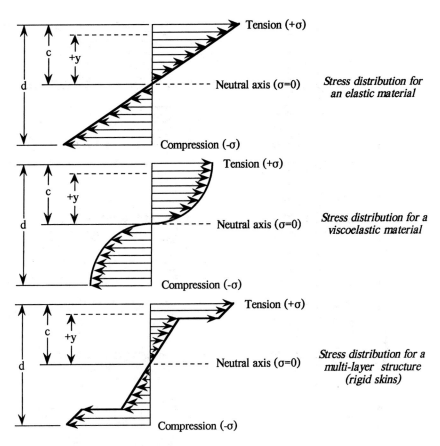

Figure 4.46 Stress distribution through the thickness of simple beams subject to bending loads. Top: Linear elastic material, middle: viscoelastic material, and bottom: structural foam (Eskins > Ecore).

The skin thickness for the foam part is given as a uniform 0.080 inch, while the foam core flexural creep modulus is given as approximately two thirds of the solid skin modulus (i.e. 200,000 lb/in^2 for the foam core vs. 300,000 lb/in^2 for the solid skin). The solid skin is taken as the reference material for the equivalent beam calculations. The neutral axis moment of inertia values for each of the four seat member cross sections are shown in Figure 4.47.

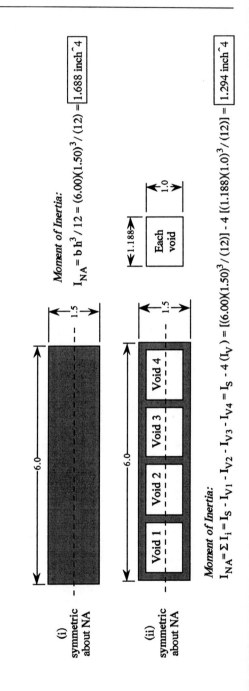

(i)
symmetric about NA

Moment of Inertia:

$$I_{NA} = b \, h^3 / 12 = (6.00)(1.50)^3 / (12) = \boxed{1.688 \text{ inch}^4}$$

Each void

(ii)
symmetric about NA

| Void 1 | Void 2 | Void 3 | Void 4 |

Moment of Inertia:

$$I_{NA} = \Sigma I_i = I_S - I_{V1} - I_{V2} - I_{V3} - I_{V4} = I_S - 4(I_V) = [(6.00)(1.50)^3 / (12)] - 4[(1.188)(1.0)^3 / (12)] = \boxed{1.294 \text{ inch}^4}$$

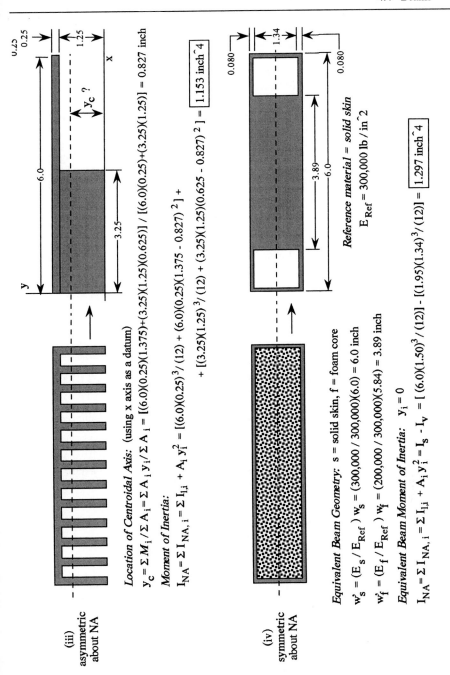

(iii) asymmetric about NA

Location of Centroidal Axis: (using x axis as a datum)

$y_c = \Sigma M_i / \Sigma A_i = \Sigma A_i y_i / \Sigma A_i = [(6.0)(0.25)(1.375)+(3.25)(1.25)(0.625)] / [(6.0)(0.25)+(3.25)(1.25)] = 0.827$ inch

Moment of Inertia:

$I_{NA} = \Sigma I_{NA,i} = \Sigma I_{I,i} + A_i y_i^2 = [(6.0)(0.25)^3 / (12) + (6.0)(0.25)(1.375 - 0.827)^2] +$
$+ [(3.25)(1.25)^3 / (12) + (3.25)(1.25)(0.625 - 0.827)^2] = \boxed{1.153 \text{ inch}^4}$

(iv) symmetric about NA

Reference material = solid skin

$E_{Ref} = 300{,}000 \text{ lb} / \text{in}^2$

Equivalent Beam Geometry: s = solid skin, f = foam core

$w'_s = (E_s / E_{Ref}) \, w_s = (300{,}000 / 300{,}000)(6.0) = 6.0$ inch

$w'_f = (E_f / E_{Ref}) \, w_f = (200{,}000 / 300{,}000)(5.84) = 3.89$ inch

Equivalent Beam Moment of Inertia: $y_i = 0$

$I_{NA} = \Sigma I_{NA,i} = \Sigma I_{I,i} + A_i y_i^2 = I_s - I_v = [(6.0)(1.50)^3 / (12)] - [(1.95)(1.34)^3 / (12)] = \boxed{1.297 \text{ inch}^4}$

Figure 4.47. Moment of inertia calculation for the solid rectangular, ribbed, hollow, and structural foam seat plank cross sections.

Loads : The external, uniformly distributed service load due to the total weight of two adults sitting across the unsupported span distance, L, of one seat member (worst case) is:

$$w_e = W_e / L = (2)(220 \text{ lbs}) / (48 \text{ inches}) = 9.17 \text{ lbs/inch} \qquad (4.23)$$

This external service load is common to each of the proposed designs. However, the internal, uniformly distributed load, w, due to the total weight of the seat member itself, W, acting over the unsupported distance, L, will vary with the specific design of the member. These load values, determined using Equation 4.24, are shown in Figure 4.48 for each of the four proposed design geometries. The specific gravity, SG, of the filled polyolefin is given as 1.40, while the nominal density reduction for structural foam member is 20%.

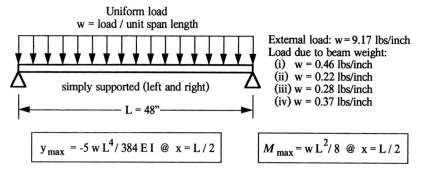

$$y_{max} = -5 \, w \, L^4 / 384 \, E \, I \quad @ \quad x = L / 2$$

$$M_{max} = w \, L^2 / 8 \quad @ \quad x = L / 2$$

Figure 4.48. Uniformly distributed loads associated with the beam weight for the four beam sections shown in Figure 4.45.

A sample calculation for the solid profile's uniform load, w, is given, where V is the volume of the profile over the unsupported distance, and w is the specific weight of water (reference).

$$w_i = W_i / L = SG \cdot w \cdot V / L \qquad (4.24)$$

$$w_i \text{ (solid)} = [(1.40)(0.036)(1.5)(6.0)(48)] / (48) = 0.46 \text{ lbs/inch}$$

Maximum Deflection Calculations: The maximum deflection at the midspan of the beam will occur at the end of the 8 hour service loading period (when the short term deflection is a maximum) on the last day of service (when the creep associated with the product weight is most significant). Using the assumptions of simple support, and uniform loading due to both the external load and the beam weight, the maximum total deflection can be determined by summing the individual deflections calculated using Equation 4.21. A sample deflection calculation for the solid section is shown, while a summary of the maximum deflection values for each of the four geometries is given in Figure 4.49.

$$y_{m,T} = y_{m,e} + y_{m,i} \qquad (4.25)$$

$$y_{m,e} = (-5)(9.2)(48^4) / (384)(300,000)(1.69) = -1.250 \text{ inch} \qquad (4.21)$$

$$y_{m,i} = (-5)(0.46)(48^4) / (384)(200,000)(1.69) = -0.075 \text{ inch} \qquad (4.21)$$

$$y_{m,T} = (-1.250 \text{ inch}) + (-0.075 \text{ inch}) = -1.325 \text{ inch} \qquad (4.25)$$

Figure 4.49 also lists the maximum tensile and compressive stresses for each geometry. The maximum tensile and compressive stresses (assuming simple support and uniform loading) occur along the outer surface at the midspan (midspan outer fiber stress), where both the bending moment and distance from the neutral axis (i.e @ $y = \pm c$) are a maximum. The maximum bending moment, at the mid-span (i.e. @ $x = L/2$) from Figure 4.42, is given by:

$$M_m = (w \cdot L^2) / (8) \qquad (4.22)$$

and can be used with Equation 4.7 to evaluate maximum stress values. The total stress due to the combined effects of the external load and the beam weight can also be found by superposition. As an example, the maximum stress values for the solid section are determined.

$$\sigma_{m,T} = \sigma_{m,e} + \sigma_{m,i} = [(w_e \cdot L^2)/(8)] \cdot c / I + [(w_i \cdot L^2)/(8)] \cdot c / I \qquad (4.26)$$

$$\sigma_{m,e} = [(9.2 \cdot 48^2)/(8)](0.75)/(1.69) = 1170 \text{ lbs/inch}^2$$

$$\sigma_{m,i} = [(0.46 \cdot 48^2)/(8)](0.75)/(1.69) = 58.6 \text{ lbs/inch}^2$$

$$\sigma_{m,T} = 1230 \text{ lbs/inch}^2$$

Taking tensile stresses as positive, the total maximum tensile stress, due to the combined loads is 1230 lb/in^2, while the total compressive stress is also -1230 lb/in^2 (due to symmetry). These maximum stress values must be compared to permissible stress levels for the material used to manufacture the product. An analysis of the summary data given in Figure 4.49 for the various geometries reveals several important points. Each proposed geometry is discussed separately.

Solid Section: The maximum tensile stresses, compressive stresses, and deflection are lowest for the solid section, however, the material and manufacturing costs associated with this baseline design are excessive. In addition, quality problems due to factors such as shrinkage voids and sink marks would be significant.

Hollow Section: Compared to the solid design, the hollow section offers over a 50% materials saving, but only a 26% increase in maximum deflection. Both the maximum tensile and compressive stresses are 28% greater than those for the solid section. A part of this type would be difficult to produce in one shot using a conventional injection molding process. However, it could be produced by welding two injection molded parts together (i.e. a clamshell design). Parts having a similar hollow cross section could also be produced using one of the gas assisted injection molding processes. Alternatively, the

Beam geometry	Moment of inertia (inch^4)	Weight per unit length (lb / inch)	NA to lower surface, - C (inch)	NA to upper surface, + C (inch)	Total tensile stress, σ_T (lb / inch^2)	Total comp stress, σ_c (lb / inch^2)
	1.69	0.46	0.75	0.75	1230	1230
	1.29	0.22	0.75	0.75	1570	1570
	1.15	0.28	0.83	0.67	1950	1590
	1.30	0.37	0.75	0.75	1590	1590

Beam geometry	y_{max} due to external load (inch)	y_{max} due to part weight (inch)	y_{max} total (inch)	Increase in deflection (%)	Material saving (%)	Increase in tensile stress (%)
	-1.25	-0.075	-1.325	Reference	Reference	Reference
	-1.63	-0.046	-1.676	+26	-53	+28
	-1.83	-0.043	-1.873	+41	-38	+59
	-1.63	-0.062	-1.692	+28	-20	+29

Figure 4.49. Summary of the maximum stress and maximum deflection values for the solid, hollow, ribbed and structural foam park bench seat members.

hollow part could be produced using continuous profile extrusion, however, end caps would need to be added to the end sections of the part for improved esthetics. The part could also be produced using the blow molding process, which is an extrusion process that permits the incorporation of integral end caps.

Ribbed Section: Compared to the solid design, the ribbed section evaluated offers more than a 38% materials saving, but a 41% increase in maximum deflection. The amount of deflection could be reduced by increasing the number of ribs / altering the rib design. While the compressive stresses for this design are only slightly higher than those of the solid section, there is a very large increase in the maximum tensile stress value, +59%, due to the reduction in the material cross section at the extremities of the rib. This would be even more of a problem if the ribs had draft angles to assist in part release. The primary advantage of this design is that it is easily manufactured in one shot using the conventional injection molding process. There are no undercuts, walls are relatively thin, and end caps / assembly features can be molded directly into the product. The specific rib design selected must be a balanced design that; permits proper material flow during injection; limits sink marks on the wall opposite the rib; facilitates part ejection; and provides the required resistance to deflection, while keeping maximum tensile stresses within acceptable limits.

Structural Foam Section: A structural foam part will have properties that are dependent upon the density reduction, density distribution, cell structure, and relative properties of the foam core and solid skin. The structural foam part deflects more than its solid counterpart, and as a result, outer fiber stress values are higher. The design is attractive since there is a material savings, and the problems associated with sink marks and shrinkage stresses are largely eliminated. The surface finish that can be achieved depends on the specific foam processing technique used to manufacture the part. Standard low pressure structural foam processing would be the simplest, lowest cost technique, and would give the product a wood like appearance. Counter pressure or expandable mold techniques could be used to improve the surface finish.

Each of the four proposed beam designs has its own relative advantages and limitations. The material consumption, processing considerations, deflections and stresses associated with each design must be evaluated and balanced in an effort to achieve the optimum design. In many cases, ratios such as the moment of inertia divided by the cross sectional area (or part weight) provide a good indication of the *efficiency* of the design with respect to bending. For example, the I/A value for the solid design is 0.188 (inch^4/ inch^2), while the I/A value for the hollow design is significantly higher at 0.304 (inch^4/ inch^2). It is true that the solid part is 26% stiffer than the hollow part, however, more than twice the material is required in order to manufacture the solid part. Efficiency in and of itself is not the only criteria, since the maximum stress values, stress distribution, and a variety of manufacturing/assembly/esthetic concerns must also be considered.

4.5   Plates

4.5.1   Introduction

While many plastic parts (or sub-parts) have beam like geometries, other parts are more appropriately described as thin, flat plates. In some cases, the product is truly a plate like structure, however, it is more common that the plate element is an integral section of a more complicated 3D molding that contains sides, edge stiffeners, intermediate ribs or other design features [1]. For example, the top of the computer housing shown in Figure 4.50 is a flat plate like element supported at the edges by the sides of the housing. Plate elements of this type are commonly loaded perpendicular to the plane of the plate. In the case of the computer housing, the plate must support both the load of the monitor resting on it, as well as its own weight. In this application, a designer is interested in evaluating stresses, strains and deflections due to the combined loading effects. The basic procedures involved are similar to those used in the beam analysis, where the designer must access the structural parameters and simplify the problem in order to evaluate the structural performance of the plate element. The designer must consider factors such as:

• Part geometry
• Edge support conditions
• Loading conditions
• Environmental conditions
• Material behavior / mechanical properties
• Safety factors

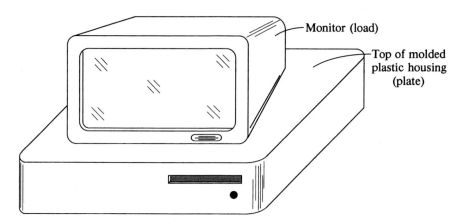

Figure 4.50 The top of the computer CPU housing is a plate like element that must support the load of the monitor.

Approximate solutions can be obtained when geometries, edge conditions, loading conditions and material behavior are idealized. Design problems involving complicated geometries, load distributions or variable edge support, cannot be described by the standard plate equations, and linear or non-linear finite element approaches must be used [1]. Their use is beyond the scope of this basic text, however, the concepts associated with the application of basic engineering formulas for stress and strain are discussed.

Engineering formulas for stresses and deflections of idealized plate elements are given in various sources [1,2]. The formulas can be applied to plates that are subject to loads normal to their plane, such as the housing in Figure 4.50, or for plates subject to in-plane edge loading (either tensile or compressive) due for example to a thermal expansion mismatch or loading by adjacent components. Engineering formulas for plates loaded normal to their plane have been derived assuming the following [2]:

• The plate is flat
• The plate has a uniform thickness
• The plate material is homogeneous and isotropic
• The thickness of the plate is not more than 1/4 the least transverse dimension
• The maximum plate deflection is not more than 1/2 the plate thickness
• All forces, both load and reaction, are normal to the plane of the plate
• The plate is not stressed beyond the elastic limit

The assumptions of isotropic behavior and elastic behavior are a particular concern for viscoelastic plastic materials, however, the formulas are useful for preliminary analysis provided the appropriate time / temperature dependent material behavior is used.

4.5.2   Sample Plate Problems

Example 4.6: Deflection of a Circular Plate: The injection molded container shown in Figure 4.51 is a household water bucket. The container is essentially a closed, drafted cylindrical sleeve (one end closed). The bottom of the container is a circular plate that is molded into the cylindrical sides of the container. The sides of the container extend downward beyond the base of the plate for stability. When the bucket is filled with water, the base (plate) will deflect due to the weight of the water, and to a lesser extent due to the weight of the base itself (neglected here).

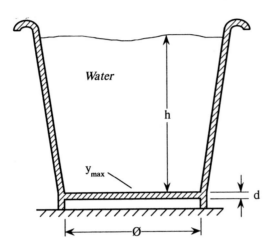

Figure 4.51. The base of the molded container is a circular plate element subjected to a uniformly distributed load (hydrostatic pressure).

Before the deflections and stresses associated with loading can be estimated, the geometry, edge support, loading conditions and material properties must be specified.

Geometry: The base of the water bucket is assumed to be a thin, flat circular plate having an unsupported diameter, Ø, of 10.0 inches, and a wall thickness, d, of 0.125 inches. This easily meets the criteria that the thickness of the plate is not more than 1/4 the least transverse dimension. The internal depth of the container itself, h, is 11.0 inches.

Edge Support: The edge support condition (around the circumference of the plate) is probably best described as "fixed", since (i) the plate is molded into the wall of the bucket, and (ii) the curvature of the sides to which the base is attached limits the vertical wall deflection. However, assuming a condition of fixed support will likely result in an underestimation of the deflection of the plate, since some vertical wall deflection is likely to occur. A worst case scenario in terms of deflection could be estimated using simple edge support, which would result in an over-estimation of deflection. The actual deflection for the base will fall between these two values, probably closer to that determined using the fixed edge condition in this case.

Loading Conditions: The load on the base of the container (assuming static loading) is due to the weight of the water acting on the plate area (i.e. creating a hydrostatic pressure). Since the water in the bucket will seek its own level, the height (or pressure head) of the water is uniform over the entire plate area.

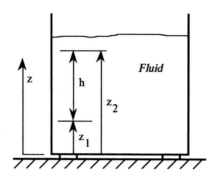

Pressure - height relationship
for incompressible fluids

$$P_2 - P_1 = -\rho g (z_2 - z_1)$$

$$\boxed{\Delta P = \omega h}$$

ρ = density
g = gravitational acceleration
ω = specific weight
h = difference in level
ΔP = pressure difference

Figure 4.52. The uniformly distributed load acting on the circular plate is determined by the height of the fluid and fluid density (pressure head).

For beam type structures, a uniform load is described as the total load, W, divided by the span length, L, and has units of load per unit length. For plate elements, uniform load, q, is described as the total load, W, divided by the area of the plate, A, and has units of load per unit area. In the case of the water container, the maximum intended service load occurs when the bucket is full (i.e. $z_1 = 0$, $z_2 = h$). The load is determined by multiplying the overall depth of the container, h, times the specific weight of water, w. The gage pressure (or uniformly distributed load) at the base of the container is given by:

$$q_{max} = \Delta P_{max} = w \cdot h \qquad\qquad (4.27)$$

$$q_{max} = (0.036 \text{ lbs/inch}^3)(11.0 \text{ inch}) = 0.396 \text{ lbs/inch}^2$$

The uniformly distributed load is 0.396 lbs/inch^2 when the container is full of water. In practice, designers should also consider the potential for an increase in this loading level due to dynamic effects or loading with higher density / specific gravity materials such as sand.

Material Properties: The water bucket is molded from a polypropylene homopolymer. The resulting deflection due to the hydrostatic load will depend on the stress-strain characteristics of the polypropylene at the end-use service temperature. The duration of loading must also be taken into account due to creep effects, as described in Sections 4.3.5 and 4.4.5. The maximum deflection associated with the hydrostatic load (water) will occur at the highest temperature / longest time of loading. For the purpose of this problem, the appropriate creep modulus is taken as 250,000 lbs/inch^2 while the polypropylene's Poisson's ratio value (i.e. the ratio of lateral to longitudinal strain) is given as 0.35.

Design Formulas: Based upon the flat, circular geometry of the plate, fixed edge support condition, and the uniformly distributed load, the appropriate formulas for stress and deflection can be selected [2]. Figure 4.53 shows the generalized diagram for flat circular plates with a uniformly distributed load and fixed supports.

Flat circular plate, uniformly distributed load, fixed support

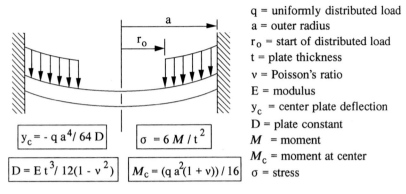

q = uniformly distributed load
a = outer radius
r_o = start of distributed load
t = plate thickness
v = Poisson's ratio
E = modulus
y_c = center plate deflection
D = plate constant
M = moment
M_c = moment at center
σ = stress

$$y_c = - q\, a^4 / 64\, D$$

$$\sigma = 6\, M / t^2$$

$$D = E\, t^3 / 12(1 - v^2)$$

$$M_c = (q\, a^2 (1 + v)) / 16$$

Figure 4.53. Classical formulas for stress and deflection for a circular plate with fixed edges, subjected to a uniformly distributed load.

In the case of the water bucket, the water is distributed over the entire plate area. For this special case, the equation for maximum downward deflection (at the center) is given by:

$$y_c = - q \cdot a^4 / 64 \cdot D \tag{4.28}$$

where D is a plate constant, a term that is analogous to the stiffness value (E·I) for a beam. The plate constant is substituted in Equation 4.28 to yield:

$$y_c = - 3 \cdot q \cdot a^4 (1 - v^2) / 16 \cdot E \cdot t^3 \tag{4.29}$$

$$y_c = - [(3)(0.396)(5)^4 (1 - 0.35^2)] / (16)(250{,}000)(0.125)^3$$

$$y_c = - 0.083 \text{ inches}$$

The maximum stress values associated with this deflection can be determined using the generalized stress equation for flat circular plates:

$$\sigma = 6 \cdot M / t^2 \tag{4.30}$$

and the unit radial bending moments (inch-lbs / inch of circumference) or unit tangential bending moments (inch-lbs / inch of radius). The moment at the center of the circular plate with fixed edges and uniformly distributed load is:

$$M_c = [q \cdot a^2 (1 + v)] / 16 \tag{4.31}$$

Combining Equations 4.30 and 4.31 yields an expression for the maximum stress at the center of the circular plate (tensile stress at the lower plate surface, compressive stress at the upper plate surface):

$$\sigma_c = [3 \cdot q \cdot a^2 (1 + v)]/8 \cdot t^2 \qquad\qquad (4.32)$$

$$\sigma_c = [(3)(0.396)(5)^2(1 + 0.35)]/(8)(0.125)^2$$

$$\sigma_c = 321 \text{ lbs/inch}^2$$

This stress value (and the stress value at the edge of the plate) should be compared to permissible stress values for the polypropylene used to manufacture the container to determine if the stress levels are within acceptable limits. The potential for crazing due to chemicals / detergents and stress concentration at the wall intersection should also be considered. The basic procedure described above can be used to evaluate stresses and deflections for a variety of other plate geometries, support conditions, and loading conditions. For example, the information given in Figure 4.54 can be used to evaluate stresses and deflections for uniformly loaded rectangular plates with fixed edges. Formulas are available for a wide range of flat plate applications.

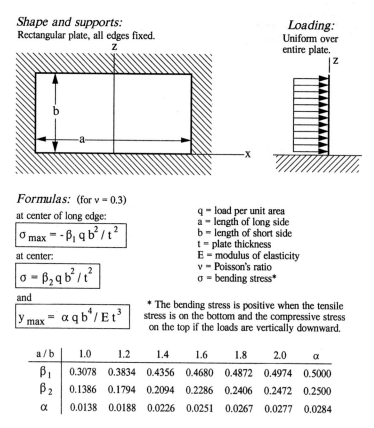

Shape and supports:
Rectangular plate, all edges fixed.

Loading:
Uniform over
entire plate.

Formulas: (for $v = 0.3$)

at center of long edge:

$$\sigma_{max} = -\beta_1 q b^2 / t^2$$

at center:

$$\sigma = \beta_2 q b^2 / t^2$$

and

$$y_{max} = \alpha q b^4 / E t^3$$

q = load per unit area
a = length of long side
b = length of short side
t = plate thickness
E = modulus of elasticity
v = Poisson's ratio
σ = bending stress*

* The bending stress is positive when the tensile stress is on the bottom and the compressive stress on the top if the loads are vertically downward.

a / b	1.0	1.2	1.4	1.6	1.8	2.0	α
β_1	0.3078	0.3834	0.4356	0.4680	0.4872	0.4974	0.5000
β_2	0.1386	0.1794	0.2094	0.2286	0.2406	0.2472	0.2500
α	0.0138	0.0188	0.0226	0.0251	0.0267	0.0277	0.0284

Figure 4.54. Classical formulas for stress and deflection of a rectangular plate with fixed edges, subjected to a uniformly distributed load.

Example 4.7 Paper Tray: Another injection molded plastic part that contains a plate like element is the stacking paper tray shown in Figure 4.55. The tray is molded from a general purpose polystyrene, and serves as a storage system for writing paper in an office environment. The shelf of the tray is a rectangular plate element that must support both its own weight, and the weight of the items placed on it.

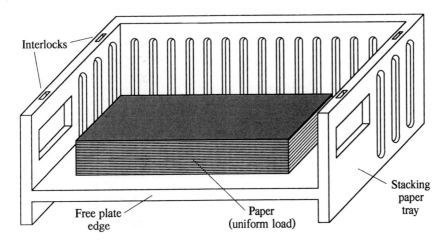

Figure 4.55. The stacking paper storage tray uses a flat, rectangular plate element to support the service load.

A designer of this product should be particularly concerned with the stresses and deflections associated with the service load (i.e. a stack of writing paper) for several reasons. Firstly, the span length (unsupported distance) along the front, unsupported edge of the shelf is relatively large for a thin walled plastic product under load, and the amount of deflection and stress are likely to be significant. Secondly, the product will be subjected to this load for an extended period of time, and creep effects (an increase in deflection with time due to constant stress) are therefore expected to be a concern. The product has an indefinite service life, and loading for a period of years is likely.

Before the stresses and deflections associated with the applied load can be calculated, the geometry of the plate element, edge support conditions, loading conditions, and material properties must be specified.

Geometry: For this initial example, it is assumed that the shelf of the tray is a flat, rectangular plate that is attached (molded into) the sides and back of the tray. The tray is designed to support paper having a width of 8.5 inches and a length of 11.0 inches. The shelf (plate) itself has a width of 9.0 inches and a length of 11.5 inches for clearance. The flat plate has a uniform wall thickness of 0.090 inch.

Loading Conditions: The plate element of the paper tray shown in Figure 4.55 will deflect due to its own weight, however, the primary function of this plate is to support a "stack" of writing paper. Like the hydrostatic load in the previous example, the load acting on the paper tray plate is probably best described as a static, uniformly distributed load acting over the entire surface of the plate (even though the plate is slightly larger than the paper). Unlike a rigid solid, such as a board, the individual sheets of paper are flexible enough that they will deflect along with the plate, and the uniform loading condition is satisfied, even as the plate deflects.

Figure 4.56. Stack of four molded paper trays with various loads (top to bottom; no load, 500 gram central concentrated load, 5 - 100 gram loads distributed over the span, and a stack of paper).

Figure 4.56 shows a set of stacked paper trays with various loads. The second tray from the top has a 500 gram weight at the midspan of the front edge, while the second tray from the bottom has five - 100 gram weights (500 grams total) distributed along the front edge of the plate. The maximum deflection and maximum stress values associated with the uniform load are significantly lower than those associated with the single concentrated load. In this case, the paper load is most closely approximated using a uniform load, however, it is sometimes good to assume all of the load is concentrated over a small area in the plate as a worst case scenario for safety, especially when the service load has some concentrated characteristics (e.g. a uniform load acting over only a small area of the plate). In this example, it is assumed that a typical load is due to a 1.0 inch high stack of paper, which generates a uniform load, q, over the surface area, A, of the plate. The uniform load due to the polystyrene plate weight itself is also considered.

$$q = W/A = [(SG_{paper} \cdot w_{water} \cdot V_{paper}) + (SG_{PS} \cdot w_{water} \cdot V_{PS})]/A \qquad (4.33)$$

$$q = [(1.2)(0.0036)(8.5)(11)(1.0)+(1.05)(0.036)(0.090)(9.0)(11.5)]/[(9.0)(11.5)]$$

$$q = 0.0424 \text{ lbs/inch}^2$$

Other anticipated loading scenarios, due to misuse / overloading or to an accidental drop should also be considered.

Edge Support: The plate element of the tray shown in Figure 4.55 is supported along a total of three edges (left, right and rear), while the entire length of the front edge is unsupported. There are no other intermediate supports. At first glance, it appears that the rectangular plate element of the paper tray has edge conditions that are best described as being fixed on three edges, and free on the fourth side, since three of the plate edges are molded into the part wall as depicted in Figure 4.57.

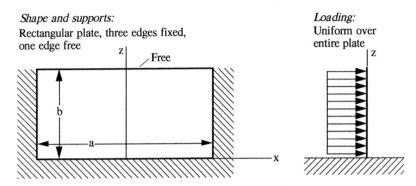

Figure 4.57. Representation of a rectangular plate with a uniform load over the entire plate, three fixed edges and one free edge.

However, at this point, consider the stacking nature of the paper tray, which has been designed with integral interlocks for stacking as shown in Figure 4.58.

Figure 4.58. Stack of four molded paper trays with no external load (left) and four trays subjected to a concentrated central loading (right). Note that the upper tray (plate) deflection is greater than that of the lower trays due to the lack of sidewall restraint.

There are several possible edge conditions that the designer might consider. The lower levels (all but the top level) of a stacked set of trays have edge conditions that are most appropriately described by three fixed edges, and one free edge. The left and right sidewall deflections for these trays are limited due to the sidewall interlock with the tray above. However, the top tray sidewalls (or the sidewall for a single free standing tray) are more likely to deflect than the lower tray sidewalls as shown in Figure 4.58 (right).

Each tray in the figure is produced from the same polymer, has identical geometry, and is subject to the same point load at the midspan on the front edge, however, the upper tray shows a significantly larger deflection at the midspan due to different edge conditions. The figure also shows that this increase in midspan deflection corresponds with an increase in the sidewall deflection. This situation would be even more pronounced for a single, free standing tray, where there is no interlocking tray above or below to restrict sidewall deflection along the front edge of tray. Under these conditions, the sides of the tray (especially at the front edge) could be considered as having simply supported edges.

Material Properties: The paper tray in this problem is molded using a general purpose polystyrene. The part is subject to loading for an extended period of time (years) and therefore a design problem of this type cannot be attempted without flexural creep data for the material grade being used. Once loaded, the deflection of the tray will increase gradually with time, at a rate that is dependent on the ambient conditions, and the flexural creep behavior of the polystyrene. While short term stress strain behavior can be used to predict short term deflection, the increase in deflection over the long term can only be predicted if creep data is available or can be generated / extrapolated. The effect of environmental conditions such as the presence of ultraviolet light and long term aging should also be considered for this long term application.

Design Formulas: The formulas that are used for stress and deflection calculations can be selected once the loading, edge conditions, and geometry have been defined. In this case, the plate geometry is defined as a flat rectangular plate that is subject to a uniformly distributed load. The edge conditions for a stack of trays could be defined as three edges

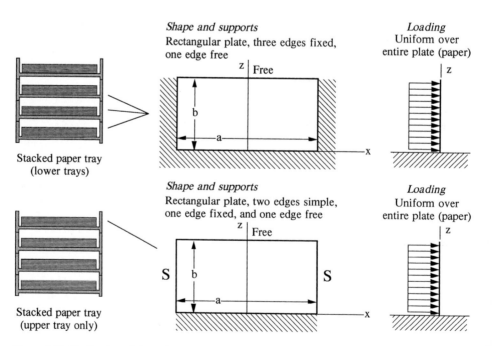

Figure 4.59. Idealized conditions of loading and edge support for the injection molded paper tray.

fixed and one free, however, it might be better to assume that the left and right sides of the plate element are simply supported as a worst case scenario for the top tray, or for a stand alone paper tray , even though the sides of the tray are rigidly supported at the back edge, recognizing that the true edge condition is somewhere between that of fixed and simple support.

A Plate with Three Edges Fixed, One Edge Free: The equation for maximum tensile (or maximum compressive) stress at the midspan of the free edge (i.e. $x = 0$, $z = b$) for a uniformly loaded rectangular plate with three fixed edges and one free edge is given by [2]:

$$\sigma_a = \beta_2 \cdot q \cdot b^2 / t^2 \tag{4.34}$$

where t is the plate thickness, b is the plate width, q is the uniformly distributed load, and the term β_2 is a constant that depends on the ratio of a/b.

Table 4.4 . β_2 Constants for a Rectangular Plate having a Uniform Load, 3 Fixed Edges and 1 Free Edge [2]

a/b	0.25	0.50	0.75	1.00	1.50	2.00
β_2	0.016	0.066	0.148	0.259	0.484	0.605

In this case, the ratio a/b is 1.278, and $\beta 2$ is found to be 0.384 by interpolation. The maximum tensile stress along the underside of the front edge midspan is:

$$\sigma_a = (0.384)(0.0424)(9.0)^2 / (0.090)^2 = 163 \text{ lbs/inch}^2 \tag{4.34}$$

Stresses and deflections at other locations along the plate surface can be calculated using similar equations. These stress values must be compared with permissible design stress values for the plastic material, while deflection values are compared with those deflections deemed acceptable for this application (i.e. based on the original design specifications / requirements).

Table 4.5 . β_2 Constants for a Rectangular Plate having a Uniform Load, 1 Fixed Edge, the Opposite Edge Free, and the Remaining Edges Simply Supported [2]

a/b	0.25	0.50	0.75	1.00	1.50	2.00
β_2	0.048	0.190	0.386	0.565	0.730	0.688

Back Edge Fixed / Sides Simple / Front Edge Free: The equation for maximum tensile (or compressive) stress at the free edge midspan (i.e. $x = 0$, $z = b$) for the uniformly loaded rectangular plate with simply supported sides, a fixed rear edge and free front edge is also given by:

$$\sigma_a = \beta_2 \cdot q \cdot b^2 / t^2 \qquad\qquad (4.34)$$

where β_2 is a constant that depends on the ratio of a/b. In this case, a β_2 value of 0.657 is obtained by interpolation for an a/b ratio of 1.278.

$$\sigma_a = (0.657)(0.0424)(9)^2 / (0.090)^2 = 279 \text{ lbs/inch}^2 \qquad (4.34)$$

The stress values along the front edge of the plate with simple side supports are significantly higher (almost two times higher) than those obtained for a plate with fixed side supports. The example is included to illustrate the importance of selecting the proper support conditions, due to their effect on the calculated stress and deflection values.

4.5.3   Plate Elements with Non-uniform Wall Sections

The plate equations used up to this point have been derived assuming that the plate is flat and has a uniform wall thickness. In reality, few plastic parts can meet the uniform wall thickness criteria. The plate like element of a plastic part may have features such as ribs, flow leaders, bosses, holes or edge stiffeners that extend up from one or both sides of the plate wall (or into the wall in the case of a hole). It may be possible to ignore the effects that a small circular boss will have on the structural behavior of a large plate as shown in Figure 4.4, however, the stiffening effects of ribs or edge stiffeners cannot be ignored without introducing significant error.

As an example, the paper tray shown in Figure 4.65 would probably be designed with an edge stiffener (i.e. a local increase in wall section) along the bottom of the front edge. The stiffener is designed to reduce deflection and stresses along the front edge. The plate equations described earlier would not be appropriate for the tray with the edge stiffener since the wall thickness of the plate is no longer uniform. Neglecting the effects of the stiffeners or other rib like features would result in significant error.

In order to obtain a crude estimate of the deflection / stress behavior for a more complicated plate geometry, the plate could be broken down into a set of perpendicular beams as shown in Figure 4.60 [30]. The tray shown in Figure 4.60 contains two beams sections that are perpendicular to one another. Beam 1 is a beam section that is supported at the right and left ends, and is subject to a uniformly distributed load. The support is either simple or fixed, depending on whether the tray is free standing or interlocked as described earlier. The load on the beam increases / decreases according to the width of the beam section selected, however, the uniform load value, w (load / unit span), is a constant. The cross section of the beam is a constant over the beam length, and design features such as the edge stiffener are simply treated according to the procedures outlined for ribbed beams. The second beam section, Beam 2 in Figure 4.60 is perpendicular to the first beam, and is a uniformly loaded cantilever beam. In this case, the cross section of the cantilever beam is constant, with the exception of the edge stiffener at the free end of the beam. Like the hook on a cantilever snap, the increase in wall section will have very little effect on the stiffness because it runs perpendicular to the direction of maximum deflection for Beam 2. The total plate deflection can be estimated from the two

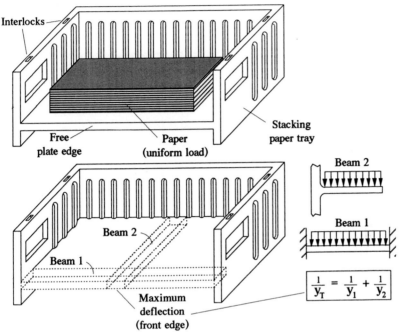

Figure 4.60. Method for estimating the deflections for plate elements of more complex geometry [30].

beam deflections. The total deflection at the intersection of the beams can be estimated:

$$1/y_T = 1/y_1 + 1/y_2 \qquad (4.35)$$

The procedure provides only a rough estimate of the deflection or stress in the local area. Computer aided finite element analyses and / or actual prototyping tests are recommended for plate like parts having a non-uniform wall thickness, or in general, for parts with more complicated geometries. A more thorough analysis of the mechanical behavior of plastic plates is given by references such as Heger [1].

4.6   Shells / Pressure Vessels

4.6.1   Introduction

Plastic materials are commonly used in applications where the geometry of the part is described as a shell, vessel or pipe. This is particularly true in plumbing, pneumatic, or chemical transport applications where plastic materials are used in the manufacture of flexible hoses, rigid pipes and a wide variety of fittings. Many automotive, food packaging and medical parts are pressure vessels. Plastic pressure vessels are most commonly used in applications where they are subject to a uniformly distributed internal pressure. For example, the molded polyester water saving toilet component shown in Figure 4.61 is designed to withstand an internal gauge pressure of several atmospheres.

Figure 4.61. The molded polyester water saving component is a pressure vessel designed to withstand continuous internal pressure.

While pressure vessels are most commonly subject to a uniform internal pressure, there are applications where parts are subject to uniform external loads. Parts used in vacuum or deep submergence applications are examples of parts subject to external loading.

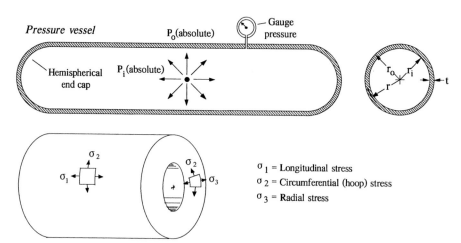

Figure 4.62. Internal pressure acting on a cylindrical pressure vessel with hemispherical end caps.

When a pressure vessel such as the closed tank shown in Figure 4.62 is subjected to an internal (or external) pressure, stresses are set up in the walls. The triaxial state of stress involves axial or longitudinal stress, circumferential or hoop stress, and radial stress. Along with these stress values, there will be corresponding axial, circumferential and radial strain values, with magnitudes that are determined by the mechanical properties of the plastic material. Formulas for the stresses and strains associated with pressure vessels of various regular geometries are given in handbook references [2].

4.6.2   Thin Walled Pressure Vessels

When the wall thicknesses, t, of a shell or pipe, subjected to a uniformly distributed internal or external load, q, is small relative to the shell radius, r, (i.e. r/t > 10), and there are no abrupt changes in curvature or thickness, thin wall design equations can be used to obtain an approximate solution. In the case of a thin walled vessel, the axial and circumferential stresses are nearly uniform throughout the thickness of shell. Formulas for the stresses and deflection for thin walled cylindrical, conical, spherical and toriodal vessels (i.e. regular geometries) are readily available. Pressure vessel equations are further categorized to cover situations where the vessel or pipe has ends that are capped or uncapped.

Example 4.8 Pressure Vessel: The water tank shown in Figure 4.62 is a thin walled cylindrical vessel with hemispherical end caps. The tank has an internal diameter of 6.2 inches and a proposed wall thickness of 0.188 inch. The vessel must be capable of withstanding a continuous static internal water pressure of 40 lbs/in^2 for a period of 20 years. The tank is produced using a glass reinforced engineering plastic. In such an application, a designer must calculate the stress level at which the tank would be expected to fail due to excessive creep or creep rupture. In this case, it is mandatory that creep rupture test data is available for the material used to produce the part.

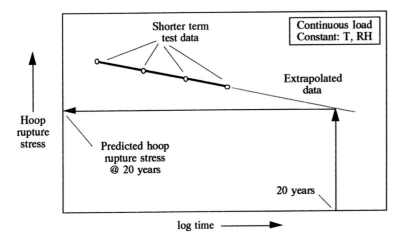

Figure 4.63. The long term tensile (hoop) creep rupture strength for pressure vessels is estimated by extrapolating shorter term test data. Real time data should be used whenever possible.

In this type of application, the designer must compare calculated stress values to the creep rupture characteristics of the material used to produce the part (vessel). The maximum stress value for the part must be well below the tensile creep rupture stress or the hoop failure stress (based on the failure stress-time relationship) determined using pipe-like test specimens [24]. The creep rupture test data must have been determined under conditions that are representative of the temperatures and relative humidities associated with the product end-use application. The adverse effects of long term exposure to water (or a more aggressive chemical), especially at elevated temperatures are particularly important with many plastic materials. The presence of weld lines would also be an important concern in this application.

Using the design equations for a closed end, thin wall cylinder, subject to a uniform internal pressure, the hoop stress away from the ends of the vessel can be determined using (tensile stresses are positive).

$$\sigma_2 = q \cdot r / t = (40)(3.19) / (0.188) = 680 \text{ lbs/inch}^2 \tag{4.36}$$

The axial stress can be determined by dividing the force caused by the internal pressure acting on the end caps, by the cross sectional area of the cylindrical shell element.

$$F_1 = \pi \cdot r_i^2 \cdot q = (3.14)(3.1)^2(40) = 1210 \text{ lbs} \tag{4.37}$$

$$A_s = \pi (r_o^2 - r_i^2) = (3.14)[(3.29)^2 - (3.10)^2] = 3.81 \text{ inch}^2 \tag{4.38}$$

$$\sigma_1 = F_1 / A_s = (1210) / (3.81) = 318 \text{ lbs/inch}^2 \tag{4.39}$$

As the wall thickness of the thin walled cylinder approaches zero, the value for the axial stress approaches 1/2 the hoop stress value.

The dimensions of the pressure vessel, specifically the radius and the axial length of the vessel, will change with both the magnitude of the internal pressure and with time due to creep. The dimensional changes can be determined if the tensile creep behavior and the Poisson's ratio of the plastic material are known. The change in radius, Δr, that would occur with changes in pressure and time can be determined using:

$$\Delta r = q \cdot r^2 \left[1 - (v / 2) \right] / E_T(t) \cdot t \tag{4.40}$$

where $E_T(t)$ describes the tensile creep modulus behavior of the material. The change in axial length, ΔL, can be determined using:

$$\Delta L = q \cdot r \cdot L (0.5 - v) / E_T(t) \cdot t \tag{4.41}$$

The stresses and deflections calculated using Equations 4.36 to 4.41 can be considered reasonable approximations for straight pipes, however, as the geometry of the vessel becomes more complicated, the results of the simplified equations are likely to be in error. This is a concern for vessels having holes, fittings, reinforcing ribs or end caps that are either molded in or attached to the cylinder in a secondary assembly operation.

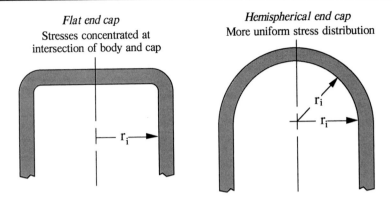

Figure 4.64. Flat pressure vessel end caps result in extremely high stress concentrations at the corners, while hemispherical end caps result in a more uniform stress distribution.

The cross sections shown in Figure 4.64 represent the classical situations of flat and hemispherical end cap designs. Studies have shown that the local stresses at geometrical discontinuities, such as the intersections of the cylinder and the base, can be 3 to 6 times greater than the nominal hoop stress value determined using Equations 4.36 [16,31]. The stresses at the corner for the part with the flat end cap are extremely high due to the combined effects of the hoop and the bending stresses associated with the end cap (plate) deflection. The hemispherical end cap is a preferred end cap design, however, its use in applications where the part must stand or end is not always permitted. The maximum stress values for most capped vessels are significantly higher than those determined using the hoop stress equation, since these values must be multiplied times a stress concentration factor, K, which depends upon the specific design of the end cap.

$$\sigma_{max} = K \cdot \sigma_2 \qquad (4.42)$$

Once the designer estimates the maximum stress, a safety factor must be applied. Once the part is designed, prototype tests are commonly conducted to determine the actual rupture stress / pressure. It has been stated earlier that the maximum stress in service should be significantly lower than the creep rupture strength. The difference in these values, or degree of safety is dependent upon the application, and quality of the test data. The operating pressure in a plastic pressure vessel often limited to one sixth the actual burst pressure determined by hydrostatic testing [31].

It is nearly impossible to calculate maximum stresses for pressure vessels of complicated geometry, and finite element techniques are recommended. In fact, material manufacturers have recommended that consultation is imperative for plastic parts subject to internal pressure [24]. While FEA can point the designer in the right direction, prototype parts, molded under realistic conditions, must be evaluated experimentally to determine burst pressures, since manufacturing related factors such as weld lines, orientation, and residual stress that superimpose on the service stress, can all have a very large effect on product performance. Prototyping is even more important for parts subjected to chemical exposure, dynamic, or fatigue loading, since these applications are more difficult to model accurately.

4.6.3   Thick Wall Pressure Vessels

The design equations for thick wall pressure vessels, cases where $r/t < 10$, are similar to the thin walled pressure vessel equations given above, however, the radial (wall) stress becomes more significant, and the variations in hoop stress through the wall cannot be neglected without introducing significant error [2,32].

Thick wall pressure vessels are described as having both an inside radius and an outside radius. When a thick wall, closed end vessel is subjected to an internal pressure, q, the hoop stress at any radius, r, can be determined using:

$$\sigma_2 = [q \cdot r_i{}^2 (r_o{}^2 + r^2)]/[r^2 (r_o{}^2 - r_i{}^2)] \tag{4.42}$$

where the maximum hoop stress occurs at $r = r_i$. The axial stress value is given by:

$$\sigma_1 = q \cdot r_i{}^2 /(r_o{}^2 - r_i{}^2) \tag{4.43}$$

The radial stress is given by:

$$\sigma_3 = [q \cdot r_i{}^2 (r_o{}^2 - r^2)]/[r^2 (r_o{}^2 - r_i{}^2)] \tag{4.44}$$

and is a maximum at r_i. The change in r_o due to the internal pressure is given by:

$$\Delta r_o = [q \cdot r_o \cdot r_i{}^2 (2 - v)] / [(E_T(t))(r_o{}^2 - r_i{}^2)] \tag{4.45}$$

Handbook references such as [2] contain an extensive listing of formulas for both thick and thin walled vessels. The concerns expressed earlier regarding the use of the thin wall design equations are equally applicable for thick wall parts subjected to internal pressure.

4.7   Torsion

4.7.1   Introduction

Parts containing beam like sections must provide torsional, rather than bending stiffness, in some applications. The boss cross section shown in Figure 4.65 is an example of a situation where a designer would be concerned with torsional stiffness.

Self threading screws or machine screws / metal inserts are commonly used as a means of assembly for clamshell type enclosures such as an appliance housing. In situations where the screw is overtightened (excessive tightening torque is applied) failure can occur in many ways. Modes of failure include thread stripping (or insert stripping), boss cracking, torsional failure of the boss, or even torsional failure of the screw. Thread stripping is a preferred mode since it offers the potential for repair, using longer or larger

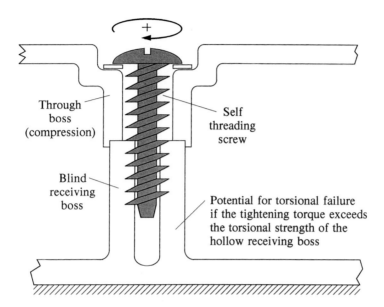

Figure 4.65. The blind self threading screw boss is susceptible to torsional failure if the screw is overtorqued, or if the boss wall is too thin.

diameter screw. The boss that receives the screw must have sufficient torsional rigidity to withstand the applied torque without experiencing torsional failure (i.e. shearing of the hollow cylinder).

4.7.2   Torsion for Circular Bars

Classical formulas can be used to estimate the stresses and angular deflections for regular geometries subject to torsional loading [2,12,24]. The formulas were derived assuming;

- The bar has a straight and uniform cross section
- The bar is solid or concentrically hollow
- The bar is homogeneous and isotropic
- Opposite twisting couples applied to the ends of the bar in planes normal to the axis
- Elastic material behavior

Some of these assumptions are not valid for plastic materials as discussed previously. This is especially true for the assumptions that assume isotropic and elastic material behavior. However, if the appropriate material properties are used (e.g. creep data for long term applications, etc.), the formulas can provide a good estimate of product torsional performance. When the geometry of the part becomes irregular, finite element techniques provide the best means of predicting torsional behavior.

When a bar such as the solid cylindrical rod shown in Figure 4.66 is subjected to a torsional load, the bar twists. The applied torque is transmitted by shear along the length

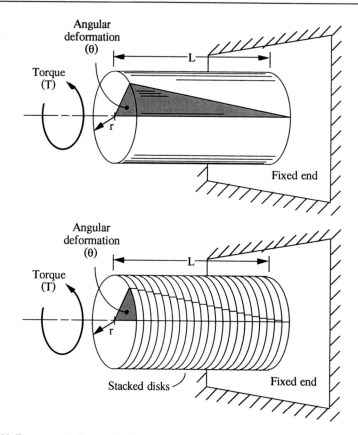

Figure 4.66. Torque applied to a cylindrical bar causes the bar to twist. The applied torque is transmitted by shear along the shaft.

of the shaft. The bar can be thought of as a series of stacked discs, with angular defections that increase with the distance from the plane of attachment. The relative rotation between discs results in a shear stress that increases with the distance from the center of the section (axis of rotation) [2,24].

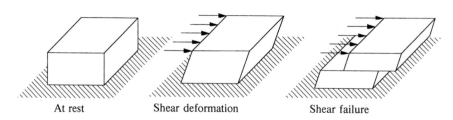

Figure 4.67. Torsional failure occurs when the shear strength of the material has been exceeded.

Material Properties: A circular shaft that has been subjected to a torque experiences failure when the shear strength (or creep rupture shear stress) of the material has been exceeded.   Shear failure occurs when adjacent layers of material actually begin sliding over one another as depicted in Figure 4.67.   Shear stress is simply the ratio of the applied force, F, divided by the shear area, A.

$$\tau = F / A \qquad \text{(4.46)}$$

Ultimate shear stress values for plastic materials are not as widely available as tensile, compressive or flexural strength values.   This is particularly true for long term creep or stress relaxation data.   When shear strength data for a plastic material is not available, the shear strength value can be estimated using the tensile yield strength value for the material [33]:

$$\tau = \sigma_T / (3)^{1/2} \qquad \text{(4.47)}$$

As a more conservative estimate, it is sometimes recommended that the maximum shear stress in a part should not exceed 1/2 the tensile yield stress of the material [12].

Shear modulus, or *modulus of rigidity*, G, is defined as the rate of change of unit shear stress with respect to unit shear strain.   Like tensile, compressive and flexural moduli values, the shear modulus of a polymer is influenced by time, stress level, and environmental factors such as temperature and relative humidity.   When shear modulus data is not available, it can be estimated using:

$$G = E / [2(1 + \nu)] \qquad \text{(4.48)}$$

where ν is Poisson's ratio and E is the modulus of elasticity.   Since many polymers have E values that vary in tension and compression, it is probably best to use the lower of the two modulus values (at the appropriate time and temperature) in Equation 4.48 for additional safety.   The actual modulus of rigidity value should be used in torsional calculations whenever possible.

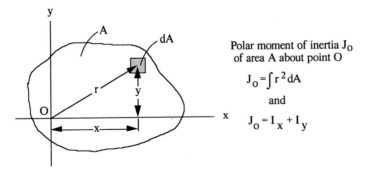

Figure 4.68. The polar moment of inertia of an area about a point is equal to the sum of the moments of inertia about perpendicular axes through that point.

Formulas for Stress and Angular Deflection: The stresses and angular deflections for a bar subjected to a torsional load are influenced by the magnitude of the load, material properties, and the geometry of the bar. In twisting applications, the polar moment of inertia, J, is of great importance [17]. The polar moment of inertia, J, of an area, A, with respect to (or about) a point, O, is given by:

$$J_o = \int r^2 \cdot dA \tag{4.49}$$

where r is the distance from O to dA. The polar moment of inertia about point O can also be determined by summing the moments of inertia (second moment of area) for the x and y axes, where x and y are axes running through O, and are perpendicular to one another.

$$J_o = I_x + I_y \tag{5.50}$$

In most cases, the polar moment of inertia required for torsional calculations is the polar moment about the centroid, c, of the cross section. However, the polar moment of inertia about any other point, O, can be found using:

$$J_o = J_c + A \cdot d^2 \tag{4.51}$$

where A is the cross sectional area, Jc is the polar moment about the centroid, and d is the distance between point O and the centroid, c. For a cylinder of radius, R, the polar moment of inertia about the centroid is:

$$J_c = I_x + I_y = (\pi \cdot R^4/4) + (\pi \cdot R^4/4) = \pi \cdot R^4/2 \tag{4.50}$$

The equations for shear stress, τ, and angular deformation, θ (units of radians), for a cylindrical member of length, L, and radius, R, subjected to a twisting moment, T, are given by Equations 4.52 and 4.53 respectively.

$$\tau = T \cdot r/J \tag{4.52}$$

$$\theta = T \cdot l/J \cdot G \tag{4.53}$$

For a solid cylinder, the maximum shear stress occurs when r = R:

$$\tau_m = T \cdot R/J = 2 \cdot T/\pi \cdot R^3 \tag{4.54}$$

while the maximum angular deformation (i.e. angle of twist) occurs at l = L:

$$\theta_m = T \cdot L/J \cdot G = 2 \cdot T \cdot L/\pi \cdot R^4 \cdot G \tag{4.55}$$

4.7.3   Torsion for Non-Circular Bars

The angular deflection for non-circular bars subjected to a twisting moment can be calculated using the general expression [2,24]:

$$\theta = T \cdot L / K \cdot G \qquad\qquad\qquad (4.56)$$

where K is a factor dependent upon the dimensions of the bar cross section. For circular cross sections, K = J, while for other cross sections, K is less than J.

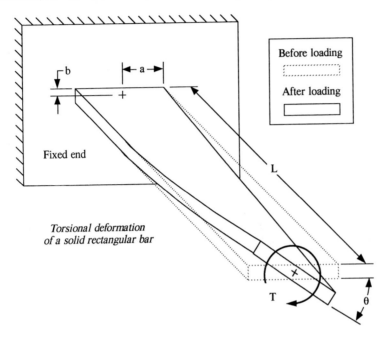

Figure 4.69. Torque applied to the bar causes the bar to twist. The torque is transmitted by shear.

Cross section geometry	Polar moment of inertia (J $_c$)	K	Maximum shear stress
Solid circular cross section 	$\dfrac{\pi}{2} R^4$	$\dfrac{\pi}{2} R^4$	$\dfrac{2\,T}{\pi\,R^3}$ @ r = R
Solid rectangular cross section 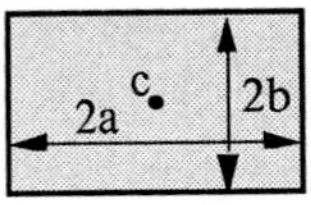	—	$ab^3 \left[\dfrac{16}{3} - 3.36 \dfrac{b}{a} (1 - \dfrac{b^4}{12\,a^4}) \right]$	$\dfrac{T\,(3a + 1.8b)}{8\,a^2\,b^2}$ @ midpoint of longer sides
Hollow circular (annular) cross section 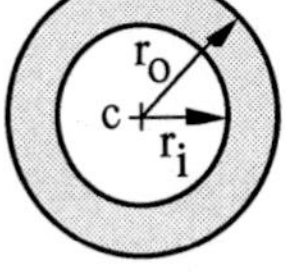	$\dfrac{\pi}{2} (r_o^4 - r_i^4)$	$\dfrac{\pi}{2} (r_o^4 - r_i^4)$	$\dfrac{2\,T\,r_o}{\pi\,(r_o^4 - r_i^4)}$ @ r_o

Figure 4.70. Polar moments of inertia and maximum shear stress values for several cross sections.

Values for K (or J) and maximum shear stress for both cylindrical and rectangular cross sections are given in Figure 4.70. More extensive listings for other cross sectional geometries are available from handbooks [2].

The torsional stiffness of injection molded plastic parts can be greatly improved by adding reinforcing ribs. Both the torsional and bending stiffness of the open box in Figure 4.71a can be greatly improved by adding internal ribbing. Reinforcing ribs laid out in an "X" or "Z" pattern are generally preferred for torsional applications, since they offer improved resistance to angular deflection [34]. The non-appearance surface (underside) of an injection molded part incorporating both conventional cross ribs and bias ribbing is shown in Figure 4.71b. This combination provides good resistance to both torsion and bending. Predicting the twisting behavior for parts having these more complicated geometries is very difficult using classical calculations, and finite element techniques are required.

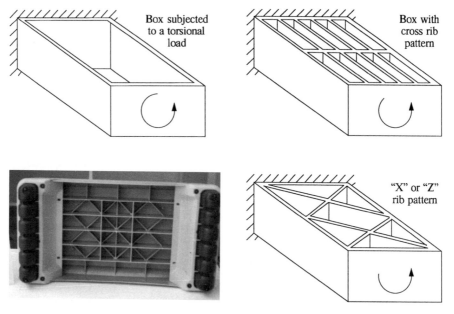

Figure 4.71. (a) Conventional cross ribbing (perpendicular to the sidewalls) have a significant impact on bending stiffness, and modest impact on torsional stiffness. The diagonal or bias ribs offer improved torsional stiffness. (b) The underside of the aerobic stair utilizes both cross and bias ribs to impart bending and torsional stiffness.

Example 4.9 Torsional Strength of a Screw Boss: The parts shown in Figure 4.72 are produced using a polyphenyleneoxide / polystyrene blend, and are assembled using a # 6 BT-25 thread cutting screw. The pilot (receiving) boss has an outside diameter of 0.315 inches and an inside diameter of 0.115 inches. The screw is driven into the boss and tightened to a torque level of 14 inch-lbs. The maximum shear stress can be determined using:

$$\tau_m = 2 \cdot T \cdot r_o / \pi (r_o^4 - r_i^4) \tag{4.57}$$

$$\tau_m = (2)(14)(0.158)/(3.14) [(0.158)^4 - (0.0575)^4] = 2300 \ lbs/inch^2$$

If the tensile yield stress for the polymer blend is listed as 7,800 lbs/inch^2 (at the appropriate strain rate, temperature, etc.), then the maximum design stress in shear for the material can be estimated to be one half the 7,800 value, or 3,900 lb/in^2. While the calculated value is well below the material's estimated maximum design stress in shear, stress concentrations in the region of the screw tip, or at the base of the boss, could result in local stress values that are significantly greater than this nominal shear stress value.

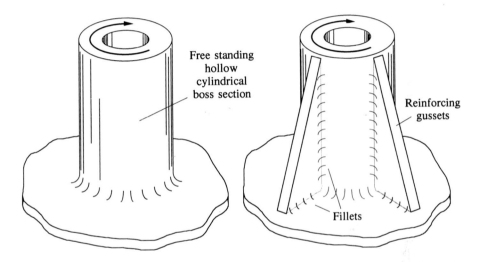

Figure 4.72. Gusset plates are commonly used to increase the bending and torsional stiffness of bosses. The gussets have the added benefit of improving mold filling characteristics by serving as flow leaders.

In many cases, reinforcing gusset plates are added to the exterior surface of the boss, as a means of improving the torsional stiffness of the boss, without increasing the boss wall thickness (and the size of the sink opposite the boss). Gussets provide the added benefit of acting as flow leaders that assist in the filling of the thin walled boss during molding.

4.8   Columns

Beams or slender columns are sometimes used in applications where they are subjected to compressive (end) loads, and therefore compressive stress. While the compressive stress on a column of uniform cross sectional area, A, under a central compressive load, F, is simply:

$$\sigma_c = F / A \qquad (4.58)$$

there is a compressive load above which a sufficiently long, slender column will become unstable and experience large lateral deflections, or buckle. Any slight deviation from straightness or any small lateral forces tend to accelerate this condition of flexural instability. The critical compressive buckling load for a straight column can be estimated using Euler's buckling theory. The theory can be applied to long, slender columns of uniform cross section, where the stiffness of the member, $E \cdot I$, is a constant over the entire column length [1]. The magnitude of the critical buckling load is influenced by the cross sectional geometry of the column, the rigidity or modulus of the polymer, E, the unsupported length of the column, L, and the support or end conditions. Some ideal end conditions are shown in Figure 4.73.

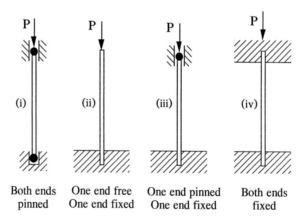

(i)	(ii)	(iii)	(iv)
Both ends pinned	One end free One end fixed	One end pinned One end fixed	Both ends fixed

Figure 4.73. Some ideal conditions of end restraint for long, slender columns subjected to an end load.

The end conditions shown in Figure 4.79 are ideal and are not likely to be realized in practice. Real life end conditions may have partial characteristics of several idealized end conditions [2]. For example, molded in columns, such as table legs, may show some change in slope at the plane of attachment when loaded in compression (due to the flexibility of the plate to which they are attached), and are therefore not truly fixed. This less than ideal degree of fixity will result in lower critical buckling loads than those predicted using a fixed end condition. The lower end (bottom surface) of a table leg is normal to the column axis and bears evenly against the loading surface, and is therefore described as flat ended.

Euler's equation giving the critical compressive load associated with the onset of buckling, F_c, can be written as:

$$F_c = \pi^2 \cdot E \cdot A / (K \cdot L / r)^2 \qquad (4.59)$$

where K is the effective length coefficient determined by the condition of end restraint, E is the bending modulus, A is the cross sectional area, and r is the least radius of gyration. The least radius of gyration can be determined using Equation 4.13 where I is the least moment of inertia about a centroidal axis. The effective length coefficient, K, has values that vary greatly with the condition of end restraint [1]. The modulus value, E, used in the buckling equation should reflect the duration of loading and the environmental conditions anticipated in service (i.e. the lowest viscoelastic modulus for safety). A more detailed description of the buckling behavior of beams and plates is given by Heger [1].

4.9   Dynamic Loads

4.9.1   Introduction

Plastic components used in appliance, automotive or other durable good applications are commonly subjected to dynamic loads involving vibration, impact, or fatigue loading. Dynamic loads, such as sinusoidal or random structural vibrations, can cause deflections and stresses that are significantly greater than those associated with static loading. The stresses and deflections associated with dynamic loading are influenced by factors such as the rate of loading, the damping characteristics of the material (viscous characteristics) and the geometry of the structure. Dynamic design is far more complex than design for static loading. In the case of vibration loading, very large stresses and deflections can result if the frequency of a pulsating load is close to the natural frequency of the structure. Parts subjected to loads of this type must have resonant frequencies out of the input frequency range. Vibration isolators are also recommended whenever possible to reduce the deflection peaks that occur at the resonances [1,39]. While dynamic design is beyond the scope of this basic text, it is worth reviewing some general concepts associated with fatigue and impact loading.

4.9.2 Fatigue Loading

Introduction: Plastic parts are commonly used in applications where loads are applied and removed periodically. The park bench shown in Figure 4.40 is an example of a product that is subjected to intermittent bending loads. The seat member of the bench is loaded / unloaded periodically (randomly) in a manner that produces a one directional square wave loading pattern. The loading function is described as intermittent rather than fatigue, since (i) the random frequency of loading is extremely low (in the range of 3 x 10^{-4} Hz) and (ii) once the seat is loaded, the load remains essentially constant (static loading). The very low frequency of loading is an indication that factors such as hysteresis heating (associated with intermolecular friction during loading and unloading) are not likely to be significant since there are sufficient time periods available for conductive / convective heat transfer (dissipation) to occur between loading cycles.

Other plastic products, such as a reciprocating machinery part, a wheel, or a gear, are subjected to periodic loading at higher frequencies. For example, the gear shown in Figure 4.75 is subjected to both a continuous rotational load and local bending loads on the gear teeth.

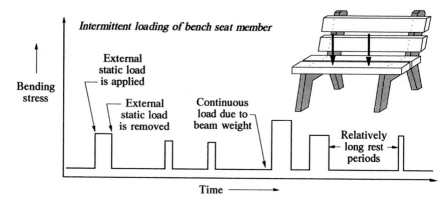

Figure 4.74. Intermittent, random, low frequency loading of park bench seat members.

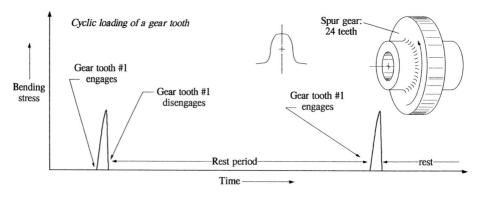

Figure 4.75. Periodic (cyclic) loading of a spur gear tooth.

Each gear tooth engages / disengages once for each revolution. Unlike the example for the park bench, the frequency of loading for the gear tooth is significantly greater. For example, a gear with 24 teeth, rotating at 60 RPM will experience a bending load every 0.4 second or at a loading frequency of 2.5 Hz. In addition, the load changes continuously during the 0.017 second loading period. Dynamic loads result in heat generation due to viscous dissipation. If the gear is produced from a polymer that exhibits significant amounts of surface frictional heating and internal viscous heating, and the rest period between loads is not sufficient for the temperature of the part to reach ambient conditions (due to conductive / convective heat transfer), the parts will operate at elevated temperatures. The problem of viscous dissipation is accelerated at high temperatures [6,37,38]. A ratio of loading period to rest period of 1/10 is commonly recommended [38].

This loading function is predictable in the case of the gear. However, in other applications, such as a part subjected to wind gust loads, the loading function is unpredictable. In most cases, hysteresis heating is not desirable. Machinery parts associated with power transmission, such as a gear, are generally designed and produced using materials that minimize the amount of energy converted to heat, in order to improve the efficiency of energy transfer, and improve the service life of the components. In other cases, such as in vibration damping applications, parts are purposely produced using energy absorbing materials, such as "viscous" thermosetting or a thermoplastic elastomers that dampen vibrations. In either case, the parts must be designed so that the local or bulk temperature rise is not excessive. In the case of the gear tooth, heating can be minimized by reducing both frictional heating and viscous heating. Local heat build up due to frictional effects can be minimized by using materials with good surface lubricity, while viscous heating can be minimized if lower loss, more elastic materials are used. In many cases, the use of filled or reinforced polymers (particularly those fillers that improve lubricity) can increase the power transmission capabilities and life of a gear assembly by increasing the stiffness of the part, and by increasing the thermal conductivity of the material [38]. Any variable that promotes heat transfer from the relatively hot dynamically loaded plastic part, to adjacent components or the surroundings tends to promote efficiency and extend the service life of the part. Increasing the diameter of a gear can reduce operating temperature by increasing the rest period between loading cycles.

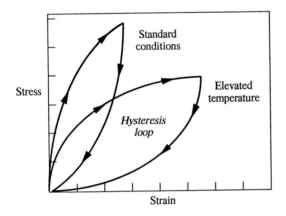

Figure 4.76. The area of a hysteresis loop is indicative of viscous energy dissipation.

Part wall thickness is also an important factor in dynamic design. Thick wall sections are commonly used to limit stress values for static loading applications, however, walls must be kept relatively thin for parts subjected to fatigue loading as shown in Figure 4.77. Part designs that have thin wall sections, and that utilize design features such as ribs or fins, can reduce operating temperatures by increasing the surface area to volume ratio of the part, while maintaining the required stiffness. Thick walls that trap heat are to be avoided whenever possible in dynamic applications for this reason, and because of the potential for internal shrinkage stresses or voids. The molding or processing conditions that are used to produce parts subjected to fatigue loads can also have a very significant impact on fatigue life. For example, residual stresses, especially those near the surface of the molding, can greatly influence the cycles to failure. Primary processing variables, or secondary processing (such as thermal treatment or tempering) that promote residual compressive stresses towards the surface of the molding have been shown to be beneficial for some polymers, while residual tensile stresses have the opposite effect [40].

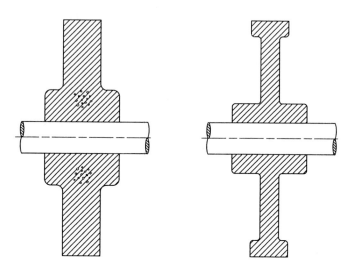

Figure 4.77. Parts subjected to fatigue loads must be designed with relatively thin wall sections to promote heat transfer and minimize the potential for shrinkage stress or voids.

Fatigue Testing: Plastic parts that are subjected to cyclic loads will fail at stresses below their static yield strength value. The cumulative effects of multiple loading cycles can cause fatigue failure at stress levels that are far below the static rupture stress value. The reduction in failure stress is linked to factors such as hysteresis, morphological changes, microvoid and craze formation. As a result, the fatigue characteristics of a part are influenced by both the material selection and the part design. Fatigue loading will decrease the time to failure for a given stress level (compared to static loading) and may result in a shift from ductile to brittle failure [41].

The fatigue characteristics of a plastic material can be determined by performing a stress or deflection controlled dynamic fatigue test. Fatigue tests are run by subjecting a series of test specimens to cyclic loading (or imposed cyclic deflection), and determining the relationship between applied stress (or imposed strain) and the number of testing cycles to failure. The failure stress, in tension, bending, compression or shear, is plotted as a function of the number of cycles on either a log-log or a semi-log scale. The asymptotic stress at very long time is usually taken as the *Fatigue Endurance Limit* of the material (i.e. a stress amplitude below which fatigue failure will not occur). The curve is known as an S/N curve (S = failure stress, N = number of cycles).

Load inputs or loading functions are typically sinusoidal in nature, however, square wave, sawtooth or other loading functions are also common. It is important that fatigue tests are run at conditions that are representative of the end-use application. Various types of loading functions are used in fatigue testing. The load input can be one directional, where the stress varies from a minimum value, typically zero, to a maximum

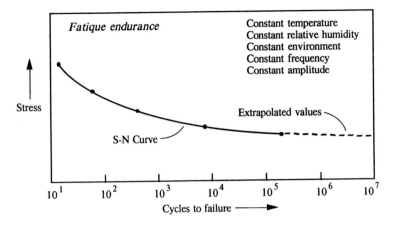

Figure 4.78. Typical S/N curve for a plastic material.

value. In other cases, parts are subjected to a reversing stress, where loads alternate from tension to compression. Completely reversing tensile and compressive loading cycles are considered to be the most severe loading conditions [37]. The results of a fatigue test are in fact influenced by a very large number of variables above and beyond the conditions of loading. Sample geometry and frequency of testing are extremely important variables, since they both have a very large effect on the amount of hysteretic heat build-up. At high frequencies, the rate of heat generation can be greater than the rate of heat dissipation. This results in a softening of the polymer, changes in morphology, and a reduction in the ability to support the stress. The frequencies that are commonly used to evaluate the fatigue properties of plastic materials range from 1 up to 30 Hz [1,36]. Accelerated tests run at frequencies equal to (or possibly greater than) 30 Hz (1,800 cycles / minute) are commonly used with metals but are generally not suitable for plastic materials. Tests run at a few cycles per second (e.g. at frequencies in the range of 1 Hz)

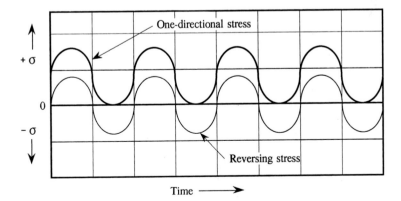

Figure 4.79. The dynamic loading function has a significant impact on the fatigue life of a plastic part. For example, cyclic stresses can be one-directional or reversing.

are best since excessive heat build-up is avoided, however, as the frequency of testing decreases, the costs and time associated with the testing procedure increase. Ideally, the frequency used in testing should be no less than that associated with the application. Test sample geometry should also be given a great deal of consideration. Factors such as specimen purity, shrinkage voids, surface area to volume ratio, surface finish, residual surface stresses, and orientation are major concerns. In theory, the use of coolants seems appropriate for accelerated tests, however, environmental factors have a very large influence on fatigue properties. For example, water has been shown to reduce the fatigue strength of polycarbonate by as much as 30% [15].

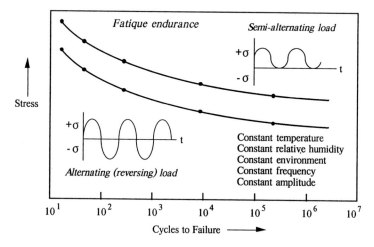

Figure 4.80. The fatigue behavior of a plastic material is influenced by the type of loading function and a number of other variables.

Guidelines that can be followed when designing plastic parts for applications involving fatigue include [36,37]:

- Design at low stress level
- Reduce frequency of loading whenever possible
- Improve heat transfer
    - avoid thick wall sections
    - use ribs / cooling fins
    - use forced air circulation
- Materials with low hysteresis
- Materials with high thermal conductivity
- Materials with high temperature resistance
- Materials with good surface lubricity

Fatigue testing is useful in ranking materials and qualitatively influencing design, however, the use of fatigue data in design calculation is of limited value. FEA techniques can provide insight into fatigue performance, however, the results are likely to be in error if the geometries, loading conditions and environments used during property testing are not truly representative of those encountered in the end-use application [12,15,36]. As a result, large factors of safety are typically used in fatigue applications (although thick wall sections should be avoided). There is no substitute for an extensive, experimental product evaluation, especially in applications involving fatigue loads [38].

4.9.3 Impact Loading

The classical equations used to evaluate the stresses and deflections for beams, plates and shells are applicable only in situations where the loads are static, or are applied very gradually. However, in many cases the external loads are applied rapidly (i.e. over a short duration of time) and the loading case is more appropriately described as impact or abrupt impulse loading.

If an item, such as a book, was dropped onto the tray shown in Figure 4.55, the resultant stresses and deflections would be momentarily greater than those associated with static loading conditions. The momentary increase in stress or deflection is associated with the kinetic energy of the fall, which must be dampened by hysteresis. If the material used to produce the part has elastic characteristics (as most plastic materials do at a high rate of loading) then the part will recover to the state of stress and deflection associated with static loading (i.e. the book resting on the shelf). However, when the magnitude of the impact load exceeds a critical value, failure will occur. Impact resistance of a component can be considered to be the relative susceptibility of the component to failure due to stresses applied at high rates [35]. Impact is a particular concern for plastic parts used at low temperatures (e.g. when the temperature drops below their glass transition temperature of the polymer).

Theoretical estimations of the stresses, strains and deflections for plastic parts subjected to impact loading are extremely complex and require dynamic analysis / dynamic test data. Crude estimates can be obtained using classical formulas for stress and strain modified for impact loading, however, it is unlikely that impact stresses or deflections can be calculated accurately using simple approximations. The values calculated using these approximate formulas may appear to be unreasonably high, when compared to the stress-strain behavior of the material generated under standard conditions [2,12,24]. However, the stress-strain behavior of a plastic material varies significantly with rate of strain as shown in Figure 4.15. Methods for assessing the impact resistance of plastic materials vary, and unfortunately, the test data is not always readily available. Further complications arise from the fact that the deformation rate may not be constant through the part being deformed. It is also unlikely that the stress distribution throughout a part subjected to a dynamic impact load are equivalent to the stress distribution for a static load. This is particularly true in situations where the body impacting the part makes uneven contact (e.g. the book dropped on the tray may make initial contact on one edge) [2].

It is difficult to design parts subjected to impact loading. The effects due to stress concentrations, such as corners, holes and the like, are even more significant for parts subjected to impact loading. The materials used to produce the part must have sufficient impact resistance at the strain rates associated with the end-use application. Above all, it is essential that parts slated for applications involving impact or impulse loading undergo thorough product testing under impact conditions representative of those anticipated in service. Again, there is no suitable substitute for thorough end-use product evaluation for plastic parts used in applications involving dynamic loads [12,24]. A rough approximation of the stresses associated with impact loading can be obtained using:

$$y_i/y_s = \sigma_i/\sigma_s = V/(g \cdot y_s)^{1/2} \qquad (4.60)$$

where V is the velocity of impact, and g is the acceleration of gravity. The subscript i refers to impact related deflection or stress values, while the subscript s refers to the static deflection or stress values.

Example 4.10   Impact Loading of a Round Plate: Consider the example of a 1.0 lb weight, dropped onto the center of the empty container shown in Figure 4.51 from a height, Z, of 12 inches.

Solid flat circular plate • Constant thickness • Uniform load over central circular area • Fixed edges

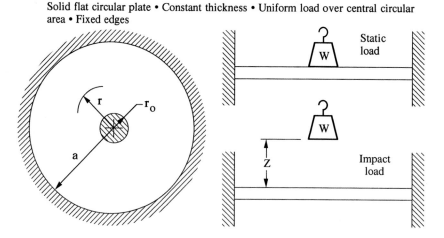

Figure 4.81. The momentary stresses and deflections due to an impact load are significantly greater than the corresponding static values.

The base of the bucket is a circular plate with fixed edges. If the weight, W, is small relative to the diameter of the circular plate and the loading occurs over a small central area, then the equation for maximum deflection (@ r = 0) under static conditions, y_s, is:

$$y_s = -[W \cdot a^2 (3+v)]/[16 \cdot \pi \cdot D(1+v)] \qquad (4.61)$$

where v is Poisson's ratio and D is the plate constant given by:

$$D = E \cdot t^3/[12(1-v^2)] \qquad (4.62)$$

Using a short term modulus value E of 300,000 lbs/inch^2, a Poisson's ratio value of 0.35, and a plate thickness, t, of 0.125 inch, then the plate constant is:

$$D = (300,000)(0.125)^3 / [(12)(1 - 0.35^2)] = 55.6 \text{ lb-inch.} \tag{4.62}$$

The maximum static deflection is:

$$y_s = -[(1.0)(5)^2(3 + 0.35)]/[(16)(3.14)(55.6)(1 + 0.35)] = -0.022 \text{ inch} \tag{4.61}$$

The velocity at the instant of impact, V, due to the drop from a height, Z, of 12 inches (assuming a zero initial velocity) is:

$$V = V_0 - (2 \cdot g \cdot h)^{1/2} \tag{4.63}$$

$$V = 0 - [(2)(386)(12)]^{1/2} = -96.2 \text{ inch/second}$$

The deflection at impact is:

$$y_i = y_s \cdot V/(g \cdot y_s)^{1/2} \tag{4.60}$$

$$y_i = -(0.022)(96.2)/[(386)(0.022)]^{1/2}$$

This maximum impact related deflection seems unreasonably high, however, the magnitude of the difference in static and impact deflection or stress emphasizes the significance of impact loading, and the importance of using generous radii and minimizing stress concentration areas for parts subjected to impact loading. Sharp radii on ribs, bosses, gussets, flanges, sharp corners, wall transitions should be eliminated. Surface imperfections or even texturing on surfaces subjected to high tensile stress could act as stress concentration [36]. Careful placement of weld lines and a reduction in residual stress and orientation are also important factors for parts subjected to impact loads. It is also useful to integrate energy absorbent components, such as flexible members, vibration dampening mounts, gaskets, or elastomeric adhesives, into products subjected to impact loading whenever possible. It should also be noted that stress-strain data for plastic materials is typically generated at low testing rates, while the instantaneous velocity of an object dropped from a height of just 12 inches is 96 inches/second or 1,152 inches/minute (at a rate that may be thousands of times greater). In order to obtain a better estimate of the products behavior, the rate / temperature / relative humidity dependent impact characteristics of the polymer must be determined using high speed impact testing equipment. Tests should be run over the range of temperatures / rates that relate (as closely as possible) to the end-use application. Materials that appear ductile at room temperature or at low strain rates, may fracture in a brittle fashion at lower temperatures or higher strain rates [35]. While this material data is useful for materials selection and initial design calculations, there is no substitute for realistic prototype testing for applications where impact loading is anticipated.

4.10 References

1. *Structural Plastics Design Manual*, American Society of Civil Engineers, ASCE Manual and Report on Engineering Practice No. 63, April (1982).

2. Roark, R. and Young, W., *Formulas for Stress & Strain*, 5th ed., McGraw Hill, NY (1975).
3. Crate, J., *Plastics Design Forum*, **9** (4), 77 (1984).
4. Lee, C., Dubin, A., Elmer, D., *SPE Annual Technical Conference*, **37**, 912 (1987).
5. Trantina, G., Minnichelli, M, *SPE Annual Technical Conference*, **37**, 438 (1987).
6. Levy, S. and DuBois, J., *Plastics Product Design Engineering Handbook*, 2nd ed., Chapman and Hall, NY (1984).
7. Rolfe, S., and Barsom, J., *Fracture & Fatigue Control in Structures, Applications in Fracture Mechanics*, Prentice Hall, Englewood Cliffs, NJ (1977).
8. Technical Bulletin, Lelij, J., *Engineering Design*, E.I. DuPont de Nemours & Co., Wilmington, DE (1991).
9. Technical Bulletin, "*Cabibre Polycarbonate Design Manual*", Dow Chemical Company, Midland, MI (1988).
10. Mehta, K., *SPE Annual Technical Conference*, **38**, 2058 (1992).
11. Technical Bulletin, Marks, F., *Engineering Design*, E.I. DuPont de Nemours & Co., Wilmington, DE (1989).
12. Technical Bulletin, "*Designing with Plastics* ", Hoechst Celanese, Chatham, NJ (1989).
13. Aklonis, J., MacKnight, W., and Shen, M., *Introduction to Polymer Viscoelasticity*, Wiley Interscience, NY (1972).
14. Throne, J., and Progelhof, R., "Creep and Stress Relaxation" in *Engineered Materials Handbook Vol 2*, ASM, Metals Park, OH (1988).
15. Technical Bulletin, "*Polycarbonate Design Manual* ", Mobay Corporation, Pittsburgh, PA.
16. Technical Bulletin, "*Lexan Design Guide* ", General Electric Company Pittsfield, MA.
17. Beer, F. and Johnson, E., *Mechanics for Engineers*, McGraw Hill, NY (1976).
18. Anonymous, *Plastics Design Forum*, **15** (6), 42 (1990).
19. Allied Signal Corporation, Morristown, NJ.
20. Technical Bulletin, "*Ultem Design Guide*", General Electric Company Pittsfield, MA.
21. Technical Bulletin, "*Delrin Acetal, Module III* ", E.I. DuPont de Nemours & Co., Wilmington, DE.
22. Technical Bulletin, "*Noryl Design Guide* ", General Electric Company Pittsfield, MA.
23. Technical Bulletin, "*Valox Design Guide* ", General Electric Company Pittsfield, MA.
24. Technical Bulletin, "*Engineering Materials Design Guide* ", General Electric Company, Pittsfield, MA.
25. Throne, J., and Progelhof, R., *SPE Annual Technical Conference*, **35**, 1637 (1989).
26. Nakayama, K., Mikio, K., and Motoichi, Y., *SPE Annual Technical Conference*, **32**, 690 (1982).
27. Lifshey, A., *Plastics Design Forum*, **5** (2), 59 (1980).
28. Campo, E. A., *Plastics Design Forum*, **7** (6), 55 (1982).
29. Stuttgart, U., *Kunststoffe*, **72** (12), 24 (1982).
30. Menges, G. and Mohren, P., *How to Make Injection Molds*, Hanser, NY (1986).
31. Technical Bulletin, Tuschak, P., *Engineering Design*, E.I. DuPont de Nemours & Co., Wilmington, DE.
32. Gebler, H. and Racke, H., *Kunststoffe*, **72** (1), 17 (1982).
33. Anonymous, *Plastics Design Forum*, **1** (5), 25 (1976).
34. Technical Bulletin, Weckman, R., *Engineering Design*, E.I. DuPont de Nemours & Co., Wilmington, DE (1988).
35. Nimmer, R., "Impact Loading" in *Engineered Materials Handbook, Vol 2*, ASM, Metals Park, OH (1988).
36. Technical Bulletin, Hawley, J., *Design Success Through Solution Engineering*, Eastman Chemical Performance Plastics.
37. Levy, S., *Plastics Design Forum*, **2** (5) 42 (1977).
38. Yelle, H., and Estabrook, F., "Fatigue Loading" in *Engineered Materials Handbook, Vol 2*, ASM, Metals Park, OH (1988).

39. Technical Bulletin, Tuschak, P., *Engineering Design*, E.I. DuPont de Nemours & Co., Wilmington, DE (1989).
40. Hornberger, L. and DeVries, K, *SPE Annual Technical Conference*, 32, 672 (1986).
41. Powell, P., *Engineering with Polymers*, Chapman and Hall, NY (1983).

5 Prototyping and Experimental Stress Analysis

5.1 Prototyping Plastic Parts

It is generally necessary to develop both models and prototype parts during the plastics product development process. The prototyping stage of product development is crucial to the success of a project, yet this aspect of development is often hurried through or underfunded. Prototype parts are used for communications, engineering studies, market studies / promotions, to evaluate product manufacturability / assembly characteristics, and to verify CAD model or print accuracy. Regardless of the medium chosen, prototyping techniques generate physical models that act as a primary means of communication between Product Marketing, Product Engineering, Tooling and Product Manufacturing groups. The use of a prototype to describe the function, size, shape, feel and look of a part inevitably leads to a more productive environment and a higher degree of interaction between the members of the product design team.

5.1.1 Introduction

Prototype parts have been characterized as being either (i) facsimile prototypes, which can serve both marketing and perhaps limited engineering functions, or (ii) processing prototypes, (i.e. those produced using prototype injection molds or tools), which are used to evaluate both the molding process and the molded part properties, before production tooling is fully committed [1,2]. It is likely that at least one, or perhaps a series of facsimile prototypes (i.e form and limited fit / function prototype parts) would have been made before one commits to the cost of preproduction or prototype tooling. The latter step can add significant time and initial cost to the process of product development. However, this step is necessary when working with new and unfamiliar materials, complex product geometries, structural parts, or tighter tolerance applications, since the *function* and *fit* of a molded plastic product are strongly influenced by the tool design and the manufacturing / injection molding conditions. Preproduction tool trial results allow the mold designer to fine tune the production mold design, and provide the design team with a potentially large number of nearly real life prototype parts, which may be required for marketing or engineering studies. It is important to note here that the use of computer aided process simulation software for injection molding has reduced the need for prototype tooling to a significant degree. Filling, cooling, shrinkage and warpage analysis packages are providing answers that were previously available only through actual molding trials [3]. A well designed simulation study will provide information on weld locations and potential part weaknesses, possible gas traps, part warpage or internal (molding) stress levels as described in Chapter 2. The results obtained using this approach are of course simulated, and are often used in concert with prototype tooling to optimize the design of the process and product. The simulation packages, at a minimum, reduce the need for major production tool modifications.

There are literally dozens of methods that can be used to produce prototype plastic parts or assemblies. The method(s) that is best for a given application depends on the quantity of prototype parts required, the size of the parts, the budget and time available, and perhaps most importantly, on how true to life the prototype must be in terms of its engineering functions. Common plastic prototype part production techniques include;

- Hand fabrication and machining of prototypes
- Photo polymerization prototyping
- Laser sintering
- Automated filament extrusion
- Laminated object manufacturing
- Polymer casting
- Molding prototypes using die cast tooling
- Molding prototypes using soft tooling
- Molding prototypes using pre-production tooling
- Structural foam prototyping

Virtually any prototyping technique can be used to produce a part that is esthetically pleasing, however, only pre-production or prototype molding techniques provide true to life information on product performance, moldability and dimensional tolerances. The chemical, mechanical, electrical, thermal and dimensional characteristics of molded plastic parts are influenced by both the primary and secondary processing operations, indicating that product performance should ideally be evaluated using the production material formulation and the primary / secondary operations to be used in production. At some point, the costs and time associated with prototype development work of this type can exceed realistic levels, and one must generally rely on simulations or less realistic prototyping methods. The safety factors used in design are directly influenced by the confidence the designer has in the prototyping and experimental test methods that have been used over the course of the product development cycle.

5.1.2   Machined and Fabricated Plastic Prototypes

Conventional machining operations such as drilling, sawing, milling or turning, and to a lesser extent grinding, are commonly used to produce prototype plastic parts. Cast, laminated or extruded plastic rod, sheet, or bar stock (i.e. semi-finished goods) can be machined to produce a plastic part or component. In many cases, these plastic parts are assembled, bonded, or in some way merged with other plastic, wood, or metal parts before they are decorated and finished to produce a final product assembly [1, 4-6].

Machined plastic prototypes can be produced to high degrees of accuracy (accuracy as good as ±0.025 mm can be achieved) provided one follows proper machining practices for plastic materials [1]. Suggested machining practices for various plastic materials are given in Table 5.1 [7]. Several general concepts should also be taken into consideration when machining plastic materials since the machining characteristics of plastic materials are very different than those of metallic materials. Some of these considerations include;

- Plastics are good insulators, and the work pieces can become hot during machining. The hot part's dimensions can be significantly different from the final equilibrium values, since many plastics have high thermal expansion coefficients. Localized heat causes expansion in the cutting area and can result in overcuts, undercuts, and even degradation.

Figure 5.1. Semi-finished thermoplastic rod and sheet stock serve as the raw material for machined plastic prototypes.

Figure 5.2. CNC machining of prototype plastic parts.

Table 5.1. Machining Variables for some Common Thermoplastics

Material	Variable	Sawing (Circular)	Sawing (Band)	Lathe (Turn)	Lathe (Cutoff)	Drilling	Milling	Reaming
Acetals	Speed (sfpm)	4000-6000	600-2000	450-600	600	300-600	1000-3000	350-450
	Feed (in/rev)	Fast,smooth	Fast,smooth	0.0045-0.010	0.003-0.004	0.004-0.015	0.004-0.016	0.0055-0.015
	Tool	HSS,carbide	HSS	HSS,carbide	HSS,carbide	HSS,carbide	HSS,carbide	HSS,carbide
	Clearance(deg)	20 to 30		10 to 25	10 to 25	10 to 25	10 to 20	
	Rake (deg)	0	0 to 15 (positve)	0 to 5	0 to 15 (positive)	0 to 10 (positive)	0 to 5 (negative)	0 to 10 (positive)
	Point (deg)					90 to 118		
	Cooling	Dry, air jet vapor	Dry air jet	Dry, air jet, vapor	Dry, air jet, vapor	Dry, air jet, vapor	Dry, air jet, vapor	Dry, air jet, vapor
Acrylics	Speed(sfpm)	8000-12000	8000-12000	300-600	450-500	200-400	300-600	250-400
	Feed (in/rev)	Fast,smooth	Fast,smooth	0.003-0.008	0.003-0.004	Slow,steady	0.003-0.010	0.006-0.012
	Tool	HSS,carbide	HSS	HSS,carbide	HSS,carbide	HSS,carbide	HSS,carbide	HSS,carbide
	Clearance (deg)	10 to 20		10 to 20	10 to 20	12 to 15	15	
	Rake (deg)	0 to 10 (positive)	0 to 10 (positive)	0 to 5	0 to 15 (negative)	0 to 5 (negative)	0 to 5 (negative)	0 to 10 (negative)
	Point (deg)					118		
	Cooling	Dry, air jet, vapor	Dry, air jet, vapor	Dry, air jet, vapor	Dry, air jet water solution	Dry, air jet, vapor	Dry, air jet, vapor	Dry, air jet, vapor
Fluoro-plastics	Speed(sfpm)	8000-12000	5000-7000	400-700	425-475	200-500	1000-3000	300-600
	Feed(in/rev)	Fast,smooth	Fast,smooth	0.002-0.010	0.003-0.004	0.002-0.010	0.004-0.016	0.006-0.015
	Tool	HSS,carbide	HSS	HSS,carbide	HSS,carbide	HSS,carbide	HSS,carbide	HSS,carbide
	Clearance(deg)	20 to 30		15 to 30	10 to 25	20	7 to 15	10 to 20
	Rake(deg)	0 to 5 (positive)	0 to 10 (positive)	0 to 5	3 to 15 (positive)	0 to 10 (negative)	3 to 15 (positive)	0 to 10 (negative)
	Point (deg)					90 to 118		
	Cooling	Dry, air jet, vapor	Dry, air jet	Dry, air jet, vapor	Dry, air jet, vapor	Dry, air jet, vapor	Dry, air jet, vapor	Dry, air jet, vapor
Nylons	Speed(sfpm)	4000-6000	4000-6000	500-700	700	180-450	1000-3000	300-450
	Feed(in/rev)	Fast,smooth	Fast,smooth	0.002-0.016	0.002-0.016	0.004-0.015	0.004-0.016	0.005-0.015
	Tool	HSS,carbide	HSS	HSS,carbide	HSS,carbide	HSS,carbide	HSS,carbide	HSS,carbide
	Clearance(deg)	20 to 30		5 to 10	7 to 15	10 to 15	7 to 15	
	Rake (deg)	15 (positive)	0 to 15 (positive)	0 to 5	0 to 5 (positive)	0 to 5 (positive)	0 to 5 (negative)	0 to 10 (positive)
	Point(deg)					90 to 110 (under 1/2") 118 over 1/2"		
	Cooling	Dry, air jet, vapor	Dry, air jet	Dry, air jet, vapor	Dry, air jet, vapor	Dry, air jet, vapor	Dry, air jet, vapor	Dry, air jet, vapor
Poly-olefins	Speed (sfpm)	1650-5000	3900-5000	600-800	425-475	200-600	1000-3000	280-600
	Feed (in/rev)	Fast,smooth	Fast,smooth	0.0015-0.025	0.003-0.004	0.004-0.020	0.06-0.020	0.006-0.012
	Tool	HSS,carbide	HSS,carbide	HSS,carbide	HSS,carbide	HSS,carbide	HSS,carbide	HSS,carbide
	Clearance(deg)	15		15 to 25	15 to 25	10 to 20	10 to 20	10 to 20
	Rake (deg)	0 to 8 (positive)	0 to 10 (positive)	0 to 15	3 to 15 (positive)	0 to 5 (positive)	0 to 10 (positive)	0 to 10 (negative)
	Point (deg)					90 to 118		
	Cooling	Dry, air jet, vapor	Dry, air jet, vapor	Dry, air jet, vapor	Dry, air jet, vapor	Dry, air jet, vapor	Dry, air jet, vapor	Dry, air jet, vapor

This information is designed as a guideline and is not to be construed as absolute. Because of the variety of work and diversity of finishes required, it may be necessary to depart from the suggestions in the table.

• It can also be good practice to stress relieve the blank or the workpiece at an intermediate stage of machining to relieve any internal extrusion or machining related stresses which could result in part dimensional changes over time or at elevated temperature.

• Heat generated in the workpiece does not dissipate through the piece as quickly as it would with metals, and part temperatures can reach the softening point of the material. However, the use of aggressive coolants should be avoided since they could result in stress cracking with some polymers. Air jets, water mist or spray, water / soap solutions, or water soluble oils may be used cautiously (parts should be examined for evidence of stress cracking). Compressed air cooling offers the additional advantage of avoiding the need for part cleaning after machining.

• It is important to avoid high local stresses and deformation of the workpiece caused by part fixturing and clamping since many plastic materials are relatively soft, while others can be brittle. In some cases, custom fixtures may need to be machined in order to support the plastic part during the machining operation. Double sided tape is sometimes used to fixture the plastic stock.

• Regular high speed tools with sharp cutting edges are acceptable for short runs, however, wide flute tungsten carbide or diamond bit tools are recommended for longer runs. Tools should be kept extremely sharp and have appropriate cutting clearances. All contact surfaces should be highly polished.

Only a limited number of types or grades of plastic materials (perhaps only several dozen) are available in a form that is suitable for machining. Generic groups of materials that are widely available in rod or bar stock include acetals, nylons, flexible and rigid PVC, polycarbonate, ABS, fluoropolymers, and some higher temperature, higher modulus materials such as polyimide and reinforced phenolic laminates. Unfortunately, prototype parts machined from these materials provide no information on processing (i.e. molding) effects. While the machined parts may be geometrically equivalent, they may not perform in the same manner as the production part [4,5].

The properties of the machined parts are most likely different than their molded counterparts, even when they are made using the same base polymer, since the additives, molecular weights, morphology, processing stresses and orientation levels in the machined part will not be equivalent to those of the molded part. In certain instances, it may be possible to machine or fabricate prototype parts using injection or compression molded plaques produced from the production polymer. While this is a step in the right direction, orientation levels, weld lines, surface characteristics, and other processing related effects will not be equivalent to those of molded prototypes [5]. It suffices to say that the choice of material for the machined prototype is critical and should reflect, as closely as possible, the properties of the polymer to be used in production, however, even then, the results of any test may be misleading since processing related effects are not considered.

Machined prototypes may or may not be expensive depending on the complexity, quality, and quantity required. In some instances, such as when the model will serve as the pattern for a casting mold, only one prototype is required, and machining is a likely candidate process. For simple parts, it may be less expensive to machine even hundreds of units before reaching the breakeven cost for an acceptable quality prototype tool, while

Figure 5.3. (left) Machined plastic parts for a prototype drive assembly, and (right) prosthetic part machined from plastic stock.

more complex parts may break even at fewer than a dozen parts. Numerical control machining equipment and CAD techniques help reduce the labor costs associated with higher production runs or for parts having complicated geometry, such as the prototype prosthetic part shown in Figure 5.3. A significant amount of set-up, fixturing, and hand finishing / decorating labor may still be required for each individual part, even when automated machining equipment is used. The conventional method of producing prototype plastic parts by machining dimensional plastic stock remains a widely used technique for the production of one or more facsimile prototype parts. The technique offers versatility and utilizes raw materials and conventional machining equipment that are readily available.

5.1.3   Some Rapid Prototyping Technologies

Several new technologies are emerging in the area of prototype plastic part manufacturing. These so called *Rapid Prototyping Technologies* are attractive since they link CAD part geometries directly with the prototype part production equipment. These new prototyping methods have also been described as *Desktop Manufacturing, Solid Object Manufacturing, Solid Imaging, Free-Form Manufacturing or Automated Fabrication.* The rapid prototyping techniques can produce prototype plastic parts or models in a matter of hours. These processes use a variety of different technologies for part production, however, each of these processes have several fundamental concepts in common:

- Defining the part geometry on a CAD system (solid model)
- Slicing the geometric model into discrete 2D slices
- Production of a physical 3D model of product, layer by layer

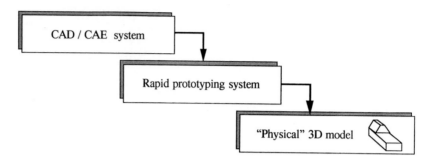

Figure 5.4. Flow chart for rapid prototyping technologies.

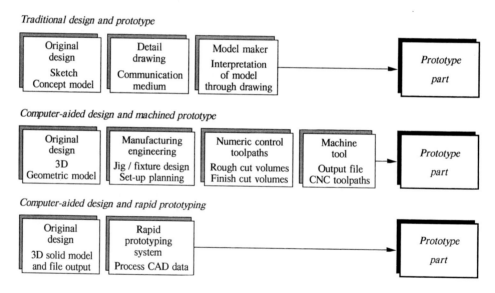

Figure 5.5. Comparison of the procedures associated with conventional model making, computer aided machining of prototypes and rapid prototyping techniques.

These prototyping methods can bring an extremely complex design to life as a conceptual facsimile prototype in a relatively short period of time. The rapid prototyping technologies eliminate the potential for misinterpretation (by the model maker), and eliminate the tool selection / set-up planning, and the fixturing steps necessary in conventional manual or CNC machining operations. Models can be produced in a matter of hours, providing a valuable communication link for concurrent product engineering. The rapid prototype models can also serve as the pattern for other plastic part prototyping techniques that may be used to provide larger part quantities or more realistic prototype parts. Rapid prototype parts can also serve as the pattern for an investment or lost wax type metal casting operation (processes which can be used for the production of cast metal cavity and core inserts).

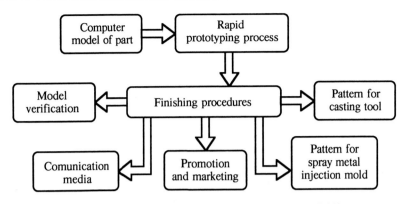

Figure 5.6. Both machined and rapid prototype parts can be used in a variety of different ways.

5.1.3.1 Photopolymerization of Prototype Parts

The first commercial Desktop Plastics Prototyping System links CAD design information with a photopolymerization process to produce prototype plastic parts [8-19]. The technique deemed *Stereo Lithography* ® by the system manufacturer [20] is capable of producing complicated prototype parts at rapid turnaround times. The process has evolved to the point where a comprehensive text has been written on the subject [21].

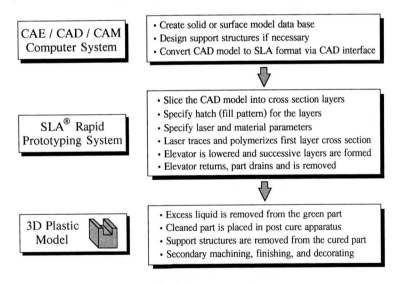

Figure 5.7. Steps associated with the production of a photopolymerized rapid prototype model. (Courtesy Computervision, Bedford, MA)

This rapid prototyping process begins by taking a CAD model, either a 3-D surfaced model or a solid model, and slicing the model into layers having thicknesses in the 0.005

- 0.020 inch (0.013 - 0.51 mm) range. These layers will ultimately be fabricated one at a time, starting from the bottom, to produce a solid, three dimensional prototype part. While the capital costs associated with this technique are relatively high (greater than the cost of CNC machining equipment), the process is capable of producing extremely complex, medium size parts in a fraction of the time required for the production of conventional prototype parts via conventional CNC machining, since set-up operations are eliminated [8]. Over the years, a number of service bureaus, firms that hire out their prototyping systems and expertise, have been established for those that wish to make use of the process but cannot justify the capital expenditure.

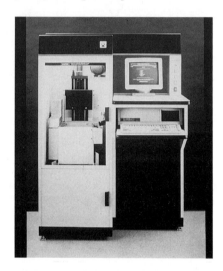

Figure 5.8. An SLA rapid prototyping system. (Courtesy 3D Systems, Valencia, CA)

Figure 5.9. Post cure apparatus used with the SLA system. (Courtesy 3D Systems, Valencia, CA)

A schematic of a typical photopolymerization model building process is shown in Figure 5.10. The rapid prototyping apparatus consists of an ultraviolet laser source and associated optics, a beam directing mirror, a vat of photopolymerizable material, a liquid leveling wiper, and an elevator, capable of Z axis movement at digital increments equal to the thickness of the CAD slices (the apparatus is linked with the sliced CAD model). The Helium-Cadmium or ionized Argon UV laser apparatus generate and focus a beam of ultraviolet light, which is directed by a movable mirror to various locations across the X-Y surface of the resin vat [19]. The elevator table sits just below the liquid surface, at a distance equal to the thickness of the "slice" (i.e. the thickness of the layer being formed). The activated laser scans the thin 2D liquid surface, in a complex manner, curing the appropriate areas (i.e. those associated with that particular layer). The ultraviolet light initiates the polymerization process which occurs only in areas exposed to the UV light.

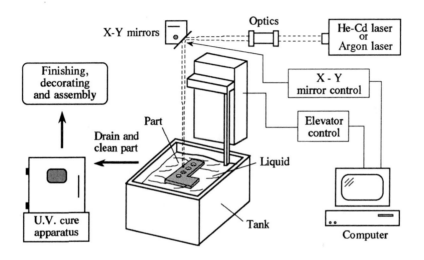

Figure 5.10. Basic schematic of a computer aided photopolymerization prototyping process.

A variety of photocurable liquids are available for use with the process. Once cured, the polymeric parts can have properties that range from brittle and glassy, to ductile, or even rubbery [21,22]. The degree of polymerization is determined by variables such as the total amount of light energy absorbed by the photocurable liquid. Once the curing of a layer (or slice) is complete, the elevator drops, the surface is leveled, and the process repeats itself. To prevent overshooting of the laser into the lower, previously scanned layers, the light must not be allowed to penetrate beyond a certain depth. This is accomplished by controlling the laser process conditions. The elevator continues to descend, layer by layer, until the uppermost layer of the part has been formed, at which time the elevator rises to the top of the bath and the part (or group of parts) is removed, drained and cleaned of surface liquids via blotting, alcohol or solvent rinse, or ultrasonic cleaning [8,9]. Drains can be incorporated into the part to facilitate movement through the bath during the build. After removal from the bath, the part is described as being in the "green" state (like any partially cured material) and must be handled carefully. The green part is then placed on a rotary table inside a high-intensity U.V. light post-curing apparatus for a short period of time to complete the cure [22]. The original materials developed for use with the SLA process tended to be higher shrinkage, brittle materials, but newer, low shrinkage, more ductile, or even rubbery materials grades have become available. One of the more flexible materials is described as having the properties of medium impact ABS [11,18]. In addition, new epoxy based resins are available with shrinkages that are an order of magnitude lower than the more conventional acrylic based resins. The lower shrinkage translates to significantly improved accuracy [11].

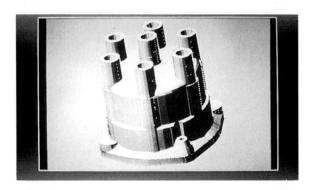

Figure 5.11. (top) Solid CAD model of an automotive distributor cap, and (bottom) prototype part produced using the SLA process. (Courtesy of 3D Systems, Valencia, CA)

The initial part CAD model is usually modified to provide an assisting support structure for the part as it is being produced (or "built") to ensure layer registration and structural integrity. Support structures are required when the part cross section contains islands of unsupported material. These legs or thin vertical strips or webs (as one might use to support the ends of a cantilever fan blade section) are carefully removed as part of the finishing operation.

The time required to construct or build a model varies with the complexity of the part and the tolerances required. Layer formation times can be decreased by creating an integral honeycomb like cross hatching structure between the inner and outer surface boundaries (vertical walls). The liquid entrapped between the walls is polymerized during the post cure [9]. The operator can control the degree of cure during the building of the part. Parts that are cured using the standard technique of hatching leave as much as 40-60% uncured liquid between the thin solid cell walls. This can result in part warpage or internal stress during / after the post cure since there is a large volumetric shrinkage associated with the polymerization. Some degree of shrinkage and warpage can continue to occur even after the part has been removed from the post cure apparatus. Advanced weave techniques have been developed which permits "in vat" cure levels as high as 96-98% within a reasonable period of time, resulting in a major reduction in the potential for warpage [19]. Part sizes up to 20 inch x 20 inch x 24 inch (51 cm x 51 cm x 61 cm) can be produced using the SLA process (on the larger equipment models). Production times are highly dependent on part size and tolerance requirements, although a typical medium size part of moderate to extreme complexity can reportedly be prototyped in several hours [8,13]. Very large parts can be produced as several sub-components keyed, dove tailed and bonded together.

A key step in the process is the initial part orientation decision. The primary appearance side of the part is often placed on top. The tolerances associated with the process vary and depend upon the CAD model, and the build parameters used. The incremental nature of this process also produces layered, step-like vertical walls for drafted or sculptured surfaces. Smaller elevation increments improve the surface for drafted, rounded and sculptured surfaces, although this does increase build time. Flat or perpendicular surfaces are easiest to work with.

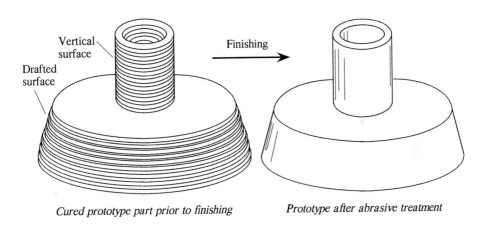

Cured prototype part prior to finishing   Prototype after abrasive treatment

Figure 5.12. (left) Prototype part before and (right) after finishing.

Cured parts require removal of the support structure and surface finishing by hand sanding, bead blasting, or machining. Depending on the part size and complexity, the cured parts can have tolerances that approach those attainable by machining (if warpage is not a problem) while tighter tolerances can be obtained with additional machining after cure [11,19]. Machining, however, is an operation that may require fixturing, and to a large degree, defeats the purpose of the rapid prototyping technology. The finished parts can then be painted, dyed, or decorated to produce the desired effect [8-10].

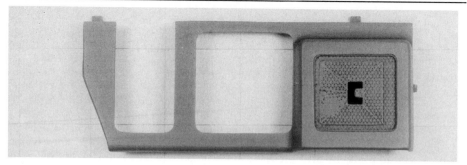

Figure 5.13. Rapid prototype part that has been finished and painted to produce the desired appearance (Courtesy Santin Engineering, Inc., Beverly, MA)

Several other rapid prototyping technologies based on photopolymerization processes have also emerged [19, 23-26]. The *Visible Light Laser Modeling System* [23] is another optical spot photopolymerization prototyping system, however, this apparatus uses a surface resin applicator rather than the vat / elevator apparatus described above, and is based on visible light laser technology [15,19]. The system also features laser beam focal length correction which allows control over the beam diameter during operation [19]. This is analogous to painting with different size paint brushes. Two other processes, *Light Sculpting* ® [24] and *Solider* ® [25], differ significantly from the processes described above in that they irradiate entire layers or slices of the photopolymer at once using UV lamps, rather than a laser spot in order to create the model. The imaging light passes through a mask which has been created for that particular layer. The mask contains both opaque and transparent areas corresponding to open and solid wall sections on the part respectively [13]. Future trends in this dynamic rapid prototyping area include larger scale production units, better tolerances, and development of new photopolymerizable resin grades spanning a wider range of properties.

5.1.3.2   Laser Sintering

Another new and emerging technology in the rapid prototyping area is *Selective Laser Sintering* ® [27]. This process is in some ways analogous to the photopolymerization / laser technique, as it uses a concentrated laser (carbon dioxide laser) to form a prototype plastic part, layer by layer. The similarities end there, however, since this process uses powdered thermoplastic material rather than a chemically reactive liquid photopolymer. This technique is especially attractive since it may be possible to produce complex prototype parts directly out of the production material (or similar material) in a relatively short period of time directly from computer models [28-29]. In theory, prototypes produced using the anticipated production material for the powdered resin could have more engineering uses, however, there are very significant differences in the molding and sintering processes, an the sintered prototypes are not direct substitutes for injection molded prototype parts.

The *Selective Laser Sintering* ® process shown schematically in Figure 5.15 begins with a solid CAD model of the part. This CAD model is positioned or oriented appropriately and sliced into sections having thicknesses ranging from 0.005 inch to 0.020 inch (0.13 to 0.51 mm). The model is built up layer by layer in a bin of powdered thermoplastic or

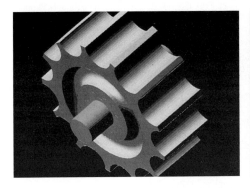

Figure 5.14. (left) Solid CAD model of a drive gear, and (right) prototype part produced using the selective laser sintering process. (Courtesy DTM Corporation, Austin, TX)

wax material. A stationary laser is reflected off of a beam directing mirror, and traces out the X-Y cross section of the part for that particular Z slice. The preheated thermoplastic powder is momentarily heated and softened by the laser to a point where welding or sintering of the particles takes place. In general terms, sintering is described as a process where the viscosity of the heated powdered polymer drops to the point where surface tension overcomes viscosity and fusion between neighboring particles occurs. The piston supporting the platform and part descends one Z-increment while the powder reservoir is raised. A new layer of powder is laid down with the leveling roller, and the process repeats until the model is complete. Another advantage of this process is that the unsintered powder surrounding the sintered part helps support structurally weak areas during the model building process [19]. In theory, any powdered material that softens or reduces its viscosity when heated can be used with this process, however, the sintering characteristics of each material must be matched with the power of the laser. Powdered thermoplastic materials such as polycarbonate, nylon, PVC and waxes have been used with this process [15,19,28,29].

The rapid prototyping technology known as *Selective Laser Sintering* ® is in its infancy, however, the interest level in this versatile process is extremely high. Perhaps the greatest area of development for this process is in the area of *Rapid Tooling*. *Selective Laser Sintering* ® has been used to produce cavity and core inserts for prototype injection molds. These cavity and core sets are created directly by sintering powdered metal in a polymer binder. The sintered parts are then heated in a furnace, producing a somewhat porous metal part. The porous part is then heated with a copper infiltrant (the copper is wicked up) to produce a dense, solid, machinable, steel alloy core / cavity that can be inserted into a standard mold frame [11,12]. This process should have a huge impact in the area of plastic prototyping, since it will be possible to produce a prototype mold cavity / core sets directly from the metal powder and a CAD model, in a very short period of time [19]. Prototype (or possibly production parts) can then be molded in these "rapid tools" using the production material. This is an advantage for a number of reasons including: (i) large quantities of prototypes can be molded at a low cost once the tool is built, (ii) realistic prototype parts can be obtained for engineering evaluation, and (iii) the processability (e.g. mold shrinkage, flow pattern, etc.) can be evaluated. The durability of the rapid tools is described as being somewhere between aluminum and P-20 steel.

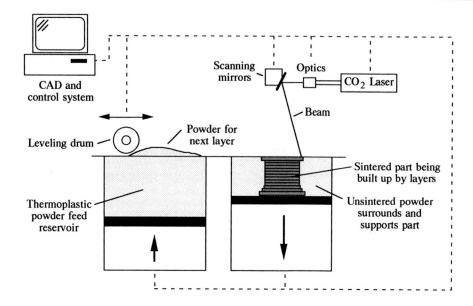

Figure 5.15. Basic schematic of the powdered polymer, selective laser sintering rapid prototyping process.

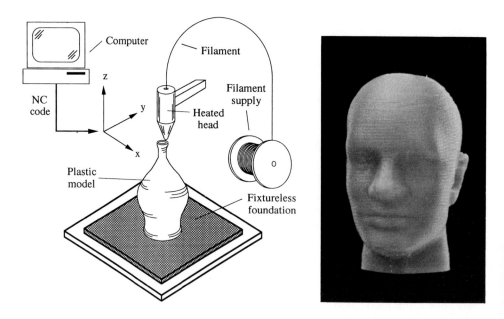

Figure 5.16. (left) Basic schematic of the automated filament extrusion prototyping process, and (right) part produced using the automated filament extrusion prototyping process. (Courtesy Stratasys, Inc., Eden Prairie, MN)

5.1.3.3   Automated Filament Extrusion Prototyping

Yet another new rapid prototyping technology is based on the use of what is essentially a very small scale, computer controlled, automated plastic wire fed extruder. The technique, *Fused Deposition Modeling* ® [30], begins with a 3D surface or solid CAD model which is sliced into layers having thicknesses ranging from 0.001 to 0.050 inch (0.025 - 0.13 mm). To actually build the model, thermoplastic filament, approximately 0.050 inch (0.13 mm) in diameter, is automatically fed through an X-Y controlled electrically heated extruder head as shown in Figure 5.16. The hot filament melt spreads over the previously formed layer, fuses to the surface, and quickly resolidifies. Support structures can be used for more complex geometries. Materials that have been used with this prototyping process include wax formulations for lost wax investment casting, machining wax and various proprietary thermoplastic formulations that can be used to build tougher prototype models. The *Fused Deposition Modeling* ® systems are available as both a desktop and floor standing units. These prototyping systems are relatively simple and produce models quickly [11,15,19,30,31].

5.1.3.4   Laminated Object Manufacturing

Another laser based prototyping system capable of building 3D solid prototype plastic parts is known as *Laminated Object Manufacturing* ® [32]. This unit uses a carbon dioxide laser tuned to a depth of one layer. Rolled sheets of precoated paper, plastic or composite material are fed into the unit where the laser traces and cuts out each cross sectional layer. Material cut from the central portions of the sheet can be removed using an automated vacuum system. Sheet thicknesses used for the laminated object manufacturing process are in the 0.002 inch - 0.010 inch (0.051 - 0.25 mm) range. The model is built from bottom to top by laminating the stacked sheets. The individual sheets are stacked on top of one another in advancing order, and are sealed to each succeeding layer using a hot roller [17,19].

5.1.4   Simulating a Production Quality Appearance on Prototype Parts

In many cases machined or fabricated prototypes must look realistic in terms of their surface color, gloss and texture. Most molded production parts are colored throughout, and have a gloss and texture that are determined by the processing conditions, material flow characteristics, and by the surface topography of the tool (the part surface can be no better than that of the tool). It can therefore be difficult to simulate these surfaces using standard prototype decorating techniques. The final appearance of the production part is an important quality, especially when products are slated for consumer applications. A designer can obtain an estimate of the surface appearance that can be expected for a material by molding test plaques having different surface finish inserts. For conceptual or marketing prototypes, the designer can simulate molded in color and surface finish on the fabricated prototype parts using custom painting techniques [33].

5.1.4.1   Molded Surfaces / Color

Mold cavity and core finishes are generally described using SPI standards [34] or textured surface standards. A mold finish comparison kit or molded surface finish plaque can improve communication between the part designer and mold maker, since tool surface appearance and surface quality can be difficult to describe verbally or in a sketch.

The surface quality of a molded part does not necessarily mirror that of the tool, especially when higher viscosity or filled / reinforced polymers are used. In many cases, objectionable surface irregularities such as gate splay or weld lines are less pronounced when molded over matte, patterned, or textured surfaces. The polymeric material to be used in production (including all additives) can be molded in lab trials to evaluate the effect of tool surface finish, heat history or other process conditions, on the final color and surface quality of a molding. Trials should take place over an extended period of time if plate-out or juicing of additives is expected to be a problem. The tool can be an older production / prototype tool, or a standard test mold, preferably a multi-surface / multi-texture test plaque.

Ideally, the test mold should produce parts with a variety of standard and textured surface finishes for evaluation. The molded prototype test part / plaque will provide the designer with a visual indication of the final product's appearance for a number of different mold surface finishes. The prototype test part can also be used to provide a good indication of how the esthetics of the part will vary with changes in processing variables such as heat history. The parts can also be used to evaluate physical properties and material shrinkage. Molded plaques are easily distributed to each member of the product design team.

Table 5.2. Simulating Molded Surface Appearance Using Hand Finishing Techniques

SPI/SPE Mold Finish Designation	Current SPI Surface Designation	RMS Surface Roughness Value (μm)	Method of Top Coat Surface Finishing
#1	A-1	0.5 - 1.0	Add clear lacquer to tinted color top coat. Wet sand 600 grit & polishing compound. Add several clear lacquer top coats. Immediate application of lacquer thinner mist to level surface.
#2	A-3	1.0 - 2.0	Add clear lacquer to tinted color top coat. Clear lacquer over tinted top coats. Surface is leveled with 600 grit dry / wet. Evenly stroked with polish compound in one direction to produce fine scratches.
#3	B-3	7.0 - 7.5	Clear lacquer added to tinted color top coat. Sand 600 grid dry / wet.
#4	C-3	12 - 15	Clear lacquer added to tinted color top coat. Sand 400 grid dry / wet.
#5	D-2	26 - 32	Flattening compounds added to tinted top coat.
#6	D-3	160 - 190	Suede compounds added to tinted top coat.

5.1.4.2   Molded Surface Simulation for Fabricated Prototype Parts

Smooth Surfaces: Machined prototypes or prototype parts generated using a rapid prototyping technology are usually given abrasive treatment and painted (or possibly dyed) to produce a visual effect that resembles the anticipated production look. Painting can be done using automotive repair finishes via spray application due to the availability of both the paints and the spray equipment, and the versatility / flexibility of the paint systems which are custom matched on a regular basis. Auto finishes are commonly available as lacquers, enamels, or urethanes, with lacquers being the most preferable for prototyping work due to their fast set up and excellent workability of the film. Enamels exhibit better gloss and flow as sprayed, but tend to show blemishes more than lacquers [33].

Michand [33] has outlined a series of lacquer finishing techniques that can be used to simulate various standard mold surfaces [34,35], once one has obtained a lacquer of proper color and hue. The thermoplastic prototype part is first sprayed with a sealer to protect the part from the aggressive solvents in the lacquer. In the automotive area, sealers are used to protect enamel finishes from lacquer touch up. Next, a primer (a high solids paint) is sprayed to create a tooth for the base coat, and to provide enough buildup to cover up sanding/machining scratches and small imperfections. Light gray primers are

Table 5.3. Current SPI Mold Surface Designations

SPI Mold Finish	SPI/SPE (old)	Cavity Finishing Procedure
A-1	#1	# 3 diamond buff (1-5 μm / 9000-7000 mesh equivalent)
A-2	-	# 6 diamond buff (4-8 μm / 5000-2500 mesh equivalent)
A-3	#2	# 15 diamond buff (8-22 μm / 1300-900 mesh equivalent)
B-1	-	600 grit Paper
B-2	-	400 grit Paper
B-3	#3	320 grit Paper
C-1	-	600 abrasive stone
C-2	-	400 abrasive stone
C-3	approx #4 (280 stone)	320 abrasive stone
D-1	-	Dry glass bead blast (#11)
D-2	#5	Dry oxide blast (#240)
D-3	#6	Dry oxide blast (#24)

recommended as they reflect more light than darker primers, assisting in surface inspection. Heavy scratches can be eliminated using filler compounds or several primer coats / sanding. Next, a lacquer base coat is applied to the primed surface. A white base coat is best for pastel top coat colors, while dark gray is used for solid color top coats. Finally, custom formulated tinted and clear lacquers are applied to the base coat. The standard mold finishes [34,35] can be simulated by following the sanding and finishing procedures outlined in Table 5.2 [31].

Current SPI standards designate 12, rather than six different mold surface finishes. The mold surface designations and surface preparation procedures outlined in the newer SPI standard are given in Table 5.3 [34].

Simulation of Textured Surfaces: Certain random textured surfaces can be obtained using pressure feed spray equipment (rather than siphon guns) where the fluid pressure can be increased beyond the capacity of the atomizing cap, producing small droplets or a course stipple. Alternatively, room temperature vulcanizing (RTV) or cure silicone castings of existing patterned / textured surfaces can be taken (as a negative) after which a positive RTV mold is cast. A viscous paint or coating is sprayed into the mold to produce a relatively flexible thin textured film, which can be bonded to the prototype part surface [33].

5.1.5   Prototype Part Casting Techniques

In situations where a few to as many as 50 prototype parts are required, low pressure casting is a potential prototyping method. Developments in both the areas of pattern manufacturing, tooling materials, and in the casting resin area, have led to the expanded use of this technique in recent years [1,36,37]. A relatively large number of prototype parts can be produced at an economical price using this technique, which is popular for electronic, communication, appliance, toy and automotive components.

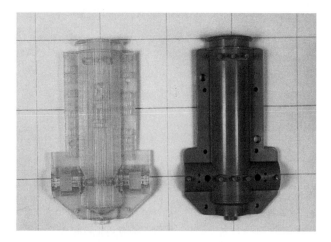

Figure 5.17. (left) Rapid prototype Stereolithography® part used as the pattern for a silicone casting mold, and (right) a colored, cast polyurethane part produced in the reusable, elastomeric silicone mold. (Courtesy Santin Engineering, Inc., Beverly, MA)

Casting can provide prototype parts in relatively large quantities (perhaps too many to fabricate via machining or rapid prototyping) that are often required for non-critical part field trials, package design programs, market studies or advertising campaigns. The cast prototyping process begins with the creation of a master pattern. The pattern can be produced from materials such as wood, plastic, soft metal or clay. Machined acrylic masters are commonly used due to the availability of acrylic stock, its good machinability / polishability, and its ability to be solvent cemented. Prototypes generated using one of the newer rapid prototyping technologies are also commonly used as masters for this type of casting process. This initial prototype part will be used as the master or pattern for a casting tool, typically produced using an RTV silicone resin. The tool will be in two or more parts, and it is therefore necessary to have well defined parting line locations and sprue / runner areas on the original master. Other common tooling materials that are used to a lesser extent include plaster and vinyl plastisol. Rigid plaster models may be adequate for a few simple, well drafted parts with no undercuts. One shot, water soluble plaster is available for more complicated geometries. Plaster has a relatively short set time, however, the tool should be completely dry before it is used, which could be as long as 72 hours for wall thicknesses in the 2 - 4 inch (51 - 102 mm) range, in order to achieve maximum strength [38]. RTV is the most common choice for the mold material as it offers good release characteristics, excellent surface reproduction, durability (typically good for up to 25 castings), chemical resistance, flexibility (allows limited undercut), low shrinkage and good handling / cure characteristics. The mold can be cast using other, less flexible materials, however, additional part ejection mechanisms would need to be incorporated. Tools can also be machined directly from a block of cast material, but it is generally easier to produce a single master, which can be used for several cast molds, than to machine and finish both a cavity and a core.

The mold building process is fast, but labor intensive. Automated mold building / part casting equipment is also available to both speed the tool building / part casting processes, and improve quality [37]. With this equipment, the mixing process is automated and is done under vacuum. Mold filling occurs under pressure, resulting in significant quality and surface finish improvements. The casting tool itself can be built in several ways. For the one shot mold tool building process, colored tape is used to identify and form the parting line on the pattern. The pattern is then coated with release agent, suspended in the center of a frame, and a transparent RTV silicone is then cast around the pattern as shown in Figure 5.18. After cure, the one piece RTV molds are then cut open at the parting line using a razor knife. In a second tool building technique, a two piece casting mold is constructed as separate halves. The cavity and core sides of the tool are poured separately (sequentially as shown in Figure 5.19). To begin the tool building process, a wood, metal, plastic, or foam board frame (a few inches larger than the part) is fabricated. The pattern (sized with both the tool and casting resin shrinkage taken into consideration) is coated with a layer of release agent before the tool is cast. The parting line for a two piece mold building process can be established using a pattern mounting board, or modeling clay. The clay or parting line mounting board form the proper parting line, the parting line location features, and support the pattern during the casting operation. The RTV resin is then de-aerated and / or vibrated and poured into the frame using a shaker table to facilitate flow. The rubbery material is allowed to cure, at which time the mold frame is inverted and the clay / mounting board are removed. The pattern is cleaned, coated with release, and the second half of the mold is poured and allowed to cure. Vents / risers and sprue hole(s) can be directly cast-in or machined after the cast tool cures. Parts should be gated in such a way as to assist in the venting of the air when the part casting resin is poured [1].

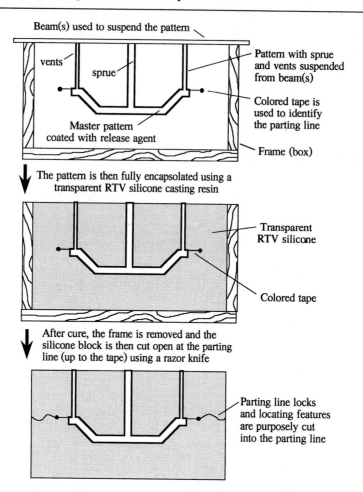

Beam(s) used to suspend the pattern

vents

sprue

Master pattern
coated with release agent

Pattern with sprue
and vents suspended
from beam(s)

Colored tape is
used to identify
the parting line

Frame (box)

The pattern is then fully encapsolated using a
transparent RTV silicone casting resin

Transparent
RTV silicone

Colored tape

After cure, the frame is removed and the
silicone block is then cut open at the parting
line (up to the tape) using a razor knife

Parting line locks
and locating features
are purposely cut
into the parting line

Figure 5.18. Steps associated with the construction of a one piece, transparent RTV silicone casting mold. The mold is cut open after the silicone cures to establish the parting line.

Machined metal or plastic mold inserts are added top the casting tool when the part geometries become more complicated as shown in Figure 5.20 and 5.21. While RTV silicones are tough materials, very thin sections / small holes can be produced more accurately with inserts due to the potential for core bending / deflection during the pour. The inserts also improve mold life for thin sections and can be used to assist in the ejection of deep undercuts such as the snap beam shown in Figure 5.21. The parts themselves are typically cast using either epoxy, thermosetting polyester, or most commonly with thermoset polyurethane casting resins. The low viscosity resins are carefully mixed and vacuum de-aerated before being poured through the sprue (filling) hole. The mixing step is critical in terms of component concentrations (i.e. mixing ratio) and air entrapment. Mixing should be done by hand or with equipment that does not introduce air. The automated casting system mixes and casts the materials under vacuum.

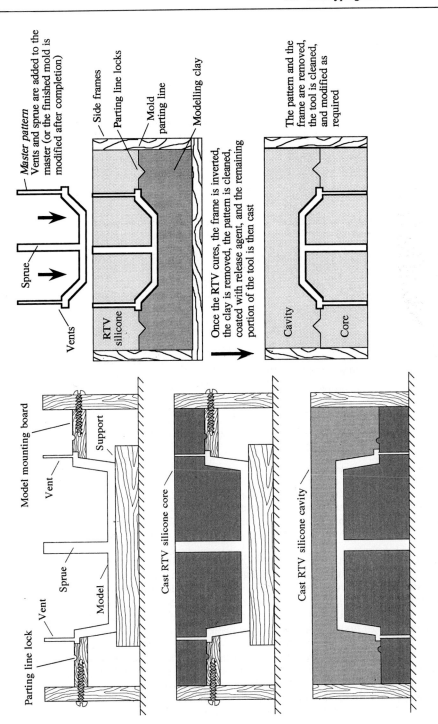

Figure 5.19. (left) Steps associated with the construction of a two piece RTV Silicone casting mold, using a model mounting board to establish the parting line and (right) construction of a two piece mold using modeling clay to support the pattern and establish the parting line.

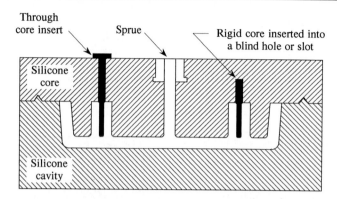

Figure 5.20. Removable metal inserts can be used to produce fine details such as the hole for a hollow boss. Alternatively, features such as holes can be machined in a secondary operation.

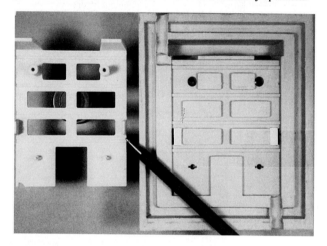

Figure 5.21. Cast polyurethane part (left) and silicone casting mold (right) used to produce the prototype part. The silicone mold contains removable aluminum inserts to assist in the production of the hollow bosses and the cantilever snap beam undercut. (Courtesy Santin Engineering, Inc., Beverly, MA)

All mixing utensils and containers should be clean and free of surface moisture, as this can affect the cure reaction [36]. Preheating the resin components or tool can temporarily reduce viscosity of the resin for hard to fill thin wall sections, however, this will also reduce pot life or working time. The cast parts are often cured in an autoclave to produce dense, void free parts [1], or using room or slightly elevated temperature cure cycles ranging from 1 to 24 hours depending on the resin grade.

Thermosetting polyurethane resins are most widely used as the casting resin because they are available in a number of grades, having a wide range of flow and toughness characteristics. Harder grades have mechanical characteristics similar to ABS (with somewhat reduced thermal properties). Additives can be mixed with the base resin formulation to produce materials that more closely reflect the characteristics of the end-use material. Flame retardant grades having a U.L. 94 V-0 rating for 1/4 inch (5.4 mm) thick specimens and transparent grades are also available [1,36,39]. Colorants can be mixed in with the casting resin or the cast parts can be painted or dyed after ejection. Shrinkages are relatively low for the polyurethane materials, however, it can be difficult to hit the target dimensions for higher tolerance items on the first attempt. In such cases, dimensional or styling changes can be made to the initial cast prototype, after which the modified model is used as a new pattern.

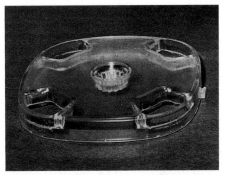

Figure 5.22. Prototype cover for an Oster Corporation part produced using a water - clear polyurethane casting resin, cast in a reusable RTV silicone mold. (Courtesy Ciba-Geigy Tooling Systems)

5.1.6   Prototype Injection Mold Tooling

The term "prototype tooling" is a term that can have different meanings to different people. To a part designer, it may indicate a relatively inexpensive, rapidly made non-production tool used to make a small number of prototype parts. To a toolmaker, it may be a tool that has been built to demonstrate whether a tool will perform as anticipated. The key points in either case are relatively low cost and relatively fast procurement as compared to production tools [38]. The SPI categorizes injection molds, or cavity inserts, according to their quality and service life (i.e. their production life in terms of the number of parts that can be produced). Prototype molds are described as molds that are constructed in the least expensive manner possible to produce a very limited quantity of prototype parts, based on the SPI's designation [40].

Prototype tooling budgets should include the costs of prototype tool modifications and the cost of 3D patterns, since a pattern is required for cast tooling (and at a minimum serves as an excellent communication aid). Even when molds are machined, models are extremely helpful. The money and time saved by skipping prototype molding steps may be small in comparison to the time and costs accrued when more expensive production tooling must be recut to accommodate the need for tool or part modifications [40]. Prototype tools are expected to produce parts that are very similar (identical would be optimum) to the expected production parts. The prototype part's production cycle time may be somewhat longer than that of the production tool due to reduced cooling capacity of prototype tooling or because the tool has manual inserts or slides. In the case of high quality aluminum prototype tools, cycles can be faster due to improved heat transfer. The

Table 5.4. SPI Mold Classification System

SPI Class Designation	Injection Clamp Size (tons)	Estimated Number Cycles	Mold Description
101		$> 1 \times 10^6$	extremely high production
102		$< 1 \times 10^6$	medium to high production
103	< 400	$< 5 \times 10^5$	medium production
104		$< 1 \times 10^5$	low production
105		$< 5 \times 10^2$	*prototype only*
401		$> 5 \times 10^5$	extremely high production
402	> 400	$< 5 \times 10^5$	medium to high production
403		$< 1 \times 10^5$	low to medium production
404		$< 5 \times 10^2$	*prototype only*

parts produced in prototype tools may also require some additional secondary operations or hard finishing. Prototype tools are typically designed to produce a limited number of parts (a few to several hundred parts, even thousands of parts in some cases) although metal prototype or preproduction tooling often end up in production for one reason or another.

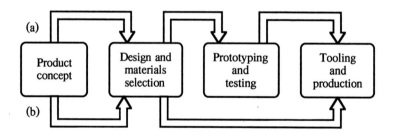

Figure 5.23. The safest and best route in product development involves prototype part production and evaluations. While route b is initially more direct, problems are not detected until production begins. The solutions are likely to be expensive and time consuming.

One of the major reasons for using prototype tools is to produce prototype parts for end-use or laboratory testing. Only injection molded samples manufacture using the production material will exhibit the true properties of the final product, because factors such as orientation, heat history, weld lines and other processing related effects are accounted for. While injection molded prototype parts and tools can be expensive relative to facsimile prototypes (especially when only a small number of parts are required), unforeseen manufacturing or processing related part performance problems are less likely to occur when manufacturing considerations are taken into account before one commits to production tooling.

The prototype tools may be single cavity (unit cavity insert) molds rather than multicavity, and may lack certain details such as trademarks or engravings. The unit cavity approach is common for smaller parts. However for larger parts, the decisions associated with prototype tooling are more difficult to make, because the cost of the prototype tool (relative to a production tool) becomes very significant. One solution is to target the problem areas. Potential problem areas for larger parts, such as the weld line on the exterior automotive panel shown in Figure 5.24, can be evaluated using much simpler prototype tooling. In such a case, it is important to keep processing conditions and critical tooling geometry as realistic as possible. The prototype tools should be constructed in a manner similar to the production tool with respect to the number, type and location of the gate(s) and cooling layout whenever possible [3,5]. In addition, it may be advantageous to design a prototype tool so that it is versatile. For example, a number of likely gating schemes could be incorporated into the tool in advance, if there is any question as to gate location as shown in Figure 5.27 [3,5].

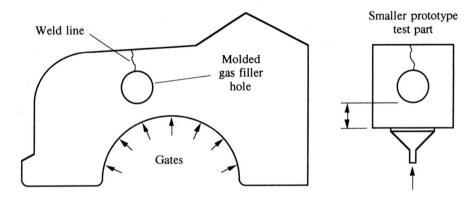

Figure 5.24. Example showing the simplification of part geometry, targeting a specific area of concern (a weld line in this case), in order to reduce cost and save time.

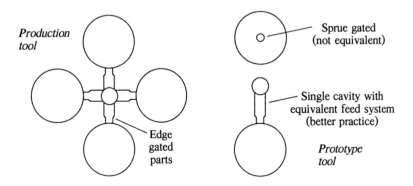

Figure 5.25. Molded prototype parts should be gated in the same manner that is planned for the production parts.

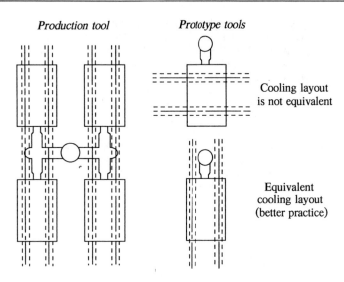

Figure 5.26. Cooling layouts for prototype molds should reflect the planned production cooling layout.

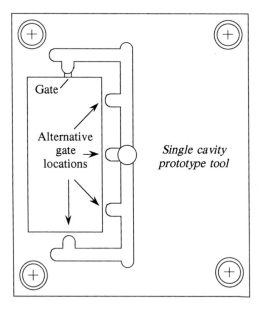

Figure 5.27. Prototype molds should be versatile. In this case, a number of possible gate locations have been incorporated into the prototype tool for potential evaluation.

In other cases, prototype parts are produced for non-engineering functions, such as those required for display, package design or marketing purposes. These parts might be produced using lower melting, non-production resins, along with softer, less expensive tooling and hand finishing, generating parts that are perfectly adequate as facsimile prototypes or models [38].

Prototype molds can be categorized based on either their production characteristics [2,4] or based on their materials of construction. The prototype injection molds can be cast, spray metal shells, sintered, or most commonly machined. Cast prototype tools require the use of a master(s) which can be made from sealed wood, plaster, plastic, wax or from a soft metal such as aluminum. The pattern material selection is dependent upon factors such as the temperature associated with the tool casting operation.

Table 5.5 Prototype Mold Classification System [2]

Prototype tool type	Production characteristics	Materials of construction
Level I	Rough part, loose tolerances Standard geometry, a few simple features Secondary operations may be required Small number of parts for initial evaluation Shortest lead time Lowest capital cost Typically sprue gated	Cast epoxy, plaster Metal dip or metal spray
Level II	Relatively tight tolerances Some mold design evaluation Hand loaded inserts / core pulls	Cast or machined aluminum, brass, kirksite, soft steel or electroform
Level III	Relatively high volume prototype work Tight part tolerances Automated ejection / side action Duplicates production gating and cooling Tool design, part performance, mold design and process conditions can be evaluated Cycle time ≈ production cycle	Machined aluminum or soft steel plate
Level IV	Single (unit) cavity preproduction mold Fully automated, production tolerances Useful as backup if production tool needs repair or doubles as production cavity insert	Hardenable steel Hardened before or after molding trials to accommodate design changes

5.1.6.1   Cast Epoxy Prototype Tools

Highly filled / reinforced epoxy casting resins can be used to produce very low cost prototype tool, of limited durability [4,8,38]. The casting resins are typically filled with aluminum, iron, or steel chips/powder to improve compressive properties, thermal conductivity, reduce shrinkage and reduce the coefficient of thermal expansion. The epoxy formulations exhibit low shrinkage and are generally room temperature cure systems, although a ramped elevated temperature post cure (for as long as two days) can be used to improve both the strength and high temperature properties of the final casting. Since the resin cures at room temperature, the pattern materials can be plastic, wood or even wax for low exotherm systems [38]. The process involves casting the filled liquid resin over a well drafted, well lubricated master, supported in a structural mold frame or chase. The frame must provide both the compressive clamping surface and be rigid enough to resist sidewall / support plate deflections due to cavity pressure. The surface quality of the tool is determined by the resin void content, filler content, pattern quality and resin viscosity. De-aeration, vibration and careful mixing will reduce void content. Some hand finishing and sealing may be required as undercuts should be avoided or filled to prevent tool damage during mold opening or part removal. The tool can be modified via conventional machining operations or by adding resin to local areas. The soft epoxy tools are more commonly used with low pressure processes such as RIM or low pressure structural foam, but can be cautiously used for prototype injection molds in some applications. However, the epoxy tool life is very limited. Strategically placed metal inserts (such as sprue bushings, runner bars, etc.) that improve the tool life are required in most applications. The prototype tools should be run at the lowest possible clamping pressure settings, molding pressures and temperatures. In addition, low temperature polymers should be run in place of higher temperature engineering polymers for facsimile prototypes whenever possible.

5.1.6.2   Metal Shell Tooling

Metal shell tooling backed with either a metal or ceramic filled / reinforced epoxy resin, or alternatively a low melting point metal alloy, are considered intermediate quality prototype tools or in some cases, very limited production tools. Tools of this type are more durable than straight epoxy molds, provide better surface detail, better tolerances, and larger quantities of parts, perhaps more than 1,000 injection molded parts if zinc or aluminum alloys are cast as the shell back up material [42,43]. The importance of low pressure mold protection, proper tool set-up, and careful maintenance cannot be overemphasized when these soft tools are used.

The metal shells necessitate the use of a pattern, which may have to withstand elevated temperatures for relatively short periods of time depending on the process that is used to make the shell. When high temperatures are a problem, the pattern can also be cored out for cooling (e.g. for water cooling) to prevent heat buildup. With some processes, the pattern must be heated.

Metal shell materials range from low melting point bismuth alloys, to hard, durable nickel. The shells are generated using dipping, spraying, electroforming, or vapor deposition processes [4,38, 42-44]. The simplest method that can be used to produce a cavity is to dip the master into a bath of molten alloy, kept just above its melting point. The cold pattern causes a thin shell to form around the pattern. Unfortunately, low melting point alloys are not very durable. A more durable metal shell can be produced using the Nickel Vapor Deposition Process [43,44]. In this process, nickel carbonyl, in gaseous form, mixed with a carrier gas, are brought into a sealed chamber containing the mandrel / pattern of the cavity or core to be formed. The mandrel (typically machined aluminum) is heated to a uniform temperature of approximately 350°F. When the nickel carbonyl gas comes in contact with the heated surface of the mandrel, the gas decomposes and a pure nickel deposit forms on the pattern (99.9% pure nickel). The deposition rates are in the 0.010-0.050 inch / hour range, and can be applied in thicknesses from less than 0.001 inch to a maximum of 1.000 inch. The process can be used to form small to very large cavity / core shells. After the nickel shell has been formed, copper tube, pattern wax or polystyrene foam channel shapes can be applied directly to / close to the rear surface of the shell. The shell is then placed within a metal chase or frame (suitable to withstand clamp and injection forces) and backed with a highly filled epoxy system . The wax / foam channels can then be cleared by heating (melting the wax) or dissolving (the polystyrene foam).

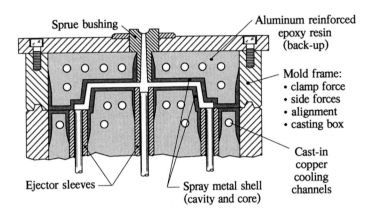

Figure 5.28. Basic Components and construction of a spray metal shell prototype injection mold.

Lower melting point metals of various types can also be arc or gas flame sprayed to produce cavity and core shells. In the spray metal shell process, an aluminum or zinc alloy wire is fed through a gun, where it is vaporized using either a gas jet or an electric arc, and is then sprayed over a pattern. The spray metal shell process can be used to produce virtually any size cavity [8,28,31]. Typical steps involved in the manufacture of an arc sprayed metal shell tool, such as that shown in Figure 5.28, are described below [42].

1) The process starts with the creation of a suitable model (pattern) that is built from well sealed wood, plaster, metal, machined plastic, clay, wax. The model can also be created using one of the many emerging rapid prototyping technologies since the arc spray process is a relatively low temperature process, and a variety of different pattern materials can be used. The parting line is then clearly defined, and the model is mounted at the parting line on a mounting board. The pattern should be well drafted, and all negative drafts or undercuts should be filled and sanded smooth. Runners and gates are added to the model as are other features such as ejector pin bushings.

2) The pattern is cleaned, and several coats of release agents, typically PVA, are added to provide an appropriate foundation for the metal spray, and to assist in pattern release.

3) The metal spray is then applied to one side of the model and mounting board. The coatings are gradually built up to a thickness approximately 0.063 inch (1.6 mm).

4) The external framework, including clamp slots, lifting bolts, alignment bushings, and cooling fittings is placed over the metal shell. The framework, typically aluminum or steel plate, must be strong enough to resist deflection due to both clamping and internal mold pressures.

5) An epoxy gel coat is then painted over the metal shell. Once this operation is complete, the cooling channels (typically copper tube) are put in place. The cooling channels should follow the contours of the shell and connect to the frame using compression fittings.

6) Once the cooling circuit is in place, a high temperature epoxy resin is mixed with aluminum chips, needles or powder. The mixture is poured over the shell (into the mold frame area) to back up the tool. It is good practice to vibrate the tool to assist in air removal, and to circulate cool water through the mold cooling channels during the exothermic epoxy cure reaction to limit the peak cure temperature and reduce the shrinkage of the epoxy.

7) Once the resin has fully cured, the tool is turned over, and the model mounting board removed.

8) The process (steps 1-7) is repeated using the reverse side of the model to produce the mating mold half.

9) The cured tool halves are separated, the model is removed, and the tool surface cleaned using warm water to remove mold release agent residue. The finished tool can be polished or plated to achieve the desired surface finish.

An alternative method of shell formation is electroforming. Electroforming can be used to produce hard nickel tool shells, with very fine definition. The tool shells will stand up to higher temperatures and pressures than conventional spray metal shells. To create the shell, a conductive (or conductive coated non-metallic) pattern is placed in an electrolytic bath where nickel is deposited until an appropriate thickness 0.050 to 0.125 inch (1.27 to 3.18 mm) is built up. The process is time consuming, however, it is well suited for complex cavities [33]. The shells can be backed with either the metal powder / chip filled epoxies or casting metals such as aluminum or a lower melting point zinc / aluminum / copper alloy.

5.1.6.3   Machined Prototype Molds

Prototype injection molds are most commonly produced by conventional machining, grinding or electrical discharge machining (EDM) techniques. These machining methods are commonly used to produce prototype molds for small parts (typically one or two cavity molds) or for larger parts that have been simplified to some degree (typically a one cavity mold) where non-critical design features and details have been eliminated. The tools are machined directly from aluminum, brass, and soft or prehardened steel plate. P-20 steel is often used for very high tolerance, higher production prototype / limited production tools. Aluminum offers the greatest advantages in terms of machinability (and therefore cost and delivery) and improved heat transfer capabilities, however, the aluminum alloys are relatively soft, with lower yield strength and abrasion resistance than steel alloys. The advantages of aluminum are most significant for medium to large tools where a great deal of machining is required. Several aluminum alloys are commonly used for prototype tools. The traditional material for aluminum molds is the 7075-T6 aircraft quality alloy. Recently, Alcoa has introduced an aluminum alloy designated QC-7, that is significantly stronger and harder that the 7075 alloy. The alloy is widely used for prototype injection molds, and is currently available in plate thicknesses up to 6 inches. The cavities, cores, and tool actions can be plated or surface treated to improve lubricity, abrasion resistance and chemical resistance. When aluminum is used as the material for prototype tool construction, steel inserts are commonly used in areas where high abrasion, bending stresses, or compressive stresses are anticipated. The number of parts that can be produced in machined prototype tools can range from thousands to tens of thousands. The potential tool life for a soft metal tool (in terms of number of cycles) is highly dependent upon a number of factors including; the materials of construction, surface treatments, the part design, the tool design, the plastic material being molded, process conditions, and tool maintenance.

Table 5.6. Property Comparison for Aluminum and Steel [47]

Property	Aluminum		Steel	
	QC-7	7075-T6	P-20	H-13
Typical hardness, Rockwell C	16	14	28 to 32	52 to 54
Typical yield strength, ksi	79 to 74	73 to 48	125 to 135	225
Thermal conductivitiy, $Btu/hr/ft^2/°F/ft$	91	75	20	16
Average coefficient of thermal expansion, $inches/°F \times 10^6$	12.8	13.1	7.10	6.10
Density, $lbs/inch^3$	0.101	0.101	0.284	0.280

Machined prototype molds have the longest lead time and highest capital cost, however, they may be produced using conventional or CNC-machining equipment (with various levels of hand finishing) and are capable of producing the maximum number of prototype parts to the highest tolerances [45]. These tools provide a realistic indication of both product and mold performance, provided the tool is cooled, vented, and gated in a manner equivalent to that of the production tool as shown in Figures 5.25 and 5.26. Soft metal prototype molds are easily modified and can be designed with significant versatility, such as alternate gate locations as shown in Figure 5.27. Prototype tools are often initially built without features such as ribs, if there is some questions as to their inclusion (i.e. steel safe design) [5]. Interchangeable insert mold constructions have also been shown to be useful for both prototype and production tools for smaller parts. The interchangeable insert tools utilize common mold frames, and as a result, can reduce the machining requirements for the tool, resulting in shorter lead times [46].

5.1.6.4   Prototyping in Die Cast Tooling

In a limited number of applications, engineering plastic materials are used as direct replacements for metals with little or no change in part geometry. While it is better practice to design the part from "the ground up", many die cast metal parts are converted almost directly with few changes. It may be possible to convert the existing die cast tool to a prototype plastics tool, and in some cases, to a limited production tool while conventional, production plastics tooling is being built [48,49].

The die cast tool could be run in a conventional thermoplastic injection molding machine, however, these tools are generally larger than standard thermoplastic molds and may require more platen area. A number of tool modifications are also required. Die cast parts are generally produced with thicker walls and sharper corners or fillet radii compared to thermoplastics. Rounding of sharp core corners or internal corner welds are modifications that would be required to reduce stress concentrations at wall intersections. The cavity and core surface finish may also need to be improved. Die cast tools are generally designed with a significant amount of venting to assist the high speed filling operation. The number or depth of the vents may need to be reduced to avoid excessive parting line flash.

The dimension of plastic parts produced in a die cast tool are likely to be different than the metal parts they replace. The molding shrinkages for zinc and aluminum are significantly lower than the mold shrinkage for a semi-crystalline thermoplastic such as nylon 6,6 which can be as high as 2.5 %. If assembly tolerances are tight, some machining may be necessary in order to obtain a proper fit. However, in metal to plastic replacement applications, the use of existing die-cast tooling for prototyping purposes is likely to save a significant amount of development time, since a large number of prototype plastic parts can be produced very early in the development cycle at a reasonable cost.

5.1.7 Low Pressure Structural Foam Prototypes

The need for prototype structural foam parts in product development is perhaps even more important than the prototyping needs for conventional thermoplastic parts. The property and design data available for these anisotropic, nonhomogeneous materials is often very limited. Unfortunately, molded structural foam parts are commonly used in applications where the parts are large, and production volumes are limited. The cost of large prototype molds can be very high, while low volume part prototyping budgets are often very small. As a result, the concept of steel safe (or aluminum safe) design is sometimes practiced with structural foam parts. In such a case, the prototypes parts are actually the first shots off of the production tool. The soft production tool dimensions are then modified based on the prototype test results. Like conventional solid moldings, structural foam prototype parts can also be described as facsimile prototype models or production (molded) prototypes. The molded prototypes are required for product testing or for an evaluation of the proposed tool design [2].

5.1.7.1   Facsimile Structural Foam Prototypes

Facsimile prototypes provide a working, life size or scale model which can improve communication, assist product promotion, provide geometric verification, or evaluate compatibility with assembly requirements. The models may also function as patterns for mold casting operations. Structural foam facsimile prototypes are most commonly fabricated from structural foam sheet stock, if it is available. The geometry of parts produced via this technique is limited, although crowned surfaces can be obtained by heating the sheet. The fabricated models should be made using materials that reflect, as closely as possible, the properties of the material to be used in the final application [2]. Hand fabricated prototypes can be generated soon after the part geometry has been conceived, however, they are of limited use in engineering testing, and are expensive on a per piece basis, limiting the technique to the production of one or a few models. Some limited engineering work, such as in locating areas of high stress or deflection, may give a rough indication where ribs or thicker wall sections are necessary. Solid facsimile models of structural foam parts having more complicated geometries can be produced using conventional prototype fabrication or casting methods.

5.1.7.2 Production Structural Foam Prototypes

Production prototypes allow a molder to produce a limited number of molded parts using virtually any polymer/foaming system. Parts generated using true to life molding techniques are more useful for engineering analysis, while the processing characteristics of the tool are simultaneously evaluated, leading to optimization of the production tool design. Various types of prototype tools are available ranging from very soft single shot tools to durable machined metal plate tools. Softer tools are less expensive and have shorter delivery times compared to hard tooling, however, they have shorter and more unpredictable service lives. Prototype tools can be built to various degrees of complexity with respect to cooling and ejection systems. However, it is important that structural foam tools are well vented. Extra care should always be observed when setting up prototype tools, as even the low clamp pressures of structural foam machines can damage soft tooling.

Structural Foam in Plaster Molds: A metal framed cast plaster tool (cast from a pattern) is perhaps the lowest cost and fastest method of producing a prototype tool for the low pressure structural foam process. However, these tools could be limited to a single shot or part. Given only one chance to make the part, the tool can be allowed to flash to relieve internal pressure and serve as an indication that filling is complete.

Structural Foam in Die Cast Tools: In instances where structural foam part is to replace a die cast metal part, the die cast tool can be modified and used for prototyping purposes as described in Section 5.1.6.4. For parts with relatively flat geometries, the parting line can be shimmed to produce a thicker flat section, while sidewalls and ribs remain thin and most likely solid. Fast fill speeds would be required to fill out thinner sections.

Structural Foam in Cast Epoxy Molds: Cast epoxy tools can be used to produce anywhere from a few to as many as 25 to 100 parts. The number of parts that the tool can produce is determined by both the complexity of the part and the molding conditions. Filled or reinforced epoxy formulations exhibit reduced casting shrinkages, increase stiffness, higher thermal conductivities and lower coefficients of thermal expansion. Cooling channels can be cast into the tool if more than a few parts are required. If no cooling and / or ejection provisions are added, the injection unit may need to be purged periodically until the part is cool and rigid enough to prevent distortion or post blowing. High internal pressures, high temperatures, and parting line wear are concerns with soft epoxy tooling. Wear plates can be added and lower processing temperature polymers should be used whenever possible. Cast silicone tools can be used in place of epoxy for very simple, shallow draw applications, when only a few parts are required.

Structural Foam in Metal Shell Molds: A more durable epoxy tool can be produced using metal shell technologies such as spray metallization, vapor deposition, or electroforming as described in Section 5.1.6.2. These thin metal shells, which are formed over a pattern, are backed with an aluminum powder, chip, or needle filled epoxy resin. The aluminum filler increases the stiffness and thermal conductivity, and brings the coefficient of thermal expansion closer to that of the shell. Cooling systems can be cast into the epoxy using copper tubing or machined along with ejection provisions. The tool is typically encased in an aluminum plate frame for support and clamping. Metal shell tools are relatively durable and can be produced at a fraction of the price of conventional machined molds.

Structural Foam in Cast Metal or Metal Plate Molds: Low melting temperature metals or alloys can be cast over a pattern to produce a durable tool directly. Aluminum, zinc alloy or even beryllium-copper (for smaller parts) molds capable of producing more than 1,000 parts with good surface reproduction capabilities can be used for structural foam parts. The metal casting techniques require higher temperature patterns and some machining after casting. Cast tools are an alternative to preproduction tooling that would generally be made using metal plates, usually aluminum, for a low pressure structural foam tool.

Table 5.7. Relative Prototype Tooling Costs [2]

Mold material	Relative cost *
Machined steel	100
Machined aluminum	50 - 70
Cast aluminum	40 - 50
Cast epoxy / metal shell	30 - 40
Cast epoxy	20 - 30

* Based on a production tool cost index of 100

Prototype tooling programs often run concurrent with production tool building due to the lead times involved, especially for the harder tools. The decision to go with machined metal or soft tooling is not straightforward since it is likely that the designer may learn more with the harder tooling; however, by that time, the production tool may be past the point where significant changes can be made easily.

5.1.8   Coordinate Measuring Machines

Accurate measurements on production parts, prototype parts or tooling can be made using coordinate measuring machines (CMMs) in a fraction of the time possible with conventional techniques. Although this type of equipment has been available for more than 25 years, integration of computer technologies and increased tolerance requirements for plastic parts have led to an increase in their use [50].

5.1.8.1   Contact Measurement Systems

CMMs consist primarily of a touch sensitive probe arm attached vertically to an overhead gantry or horizontally to a vertical guidebar. The three axes of motion are achieved by having the probe move in an x-y plane, while z axes motion is provided by the gantry or guidebar. In certain cases, the probe can rotate for additional flexibility. Parts are placed on dimensionally stable granite surface block tables and the servocontrolled probe is brought to the parts surface (automatically or manually). When the probe touches the workpiece, the point of contact is defined in terms of the x-y-z axes of the coordinate system. The probe then moves to the next point of measurement and so on. The data are interpolated to determine the distances between the points and translated into part dimensions. The CMMs are extremely useful for evaluating the differences between actual and target dimensions on molded prototype parts, especially for parts with contours and irregular surfaces.

5.1.8.2   Non Contact Measurement Systems

Coordinate measuring machines are routinely measuring to 0.0001 inch (0.0025 mm) and are therefore susceptible to humidity, vibration and temperature drift. Granite tables, ceramic machine components and environmental control have been used to address the problem, however, the use of contact measurement probes can still be a particular problem with flexible or soft plastic parts. Non contact coordinate measuring equipment, using lasers and video cameras, are promising new technologies. One system uses laser triangulation to lock onto a point, and analog LVDTs to determine the position of the probe axis [50]. Another system consists of a fixed platform with a rotating camera. As the camera rotates, a laser-based digitizer takes more than 250,000 three axis measurements in a matter of minutes. These measurements can be viewed on a computer screen and downloaded to NC machine equipment [8]. While the non contact technology offers a number of advantages, it can be sensitive to the surface finish and lighting conditions one might encounter when measuring inside dimensions. Future technologies such as magnetic resonance imaging may be able to both measure part dimensions and detect material flaws at the same time.

5.2   Experimental Stress Analysis

5.2.1   Introduction

Prototype plastic parts are commonly used to verify the performance of a proposed part design. The verification requirements range from geometric to structural, depending on the end-use requirements of the part. Parts intended for engineering applications are likely to require several prototyping steps, where environmental and structural characteristics of both the molding material and part geometry are evaluated. Ideally, the design engineer would like to evaluate molded prototype parts made using the production material formulation, however, the costs and time associated with a full product evaluation can be extensive. Design engineers may work with facsimile prototypes (such as machined or cast polyurethane parts) rather than production prototypes initially. The costs and turn around time for these facsimile prototypes allow the designer to evaluate the basic design, and potential problems related to part geometry. Based on the results of the initial studies, the part design would be altered, and a series of production prototypes, those produced using preproduction or prototype tooling, would then be evaluated in terms of product performance. Processing related factors, such as weld line strengths or morphological / orientation effects, can be evaluated using these molded prototypes.

A common objective of an experimental engineering study is to evaluate the performance of a true to life part subject to typical or worst case environment and loading conditions. Unfortunately, the product engineer may not be able to quantitatively define the typical or worst case service load or environment during the end-use application. It may be necessary to monitor service loads and environments as part of an overall prototype product evaluation program, although ideally, their limits should have been quantified very early in the design process. It is also important to develop a database of product testing results for future application for similar product development projects.

This section will discuss some of the basic techniques that can be used to evaluate the stress level in prototype or production parts. It is important to indicate that experimental stress analysis techniques do not measure stress, rather they measure strain or deformation (usually surface strain). The measured strains are then converted into stress using linear or non linear stress-strain relationships, i.e. the appropriate modulus for the material being tested. Plastic parts are produced in a wide range of sizes and shapes, and are subjected to various types of loads and environmental conditions. As a result, a number of experimental stress analysis techniques are commonly used. These techniques include simple extensometer measurements, brittle coatings, electrical strain gaging, solvent testing, photoelasticity and direct optical measurement. The selection of the most appropriate technique(s) is determined by such factors as whether the test is a field or laboratory test, the type of strain to be measured (uniaxial, biaxial, tension, shear), the expected range of strain, the resolution of strain field required, and the operating environment. In many cases, a combination of experimental techniques is most appropriate [51,52].

5.2.2   Brittle Coatings

Brittle coatings in the form of sprayed lacquers can be used to evaluate the surface strains in plastic parts. These coatings are especially useful when the direction and distribution of the strain are unknown. The brittle coatings are strain sensitive lacquers that are sprayed over the entire surface of the part to be evaluated (or as stripes), are allowed to dry, and are observed during / after external loading. The brittle coatings, available in a series of strain sensitivities, will show cracks that run perpendicular to the direction of the largest principal stress and are parallel to each other. The crack pattern will give an indication of the overall strain distribution, including the magnitude and directions of the strains [6,51,52,54,56].

This technique is an excellent method for obtaining a quick indication of high stress areas on a part (indicating the need for a design change) or for pinpointing the high stress location for more extensive strain gage testing. The coatings are formulated to crack at specific threshold values of strain, allowing a designer to approximate the maximum principal stress level. The stress value in the region of the crack is determined using the appropriate modulus value for the polymer, and the brittle coating's threshold strain:

$$\sigma_p \geq E_p \, \varepsilon_t \qquad\qquad\qquad (5.1)$$

The test is by nature incremental, providing crude strain sensitivity in comparison with a strain gages [51,52]. However, the brittle coating technique has the advantage of displaying the entire strain field and strain gradient. The technique is described as semi-quantitative and calibration samples of regular geometry, for which stress or strain can be calculated, should be used in combination with the experimental analysis.

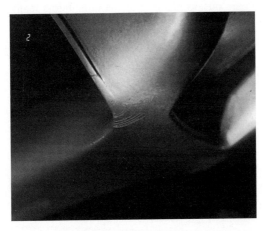

Figure 5.29. Cracks appear in a coated prototype housing after being loaded. (Courtesy Miles Corporation, Pittsburgh, PA)

Brittle coatings provide an excellent indication of potential problem areas on a part, however, the technique does have limitations. The coating is a paint containing chemicals or solvents that could interact with the surface of the plastic part to be coated. In addition, the coating should be as thin as possible to avoid magnification effects. The method also assumes perfect adhesion between the strain sensitive coating and the part to which it is applied. The use of sealers or primers may improve stress transfer and act as barriers, but should be used only in cases where they are absolutely necessary due to coating thickness build up and related magnification effects. Residual stresses are not easily determined using this technique, and as a result, the coatings are primarily used in the evaluation of external assembly or end-use loading related stresses. In addition, a relatively large number of prototype parts may be required for a thorough experimental analysis. The principle stress value determined using this technique is only an estimate since the test results are affected by factors such as the composition of the coating, the coating temperature, the thickness, the environmental conditions and the biaxiality of the stress field. More quantitative techniques, such as strain gage studies, are a good follow up to the brittle coating strain measurement technique [54].

5.2.3 Strain Gages

The most widely used tool for experimental stress analysis is the bonded electrical resistance strain gage. Strain gages are useful for quantitative analysis of surface strains associated with either external loads or internal stress release [51,53,54,55]. The resistance, R, for an electrical conductor or length, L, and uniform cross sectional area, A, is given by:

$$R = \rho\, L\, /\, A \qquad\qquad (5.2)$$

where ρ is the resistivity of the conductor. If the conductor is stretched or compressed, its resistance will change due to changes in the conductors length and cross-sectional area, and the conductor's piezo resistance, an indication of the dependence of resistivity on mechanical strain. Conductors bonded to the surface of plastic parts will transform surface strains caused by a stress, into electrical resistance changes in a linear manner [45,57].

Figure 5.30. Typical uniaxial foil strain gage. (Courtesy Micro-Measurements Division of Measurements Group, Inc., Raleigh, NC)

While many types of strain gages are available for use as transducer elements, bonded metal-foil strain gages are used almost exclusively for general purpose stress analysis work. The gage is an extremely thin, small, strain sensitive electrical resistor bonded to a flexible backing material to assist handling. When the gage is bonded to the part under test, it transforms surface strains caused by stresses into electrical resistance charges. The conductive sensing elements are formed from sheets less than 0.0002 inch (0.005 mm) thick using a photoetching process. The foil geometry is such that it maximizes the length of the conductor along a particular axis. The linear grid shown in Figure 5.30 is designed with fat end turns to reduce transverse sensitivity, a spurious input since this particular gage is intended to measure strain component along the length of the grid element (uniaxial). Foil gages also contain integral soldering tabs or presoldered leads [57].

The gage alloys used on most gages are copper / nickel, (constantan) or nickel / chromium alloys for very low or higher temperature work [51,55]. Semiconductor or piezo electric gages are newer technologies providing high precision strain measurements for very low strain or dynamic applications [51,53,57]. The foil gages come mounted on a flexible carrier film having a thickness of approximately 0.0010 inch (0.025 mm), bringing the overall thickness of the gage to 0.0012 inch (0.037 mm), plus the thickness of the adhesive layer, between the film and the surface of the part. The magnification error is expected to be significant only for thin wall sections, and can be nearly eliminated

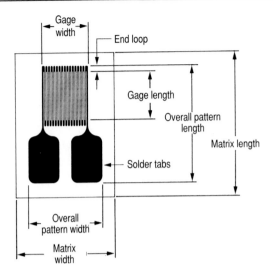

Figure 5.31. Nomenclature and features of typical foil strain gage. (Courtesy Micro-Measurements Division of Measurements Group, Inc., Raleigh, NC)

analytically. The adhesives used for strain gage testing (i.e. to bond the foil gage to the plastic part) are typically reactive monomeric adhesives. These adhesives offer good strength characteristics and low viscosity, generating a thin bond line. The quality of the adhesive joint is critical to the proper operation of the strain gage, since it is the link between the specimen and the carrier film. Problems may arise in the bonding area when working with very low surface energy plastic parts, or working in extreme temperatures and humidities. Parts should be cleaned and handled in accordance with standard adhesive bonding preparation practices for the plastic material being evaluated.

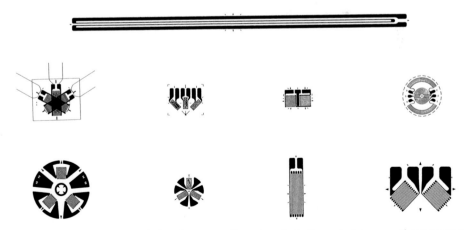

Figure 5.32. Common bonded foil strain gage configurations including uniaxial gages, planar rosettes, and stacked rosettes. (Courtesy Micro-Measurements Division of Measurements Group, Inc., Raleigh, NC.)

Strain gages vary in the active grid size from approximately 0.010 inch to as much as 4.0 inch (0.25 to 102 mm). It is not possible to obtain a measure of strain at a geometric point since the grid covers a finite area, thus the gage reads an average strain over the area. If the strain gradient in the part beneath the grid is linear, the average value can be associated with the midpoint of the gage length. If the gradient is not linear, the point at which the gage's reading applies is somewhat uncertain. This uncertainty diminishes as gage size decreases, indicating that smaller gages are more appropriate for steep strain gradients, such as those occurring at wall intersections [57].

The gage sensitivity to strain, known as the gage factor, is the ratio of unit resistance change ($\Delta R/R$) to unit strain ($\Delta L/L$) and is given by:

$$G_f = \text{Gage factor} = (dR/R)/(dL/L) = 1 + 2\nu + (d\rho/\rho)/(dL/L) \qquad (5.3)$$

where ν is Poisson's ratio for the gage material. The gage factor is determined by the sum of the resistance change due to the length change, the resistance change due to the area change, and to the resistance change due to the piezo resistance effect. The strain in the gage (and part) can then be determined by measuring the change in resistance due to loading:

$$\varepsilon = (\Delta R / R)(1 / G_f) \qquad (5.4)$$

The resistance of an individual unstrained strain gage is relatively easy to measure, however, measurement of the gage factor requires cementing the gage to a specimen for which strain can be accurately calculated theoretically (i.e. regular geometry, homogeneous, elastic material) which would render the gage unusable. The gage-factor numbers supplied with purchased gages have not been determined individually, but are an average value obtained using samples from the same production run [57].

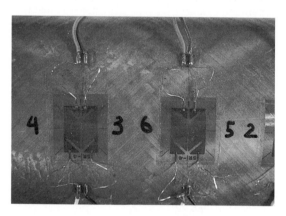

Figure 5.33. Example of a bonded foil strain gages used to evaluate surface strains for a plastic part.

A series of multi-element strain gages having various configurations are also available. Strain gage rosettes, as they are called, reduce set up time and improve accuracy by eliminating the need for precise alignment of multiple, individual, single axis gages. For example, a three gage rosette, such as the planer rosette shown in Figure 5.34, will allow one to determine the magnitude and direction of an unknown surface stress [51,52, 54-57]. Ideally, the three gages would be mounted at different angles, but at the same point. However, a stacked rosette suffers from disadvantages associated with heat build up and strain magnification errors, which may outweigh the advantages of the stacked point design [57]. In cases where the principle axes of a biaxial stress field are known, only two independent strain measurements are required to determine the principle stresses. This could be done using a two gage 90° rosette where the gage axes are in line with the principle axes [51]. Brittle lacquers can be useful for determining the location and the direction of the principle stresses before strain gages are mounted on replicate parts to evaluate the magnitude of the surface strains [53].

120° rosette

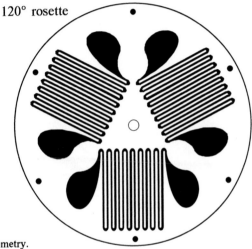

Figure 5.34. Typical planar rosette geometry.

The measuring instruments used for the detection and presentation of the output from an electrical resistance strain gage are most often based on a wheatstone bridge circuit, in which the experimental strain gage forms one of the bridge legs. Temperature and humidity effects are important considerations in strain gage experimentation, since strain induced resistance changes can be quite small. Changes in temperature influence both the resistivity of the gage foil and the dimensions of all system components, while variations in relative humidity can change dimensions of hydroscopic adhesives, carriers and plastic parts. The thermal or moisture induced expansion mismatch between the gage and the underlying materials can result in significant error. Temperature compensated gages can be used, or the effects can be compensated for, or balanced out, by mounting a second strain gage (identical to the active gage) to an unstressed, dummy part. The dummy and active gages are placed on adjacent legs of the Wheatstone bridge circuit, thus resistance changes associated with changes in the environmental conditions have no net effect on the bridge output [57].

Residual stresses, such as those introduced during the injection molding process, can be evaluated using strain gage techniques. Residual stress are important because they can lead to environmental stress cracking, warpage at elevated temperature, or may contribute towards product failure when service loads are superimposed on them. The residual (molding) stresses can be estimated using a strain gage "demolding test" [58] or a blind hole drilling technique [54]. The demolding tests are essentially unfixtured, elevated temperature stress relieving procedures, where the part is instrumented with strain gages. In the blind hole drilling technique, a rosette (typically a 3-element 120° planer foil gage) is mounted at the location of the strain measurement on the surface of the internally strained part. Drilling a small blind hole at the center of the rosette relieves the residual stress at that point, resulting in a measurable strain in the strain gage elements around the hole.

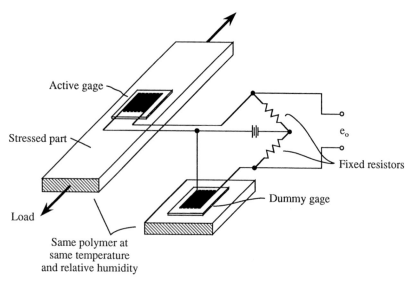

Figure 5.35. Wheatstone bridge circuit used with an active strain gage, and a dummy gage to compensate for temperature variation.

Bonded foil strain gages are perhaps the single most important tool for quantitative stress analysis. This technique has the potential to be sensitive to strains as low as 1 μm/m, can be used over a wide range of environmental conditions, and can be useful in the evaluation of residual stress. The primary limitation of the bonded foil strain gaging technique is that it provides only an average indication of the surface strain over a local area, rather than a stain gradient [51].

5.2.4   Solvent / Chemical Testing

The presence of internal or external stresses in a plastic part will reduce the solvent resistance of the part. This phenomenon can be a problem in service, where parts may craze, crack or fail at relatively low stress levels when exposed to a hostile chemical environment. However, the environmental stress cracking behavior of a particular polymeric material, when exposed to a particular solvent system, can be characterized and quantified, resulting in a potentially useful tool for experimental stress analysis.

One solvent based stress analysis approach uses two solvents of different strength, mixed together in a series of volume ratios. The strong solvent would be aggressive for the polymer in question, while the second solvent would be a miscible non-solvent. The term strength is most easily quantified as solubility parameter.   As a general approximation, in the absence of strong interactions such as hydrogen bonding, solubility of a polymer in a solvent can be expected if the difference between the solubility parameter of the solvent and the polymer is less than about 1.7 to 2.0.

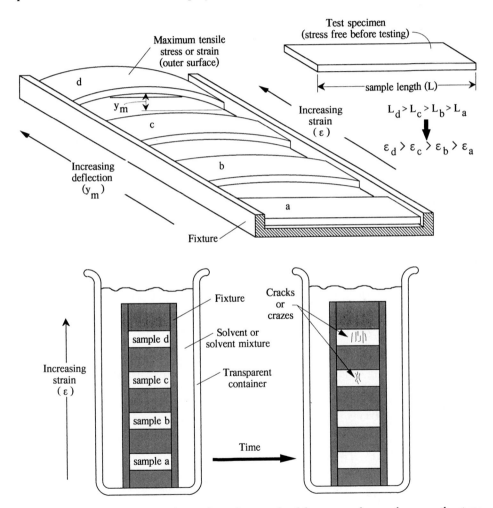

Figure 5.36. Solvents can be used to evaluate the stress level for many polymers, however, the stress crack resistance of the polymer must be quantified. Calibration samples produce from the same base polymer as the part being studied can be used to establish the relationship between tensile stress level and the appearance of cracks (in the presence of particular solvent).

Polymethyl methacrylate, having a solubility parameter of 9.10, would be expected to dissolve in benzene with a solubility parameter of 9.15, but not in methanol, with a solubility parameter of 14.5 [59]. Solvents / nonsolvent mixtures can be made up in various ratios, to produce solvents of various strength. For example, in the case of polycarbonate, mixtures of toluene and n-propyl alcohol or ethyl acetate and methyl alcohol have been used experimentally with good success [54].

The stressed plastic parts are dipped into containers, or coated with the solvent mixtures at a specific temperature for a specific period of time. The parts are then cleaned and dried of excess liquid. The appearance of cracks or crazes on the surface of the part indicates that the stress levels at that location of the part are equal to or higher than the critical stress level of that particular solvent mixture. This critical or threshold stress level for each solvent mixture / material would be determined in a set of calibration experiments with externally loaded samples of regular geometry, molded in the same polymer, for which theoretical stress calculations can be correlated with the onset of crack formation. The relative effects of residual and load related stresses must be separated using proper sample preparation and stress relieving techniques. Cracks develop perpendicular to the direction of the stress. The onset of crack formation can be correlated through the calibration samples to stress in the molded part using an appropriate ranking system. The accuracy of the test is determined by the number of solvent mixtures used (i.e. stress increment between critical stress values) and the judgment of the investigator, as the visual inspection can be to a large degree subjective.

A second approach to solvent stress analysis is to use one solvent of appropriate strength or solubility parameter, and evaluate the time duration from solvent application to crack initiation [52,60]. For this method, parts must be continuously exposed to the solvent or solvent vapor. The method is especially appropriate for a semi-crystalline materials such as high density polyethylene, which exhibits resistance to most solvents. The stressed parts can be placed in a transparent container along with the solvent or solvent vapor and inspected using time lapse photography or periodic visual inspection. The test can be accelerated by increasing the test temperature, although any significant internal stress relief at the higher temperature could invalidate the result. Cracks appear first at the areas of highest stress. A quantitative correlation can be obtained by placing stressed control samples of regular geometry (with stress levels that can be calculated theoretically) in the same enclosure as the part [58].

Solvent stress analysis techniques are quick, semi-quantitative tests that are especially useful for determining residual stress levels in molded plastic parts, however they can also be useful for evaluating load induced stress. It is important to note that proper safety precautions and proper ventilation should be utilized when working with potentially hazardous organic solvents.

5.2.5   Photoelastic Testing

Photoelasticity is a full-field, visual technique for measuring stress. Some isotropic plastic materials exhibit a temporary, double refractive index when stressed. The index of refraction will change with the level of stress (or strain), making this optical property the basis of the photoelastic testing technique. When a model or part made from a photoelastic material is loaded and viewed under polarized light, colorful fringe patterns are observed as shown in Figure 5.37. The fringe pattern or contours can be viewed analytically to provide an accurate indication of the magnitude and direction of the stress at a given location. The technique is useful for evaluating both processing related and externally induced stresses.

When the photoelastic material is stressed, the material becomes birefringent. Polarized light passing through the stressed material splits into two beams, each vibrating along a principle stress direction and traveling at a different speed. The phase shift between the two beams produces the colorful fringe pattern observed using the polariscope. Using the polariscopes measuring system, the plane of vibration is established to permit measurement of the principle stress directions. The phase shift is measured by optical compensation to determine the stress magnitude [51,62].

Photoelastic testing is done using either two dimensional photoelastic models, three dimensional photoelastic models, or parts coated with a photoelastic material. Photoelastic model analysis is most useful at the early stages of product design where facsimile prototype parts can be made using a transparent photoelastic material such as polycarbonate, polymethylmethacrylate or cast polyester. Two dimensional models are generally cut from a flat, stress free cast sheet, typically 0.250 inch (5.35 mm) thick, following machining practices which minimize machining stresses. The sheet is placed in a transmission polariscope along with wave plates of specific relative retardations. Part size is limited by the size of the polariscope, and scale models, such as the automotive panels shown in Figure 5.37, are sometimes evaluated. This experimental stress analysis technique is especially useful for evaluating stress concentrations due to holes, notches or other surface discontinuities [6,54,58,61,62].

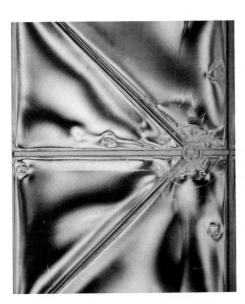

Figure 5.37. The residual molding stress levels for a part produced from Lexan® polycarbonate resin are evaluated using photoelastic analysis. The part on the left was molded via conventional injection molding, while the part of the right was molded using a lower stress injection - compression molding process. (Courtesy GE Plastics, Pittsfield, MA. Lexan® is a registered trademark of the GE Plastics).

More complex three dimensional photoelastic models can also be evaluated. In one technique, the three dimensional models are loaded or strained while at an elevated temperature in an oven, and cooled slowly back to room temperature to freeze in the photoelastic pattern [51,62,63]. The models or model sections can be cut into two dimensional thin slices using slicing techniques, and analyzed using a light transmission polariscope or microscope equipped with a polarizer / analyzer and a variable intensity light source. Sections of the part can be backed or embedded in a cast epoxy before slicing to maintain the dimensional stability of the part during the cutting operation. Small section slices of the part can be mounted on a microscope slide and viewed under polarized light.

Another widely used photoelastic technique involves coating a plastic part with a thin, uniform layer of a photoelastic material and using a reflection polariscope to analyze the effects of external loading. The technique is extremely attractive since it can be used with parts of virtually any size, shape or material, even those that are opaque. Prototype parts molded using the production material can be coated and evaluated. The surface strain distribution is displayed over the entire area, even for very steep strain gradients.

5.2.6   Optical Strain Measurement Techniques

A number of direct optical measurement techniques are also used in the area of experimental stress analysis. These techniques are commonly based on the principles of optical interference and include Moire, laser or holographic interferometry.

Moire Techniques: Moire is the name given to the optical effect one observes when two closely spaced grids of parallel opaque lines, with equal width transparent bands between, are superimposed. If the line spacing or orientation of one grid changes, periodic mechanical interference of transmitted or reflected light occurs, and a pattern is produced. The concept is used in stress analysis by bonding one of the identical grids to the part before it is loaded, using the other grid as a viewing reference. The grids are aligned precisely before the test part is strained. When the part is loaded, surface strains on the part and bonded grid deform the grid shape, causing fringes to appear when viewed through the reference grid [6,51]. The interference is due only to geometric blocking of the light (ordinary white light) as it passes through or is reflected from the grids. The Moire technique can also use photographic imaging techniques to produce and project grid images. The technique may be useful for high temperature work or where large plastic or elastic strains are involved, however, it is limited in many applications due to practical difficulties associated with making accurate strain measurements for small strains or steep strain gradients [39].

5.3   References

1. Metelnick, J., *Plastics Design Forum*, **14** (3) 31 (1989).
2. Anonymous, *Plastics Design Forum*, **3** (3) 72 (1978).
3. Anonymous, *British Plastics*, July / August, 17 (1984).
4. Shimel, J., *Plastics Design Forum*, **9** (1) 75 (1984).

4. Shimel, J., *Plastics Design Forum*, **9** (1) 75 (1984).
5. Kelly, W., *British Plastics and Rubber*, July/August, 12 (1984).
6. Ehrenstein, G. and Erhard, G., *Designing With Plastics*, Hanser, NY (1984).
7. Technical Bulletin, *CadCo Engineering Plastics*, Cadillac Plastic and Chemical Co., Troy, MI.
8. Deitz, D., *Mechanical Engineering*, **112** (2) 34 (1990).
9. Dowler, C., *Plastics Engineering*, **45** (4) 43 (1989).
10. Anonymous, *Modern Plastics*, **66** (3) 84 (1989).
11. Ogando, J., *Plastics Technology*, **40** (1) 40 (1994).
12. Kirkland, C., *Injection Molding*, **1** (3) 41 (1994).
13. Lindsey, K., *Modern Plastics*, **67** (8) 40 (1990).
14. Technical Bulletin, 3D Systems Incoporated, Valencia, CA.
15. Leonard, L., *Plastics Design Forum*, **16** (1) 15 (1991).
16. Lindsay, K., *Modern Plastics*, **68** (6) 216 (1991).
17. Gabriele, M., *Plastics Technology*, **37** (6) 45 (1991).
18. Charnas, D., *Plastics News*, **3** (21) 7 (1991).
19. Ashley, S., *Mechanical Engineering*, **113** (4) 34 (1991).
20. 3D Systems, 26081 Avenue Hall, Valencia, CA 91355.
21. Technical Bulletin, *Cibatool* SL XB 5081, Ciba-Geigy, East Lansing, MI.
22. Jacobs, P., *Rapid Prototyping and Manufacturing*, Society of Manufacturing Engineers, Dearborn, MI (1992).
23. Quadrax, 300 High Point Avenue, Portsmouth, RI 02871.
24. Light Sculpting, 4815 N. Marlborough Drive, Milwaukee, WI 53217.
25. Cubital, P.O. Box 330, Herzlia B 46103, Israel / Cubital America Inc., Troy, MI.
26. DuPont Somos Venture, New Castle Corporate Commons, Two Penns Way, New Castle, DE 19720.
27. DTM Corporation, 1611 Headway Circle, Building 2, Austin, TX 78754.
28. Anonymous, *Plastics Technology*, **36** (13) 23 (1990).
29. Meyer, A., *Micro CAD News*, January / February, 25 (1990).
30. Stratasys Inc., Eden Prairie, MN.
31. Fallon, M., *Plastics Technology*, **36** (8) 50 (1990).
32. Helisys, Inc., Torrance, CA.
33. Michaud, G., *Plastics Design Forum*, **6** (3) 56 (1981).
34. *Mold Finish Standards*, Moldmakers Division, The Society of the Plastics Industry, Washington, DC 20005.
35. Haaxma, H., *Mold Finishing and Polishing Manual*, I. T. Quarnstrom Foundation / Society of Plastics Engineers, Brookfield, CT (1985).
36. Sheehan, J., Technical Paper, Society of Plastics Engineers RETEC, Rochester, NY, L-1 (1990).
37. MCP Systems, Inc., 511 Commerce Drive, Fairfield, CT 06430-5541.
38. Schwartz, S., *Plastics Design Forum*, **10** (2) 57 (1985).
39. Geresy, W., *Plastics Design Forum*, **10** (2) 70 (1985).
40. *Standard Classification of Injection Molds*, Moldmakers Division, The Society of the Plastics Industry, Washington, DC 20005.
41. Brewer, D., *Plastics Design Forum*, **7** (3) 95 (1982).
42. Technical Bulletin, # 300-D10622, TAFA Incorporated, Concord, NH.
43. Hanna, S., *Obtaining Durable Molds from Rapid Prototype Patterns*, MS Project, Department of Manufacturing Engineering, University of Mass Lowell (1992)
44. Microtech, Incorporated, Toronto, Canada.
45. Dryce, D. M., Structural Plastics Conference, Society of the Plastics Industry, 146 (1992).
46. Technical Bulletin, Master Unit Die Products, Inc. P.O. Box 520, Greenville, MI 48838.
47. Galli, E., *Injection Molding*, **1** (1) 53 (1994).
48. Mannis, F., *Plastics Design Forum*, **2** (3) 52 (1977).

49. MacDermott, C., Selecting Thermoplastics for Engineering Applications , Marcel Dekker, Inc. NY (1984).
50. Anonymous, *Plastics Technology* , **36** (5) 67 (1990).
51. Corby, T. and Redner, S., *Plastics Design Forum* , **6** (1) 43 (1981).
52. Crites, N., *Product Engineering* , October 16, 90, (1961).
53. Rowand, R., *Plastics News* , **1** (33) 6 (1989).
54. Mehta, K., SPE Annual Technical Conference, **32**, 155 (1986).
55. Crites, N., *Product Engineering* , February 19, 69, (1962).
56. Roark, R., and Young, W., *Formulas for Stress and Strain* , McGraw Hill, NY (1975).
57. Doebelin, E., *Measurement Systems* , McGraw Hill, NY (1984).
58. Levy, S., *Plastics Design Forum* , **9** (4) 83 (1984).
59. Billmeyer, F., *Textbook of Polymer Science* , Wiley Interscience, NY (1971).
60. Standard Test Method D1693, American Society for Testing and Materials, Philadelphia, PA, **8.02**, 53 (1989).
61. Sullivan, T. and Matsuoka, S., SPE Annual Technical Conference, **35**, 790 (1989).
62. Crites, N., Grover, H., and Hunter, A., *Product Engineering* , September 3, 57, (1962).
63. Miller, H., *Plastics Design Forum* , **6** (4) 33 (1981).

6 Assembly of Injection Molded Plastic Parts

6.1 Introduction

Many injection molded plastic parts are simply a component of a larger product assembly. Molded plastic parts are combined with one another, or with components produced from other materials to produce the final product. The fastening or assembly method that is used must establish mechanical continuity between the various parts that make up the product. In many cases, this product assembly process is a secondary manufacturing operation, or in other cases, the burden of assembly is shifted to the consumer. In either case, it is highly desirable to minimize the number of parts and materials that make up a particular product in order to simplify and minimize the costs associated with assembly and manufacturing [1,2]. A major objective in the design of most plastic products is to minimize assembly operations by consolidating functions, and molding the fasteners directly into the plastic parts themselves. Plastic parts produced using the injection molding process are ideally suited for *Design for Assembly* (DFA) since the injection molding process is capable of producing parts with extremely complicated geometries. *Design for Assembly* is a philosophy that is widely accepted as a means of improving both product quality and reducing manufacturing costs. Even the elimination of a single very low cost screw or washer can have a significant impact on the bottom line when handling costs and assembly time / equipment / labor costs are taken into consideration.

The DFA concept is simple. Minimize the number of parts required to produce a product by incorporating as many assembly features as possible into the molded parts. Avoid the use of fasteners such as screws, inserts, and the like (particularly those mechanical fasteners that require rotation), should be avoided whenever possible as should other assembly operations such as adhesive bonding or welding. Unfortunately, this may be difficult to accomplish in practice. This is largely due to the fact that the moldability of a part is very closely related to the complexity of the part geometry (i.e. complex parts tend to be more difficult to tool and mold). The savings in assembly costs must be balanced against the cost of the more complicated tooling and a more complicated primary molding operation. Mold reliability and maintenance issues also become more significant as tool complexity increases. Consider the example shown in Figure 6.1.

The original methods of golf ball production involved both a primary injection molding operation and a secondary assembly (compression molding / welding) operation. For this process, injection molded thermoplastic shells are placed over the premolded elastomeric core. The three parts are then placed into a heated compression mold, where the outer shells soften, form the surface detail, and weld together. The compression mold is then cooled to resolidify the thermoplastic shell, and the finished assembly is ejected. The golf ball can also be produced in a one shot process by placing the elastomeric core inside the injection mold cavity and injecting thermoplastic melt around it. The elastomeric core is initially stabilized by support pins that are sequentially retracted during or at the end of fill. The latter one step process does eliminate the need for secondary welding or forming operations, however, it does necessitate the use of a significantly more complicated and expensive primary processing operation. In addition, the designer must consider the fact that the part "quality" will be influenced by the manufacturing and assembly processes used.

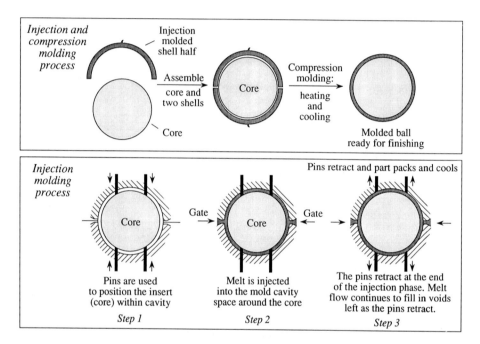

Figure 6.1. Processes used in the manufacture of golf balls can involve (i) injection molding followed by compression molding, or (ii) injection molding with a more complex mold.

The quality of parts produced using competitive fastening systems may not be equivalent. For example, it is relatively easy for a designer to eliminate the use of self threading screws (or other types of mechanical fasteners) by incorporating a molded cantilever snap beam directly into the molded product. The molded snap beam assembly method is desirable because it eliminates one component, the self threading screw, and simplifies assembly by replacing an operation that requires rotation, with one that meets the desired objective of simple "push-on" assembly. While these two fastening methods do compete, the overall performance of the two end products would in fact be quite different. For example, if the snap beam fails during service (or during product repair), the entire molded component must be scrapped. On the other hand, stripped screw threads are generally repairable using a longer or larger diameter screw. Preload and vibration control can also be more difficult to control with snap fits, while screws offer infinite control over preload. The point here is that both manufacturing and performance criteria must be considered. In some cases, no one assembly technique is deemed to be adequate, and a "belt and suspenders" approach is taken, where a primary assembly technique such as adhesive bonding is used, along with a few strategically placed reliable mechanical fasteners for additional safety.

A number of assembly techniques will be discussed in this chapter. The techniques include:

- Press fit assembly
- Snap fit assembly
- Mechanical fastening techniques
- Welding techniques
- Adhesive bonding
- Solvent bonding

The selection of the assembly method that is most appropriate for a particular product involves a number of considerations above and beyond economic considerations. The materials that will make up the components to be assembled are one of the most important considerations. For example, polyethylene may be an ideal candidate for press fit and snap assemblies due to its ductility, however, its superior chemical resistance and low surface energy all but prevent the use of adhesives with this material. Welding techniques are appropriate for thermoplastics, but not thermosets. Coefficient of thermal expansion is also an important material consideration, especially when assembling components produced from different materials, or when the assembly process involves the addition of a third material, such as in the case of adhesive bonding or mechanical fastening.

Esthetic requirements also have an impact on the selection of the assembly method. Self threading screws can be used in conjunction with a blind boss to produce a clam shell assembly when only one appearance surface is required, however, their use may be prohibited in applications requiring improved esthetics on both the upper and lower surfaces of the clam shell. Environmental and structural performance requirements will also influence the selection of the fastening technique. For example, mechanical fastening or welding of a particular thermoplastic product may be preferred over adhesive bonding when the end-use application involves high temperatures and high humidities. There are also a variety of structural concerns associated with product assembly. They include the performance of the fastening system under impact loading, fatigue loading, static loading, and the effects of residual or thermally induced stress [3].

One of the most important factors that must be considered when evaluating assembly methods is functionality, or the ability to reverse or disassemble the components for repair or recycling. Adhesive bonding and welding processes are generally considered to be irreversible, while snap fits, press fits and mechanical assembly techniques offer the potential for disassembly. For example, parts assembled using self threading screws can be used where one or two disassembly / reassembly cycles are anticipated (for example in appliance repair), while more durable machine screw / insert assemblies are used when frequent assembly is anticipated (for example in photocopy machine maintenance).

In recent years, the *Design for Disassembly (DFD)* philosophy has become very important as a method to improve the recyclability of multi-material, multi-component products by reducing the costs associated with the "separation" of the individual components [4,5]. This relatively new design philosophy is being practiced in areas such as automotive, computer, and appliance manufacturing. The DFD concept is simple; (i) minimize the number of materials and parts that are used in the manufacture of the product, (ii) utilize materials that are easily recycled, and (iii) use reversible assembly techniques. DFD dictates that secondary operations such as painting, printing, metallization or plating should be avoided whenever possible.

Fastening methods have been described as being the heart of design for disassembly. Molded in fasteners such as interference or reversible snap fits are the preferred method of assembly for DFD. While snap type assemblies are preferred, the use of reversible mechanical fasteners (such as screws), is also accepted in DFD, their use being preferred over more permanent assembly techniques such as welding or adhesive bonding. Processes such as electromagnetic welding or temporary adhesive bonding also show promise, however, residual adhesives that can have a negative impact on the performance of the recycled plastic material (depending on the relative compatibility between the adhesive contamination and the plastic resin).

6.2   Press Fit Assemblies

6.2.1   Introduction

The simplest means of assembling plastic parts is to utilize their elastic or spring like characteristics to produce press fit assemblies. Press fitting assembly methods are most commonly used with cylindrical plastic parts such as the hub / shaft assembly shown in Figure 6.2, however, many other geometries are possible. Press fit assemblies rely on the interference between the two components to keep the components locked together. The concept is ideal for cylindrical parts since the stresses and strains associated with the interference are distributed uniformly around the circumference of the part [6,15].

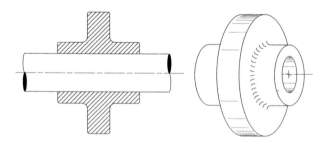

Figure 6.2. Molded plastic parts such as gears, wheels or bearings are commonly mounted on shafts using a press fit.

Gears, pulleys, bearings, and other annular parts are commonly attached to metal or plastic shafts using the press fit technique. The principle advantage of this technique is its simplicity. Parts are molded without undercuts, and no additional mechanical fasteners, such as set screws or key ways, are needed. It should be noted here, however, that press fit hubs are subject to long term tensile stresses, and as a result both the tensile stress relaxation properties of the material and the potential for crazing or cracking must be taken into account when designing press fit assemblies. This can be a particular concern for hubs molded with a series of pin gates or internal spoke gates, which in turn create a series of weld lines perpendicular to the direction of the tensile stress. Disc or diaphragm gates are preferred for press fit applications, since weld lines are eliminated.

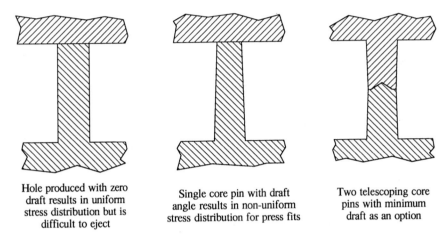

Hole produced with zero draft results in uniform stress distribution but is difficult to eject

Single core pin with draft angle results in non-uniform stress distribution for press fits

Two telescoping core pins with minimum draft as an option

Figure 6.3. Core pins with excessive draft result in non-uniform stress distributions for press fit hubs. Hubs with zero draft are more difficult to mold. The telescoping core pins offer a balance in terms of stress distribution and moldability.

An additional manufacturing concern for press fit hubs is the draft angle used to mold the inside diameter of the hub itself. Draft angles are added to facilitate demolding or ejection of the part from the mold, however, their use results in a non-uniform stress distribution for the hub after press fitting. If possible, hubs should have a zero or minimum draft angle. If draft angles are used to facilitate release, two core pins, one extending from the cavity and one from the core, can be used as shown in Figure 6.3. This approach is preferred over the single core pin as it reduces the amount of draft required and results in a more balanced stress distribution in the final assembly. Holes molded with excessive draft angles could require reaming to size before assembly.

6.2.2   Material Considerations

In theory, the press fit assembly process can be used with any thermosetting or thermoplastic material, however, in practice, the use of press fit techniques becomes significantly easier with more ductile polymers. Consider the typical application of a molded plastic hub such as a gear, pressed over a solid steel shaft. The torsional strength of a given assembly is determined by both the material properties and the amount of diametral interference. Rigid, glassy polymers such as phenolic or polystyrene have breaking strain values that are less than 1.0%. The design strain values that can be used, especially for longer term applications where stress relaxation can occur, cannot exceed perhaps 10 - 40% of this breaking strain value. Permissible interference values are directly related to design strain values, and as a result, the difference in the inside diameter of the hub and the outside diameter of the shaft may be less than the combined manufacturing tolerances of the hub and shaft. When more ductile polymers such as unreinforced an polyethylene, nylon, or acetal are used, the design strain values are large enough (relative to the combined manufacturing tolerances) that press fitting becomes a practical assembly option as shown in Figure 6.4.

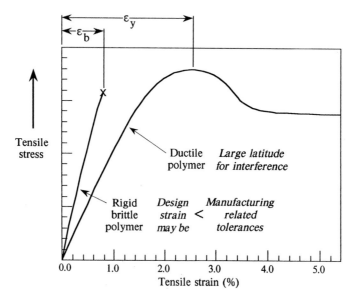

Figure 6.4. Typical stress-strain behavior for rigid and ductile polymers. Many rigid polymers are too brittle for press fit applications. Tough, ductile polymers are more forgiving when considering the effects of manufacturing tolerances.

The hub in a press fit assembly is subject to tensile loading, while the shaft is subject to compressive loading. The properties of both the hub and shaft materials must be taken into account when designing press fit assemblies, especially when the shaft is produced using a plastic material. Tensile stresses in the hub are the primary concern in most cases. Tensile stress levels for the hub should be kept as low as possible in order to provide a more reliable long term assembly. If the design stress values are low, the decay in torsional (or axial) strength due to stress relaxation will be reduced. In addition, the potential for failure due to crazing, cracking, weld lines or chemicals is reduced at lower stress levels. Unfortunately, the axial and torsional strength of a press fit assembly are also directly related to contact pressure and therefore the tensile stress level. The force, F, required to cause relative movement between the hub and the shaft can be given by:

$$F = \mu \cdot P \cdot A \qquad (6.1)$$

where μ is the coefficient of friction between the shaft and hub, P is the contact pressure (directly related to design stress), and A is the surface area of contact. The coefficient of friction for a given hub / shaft material pair is essentially a constant (it does in fact vary with stress level and surface quality). The optimum press fit design is achieved when the designer uses an interference value that results in low stress levels, but maximizes the surface area of contact as shown in Figure 6.2. Larger diameter shafts can also be used when possible. Additives that reduce the coefficient of friction of the polymer will reduce the torsional strength of the assembly. Additives such as mold releases or lubricants, should be avoided in press fit applications. The mating surfaces should be very clean and free from any type of chemical contaminate that could result in delayed failure [16]. Press fit assemblies subject to temperature variations should be produced with materials that have similar coefficients of thermal expansion whenever possible, to avoid changes in the effective interference due to the coefficient of thermal expansion mismatch.

6.2.3   Design of Press Fit Assemblies

The designer's objective in most press fit applications is to produce an assembly that has adequate resistance to both torsional and axial movement, while keeping component stress levels (especially tensile stress) within acceptable limits. The tensile stress level for a given shaft / hub material combination is determined by the overall geometry of the components and the interference value used. In most cases, the outer hub dimensions and often the shaft diameter are dictated by the end-use application. The designer must determine an acceptable interference value for each application. One way to determine the acceptable interference is to consult material manufacturers, who can provide graphical representations of interference limits (maximum recommended interference value), such as that shown in Figure 6.5.

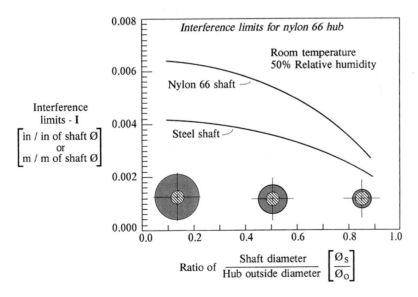

Figure 6.5. The amount of interference for a press fit can be determined using design equations, or graphs similar to that shown, indicating the maximum recommended interference for a particular material.

The information presented in figures of this type is material specific and is applicable only within a limited range of environmental conditions. Using the information given in Figure 6.5, the interference limit, I, for a nylon hub and steel shaft can be determined. Consider the following example.

> Steel shaft diameter, $\emptyset_s$ = 0.400 inch
> Nylon hub outside diameter, $\emptyset_o$ = 1.000 inch
> then $\emptyset_s / \emptyset_o$ = 0.400 inch / 1.000 inch = 0.40

From the graph, the I limit value is 0.0036 inch / inch shaft diameter. The interference value for the 0.400 inch diameter shaft would be:

> I = 0.400 inch x 0.0036 inch / inch shaft diameter = 0.0014 inch

The hub inside diameter, $\emptyset_i$, is then:

> $\emptyset_i = \emptyset_s$ - I = 0.400 inch - 0.0015 inch = 0.3985 inch

The molded gear, after mold shrinkage; should have an inside diameter no less than 0.3985 inch to stay within the material manufacturers recommended strain limit.

Figures 6.5 shows that the permissible interference increases as the ratio of the radial wall thickness to shaft diameter increases. The figure also shows that the recommended interference increases when nylon, rather than steel, is used for the shaft material. This is due to the fact that the softer nylon shaft (relative to steel) actually deforms after the pressing operation. Even though the interference values are greater for the nylon hub / shaft combination compared to the nylon / steel combination, the effective (net) interference and tensile stress level in the plastic hub after pressing is approximately the same in both cases.

While the information presented in Figure 6.5 is extremely useful, it is limited, since it is both material and environment specific. As a more general approach, Equation 6.2 can be used to determine the interference value for any hub / shaft material combination:

$$I = [(\sigma_D \cdot \emptyset_s)/W] \cdot [[(W + v_h)/ E_h] + [(1 - v_s)/E_s]] \qquad (6.2)$$

where: I = diametral interference (inch)
σ_D = design stress level (lbs / inch^2)
$\emptyset_o$ = hub outside diameter (inch)
$\emptyset_s$ = shaft diameter (inch)
E_h = hub modulus (lbs / inch^2)
E_s = shaft modulus (lbs / inch^2)
v_h = Poisson's ratio for hub material
v_s = Poisson's ratio for shaft material
$W = [1 + (\emptyset_s / \emptyset_o)^2] / [1 - (\emptyset_s / \emptyset_o)^2]$

The interference, or difference in the shaft diameter and the hub inside diameter, can be determined if the shaft and hub outside diameters, and material properties are known. When the shaft and hub are produced in the same polymer, the hub and shaft properties are equivalent, and the expression reduces to:

$$I = [(\sigma_D \cdot \text{Ø}_s)/W] \cdot [(W+1)/E] \qquad (6.3)$$

where E is the modulus of the polymer (assumes tensile modulus is equal to compressive modulus). Equation 6.2 can also be reduced to a simpler form when a polymer hub is used with a metal shaft. For the metal shaft, $E_s \gg E_p$, and the I can be found using:

$$I = [(\sigma_D \cdot \text{Ø}_s)/W] \cdot [(W + v_h)/E_h] \qquad (6.4)$$

This form of the equation is most commonly used since plastic hubs are typically used with steel shafts. The material property values used in the expression should be those that correlate with the end-use conditions.

The designer must determine what level of tensile stress (or strain) that is acceptable for the hub material. The design stress value is not a constant value but changes with variables such as temperature, relative humidity, chemical environment and time. As the service life of a plastic product increases, the recommended design stress levels decrease. Consider the press fit hub / shaft assembly in Figure 6.6. Press fit hubs are sometimes pushed over shafts that have been turned down to provide positive axial location.

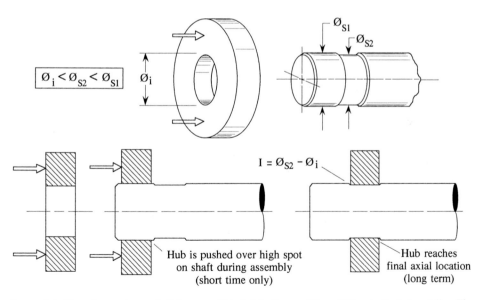

Figure 6.6. Use of an undercut shaft for press fit hub / shaft assemblies will locate the hub axially. The stresses associated with both the long term and short term interference (as the hub is pushed onto the shaft) must be considered by the designer.

The hub inside diameter and shaft diameter at the point where the shaft is undercut, should be designed using an interference value that is suitable for a long term application. The interference value (and strain level) are significantly higher when the hub is pushed over the shoulder onto the shaft during assembly, though for only a very short period of time. Acceptable short term stress (or strain) values could be used for this very short term assembly interference calculation. The tensile stress values that are suitable for long term press fit applications are determined by the stress relaxation characteristics of the polymer, and are often less than 20-25% of the short tensile yield stress for the material. In general, the design stress values for long term applications should be kept as low as possible, in order to minimize stress relaxation and the potential for premature failure due to slippage or cracking. However, when the hub is pushed over the shoulder on the shaft (the portion of the shaft that has not been turned down) during installation, the stress levels reach a higher value, perhaps 40 - 60% of the tensile yield stress, for a very short period of time.

The force required to push a press fit (undersized) hub over a shaft is important for a number of reasons. The push-on force, F, determines the assembly characteristics, torsional strength, and axial strength of the assembly. The push-on force can be determined using:

$$F = \mu \cdot P \cdot A = \mu \cdot P \cdot \pi \cdot \emptyset_s \cdot L \qquad (6.5)$$

Where L is the axial length or width of the hub. The contact pressure, P, can be determined using:

$$P = \sigma_D / W \qquad (6.6)$$

The push-on force value, P, is the force required for assembly, and is related to the torsional strength (slippage torque), T, of the assembly.

$$T = F \cdot \emptyset_s / 2 \qquad (6.7)$$

Push-on or assembly force values for the hub / shaft assembly can be reduced using lubricants that reduce the coefficient of friction between the polymer hub and metal shaft, however, lubricants will also reduce the torsional strength (i.e. slippage torque) of the press fit assembly. The combined effect of the lubricant and the surface tensile stress in the hub can also lead to problems such as stress cracking over the long term. The preferred method of reducing assembly stresses is to cause a temporary change in the interference value by cooling the metal shaft, heating the polymer hub, or both. The most common approach is to simply cool the shaft using a freezer, as this eliminates the potential for problems such as oxidation, warpage, or softening of the polymer hub that could occur if the hub was heated. The temporary change in the shaft diameter, $\Delta\emptyset$, is given by:

$$\Delta\emptyset_s = \alpha_s \cdot \emptyset_s \cdot \Delta T \qquad (6.8)$$

where α is the linear coefficient of thermal expansion for the shaft, and ΔT is the temperature change.

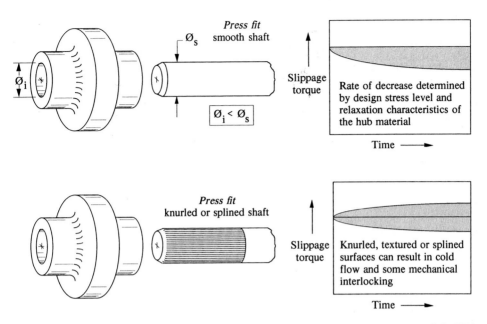

Figure 6.7. The shafts used with press fit assemblies can be smooth, textured or even knurled. With smooth shafts, torsional strength can decrease with time due to stress-relaxation effects. The torsional strength for textured or knurled shafts involves some degree of mechanical interlock.

Torque retention is a significant problem for press fit assemblies, due to stress relaxation. Once a hub is pressed into place over a smooth metal shaft, the contact pressure and torsional strength decrease over the long term as shown in Figure 6.7. However, if the same hub is pressed over a knurled, splined, textured or bead blasted surface, the creep or cold flow of material into the various topographical features can result in a more constant or even an increase in torsional strength over time. Smooth shaft surfaces are recommended for rigid, amorphous polymers, while rougher surfaces can be used with more ductile, semi-crystalline polymers that are less sensitive to stress concentration effects. Mechanical design modifications, such as keyways or other shaft geometries, can also be used to increase the torsional strength of a hub / shaft assembly, however, their use negates the need for and simplicity of the press fit assembly concept.

6.3   Snap Joint Assemblies

6.3.1   Introduction

Snap or interference fit assembly methods for molded plastic products provide an attractive alternative to more conventional assembly approaches. The use of snap joint assemblies is increasing at a rapid rate, since parts assembled using the snap technique satisfy the requirements of both *Design for Assembly* and *Design for Disassembly*. From an assembly viewpoint, snap joints are economical because they are molded directly into the product as an integral feature. This eliminates the need for additional parts / materials such as mechanical fasteners or adhesives. The assembly operations associated with snap fit assemblies are also relatively simple, usually requiring only straight insertion. There is no need for rotational motion or part fixturing. The snap joints can also be designed to be reversible, permitting access for repair and improved product recyclability. Snap assemblies are simple, yet they are perhaps the most versatile means of plastic product assembly [6-14].

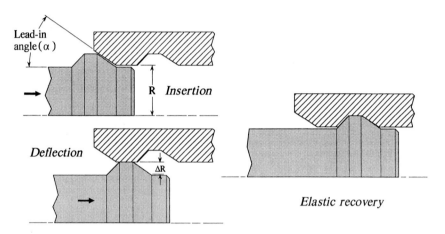

Figure 6.8. Insertion, deflection and recovery. While there are many different snap fit geometries, the snap fitting process always involves a momentary deflection during assembly / disassembly, followed by elastic recovery.

Snap joints can have a variety of geometries, however, the principles of operation remain the same in each case. When two parts are joined using the snap assembly process, a protruding feature on one component, such as a hook or beam, is deflected briefly during the product assembly operation due to an interference, after which the protruding part recovers elastically, and catches in an undercut or indentation on the mating component. The deflection during the assembly operation can be relatively large resulting in high stress or strain levels, however, once the assembly is snapped in place, the components are generally designed to be in a relatively stress free state (unlike press fits) [6].

Perhaps the most significant disadvantage associated with the use of snap assemblies is the consequence of joint failure. Snap assemblies that undergo repeated assembly operations can fail due to fatigue: Even one time assembly applications can fail due to improper handling. This can be a particular problem for snap assemblies produced from brittle, filled, or fiber reinforced polymers. Since the snap member is an integral feature of the molding itself, snap failure can mean component failure. Snaps are difficult or impossible to repair. As a result, it may be desirable to "overdesign" the number of snap joints required for a particular product to account for the possibility of individual snap damage. The redundancy may have some impact on the tool and ultimate product cost, however, the useful service life of the part may be extended. Strain limiting features, adjacent to, the deflecting component, can also be added to limit the permissible deflection and minimize the potential for snap damage.

Another disadvantage associated with the use of snap joint assemblies is the need for tighter control over part tolerances. The tightness of a snap assembly is controlled by both the snap geometry and the stress state after assembly. Excessive interference or stress can lead to the potential for joint failure, while a lack of interference may result in poor location or a loosening of the parts. Preload control can also be difficult to accomplish with snap assemblies, however, creative joint design and careful control over part tolerances improve the ability to control the preload.

6.3.2   Types of Snap Joints

Snap joints are commonly categorized as (i) snap hooks or beams, (ii) annular or ring snaps, (iii) ball and socket snaps, or (iv) torsional snap joints. Snap joints are further categorized as being either separable or non-separable [6,12,14]. Annular snap joints can be used to assemble rotationally symmetric parts. The annular snap joints shown in Figures 6.9 to 6.11 represent common configurations.

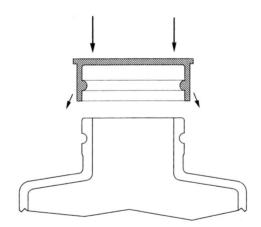

Figure 6.9. Annular snap fits are commonly used with more flexible polymers. A common application for an annular snap assembly is a push on bottle cap.

The bottle cap shown in Figure 6.9 has a circumferential bead that deflects briefly during assembly as it is pushed over the neck of the bottle. The design permits both assembly and disassembly, and is therefore described as reversible. Unlike press fits, snap assemblies are usually designed to be in a stress free (or very low) stress state after assembly.

The cylindrical components shown in Figure 6.10 differ from one another in that the component on the right is reversible, while the one on the left is self locking. The separable joint incorporates both a lead-in and a return angle or "ramp" that permits both insertion and separation, while the inseparable joint is self locking because it incorporates a 90° return angle. These lead-in and return angles can be used as one means to control the relative "push on" and "pull off" forces for a given snap geometry.

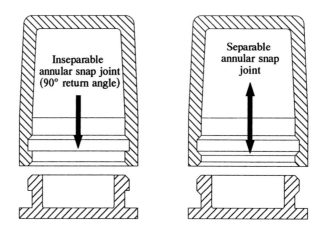

Figure 6.10. Snap assemblies can be designed to be either separable or inseparable.

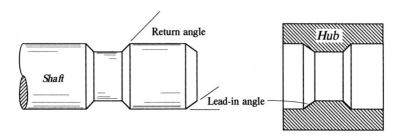

Figure 6.11. The snap fit lead-in and return angles influence the push-on and the push-off forces.

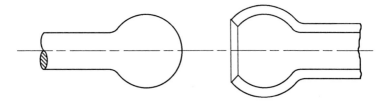

Figure 6.12. Example of a ball and socket snap fit assembly.

The ball and socket snap assembly shown in Figure 6.12 is a modification of the annular snap. Annular snap assemblies are used most commonly with ductile or flexible materials. Push-on / pull-off forces for parts produced in more rigid materials can be extremely high. For these more rigid materials, slotted annular snaps such as that shown in Figure 6.13, are commonly used.

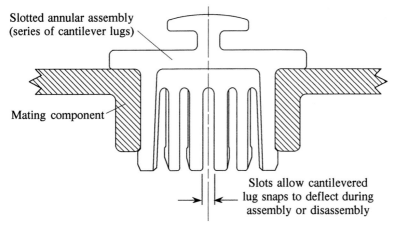

Figure 6.13.   The slotted annular snap assembly is actually a series of cantilever snap beams. This approach is more suitable for rigid polymers.

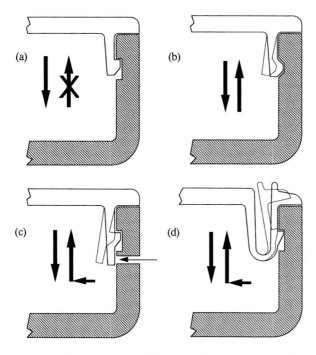

Figure 6.14. Cantilever snap beams are commonly used for the assembly of plastic parts. A variety of both separable and inseparable configurations are possible.

The slotted annular snap shown in Figure 6.14 is actually a series of cantilever beams or lugs that extend in the plane of the cylindrical wall. The forces of assembly and the strength of the assembly can be controlled by the number and the design of the individual cantilever sections that make up the slotted annulus.

The most commonly used snap joint utilizes a cantilever beam that deflects and snaps into an undercut on the mating component. These cantilever beam snaps can be designed to be reversible or irreversible, and can be molded directly into the part at the desired locations. The cantilever beams are either an extension of the part walls (i.e. in-plane beams), or extend up (most commonly perpendicular) from the nominal wall (i.e. out-of-plane beams). A variety of cantilever beam configurations are shown in Figures 6.14 to 6.24.

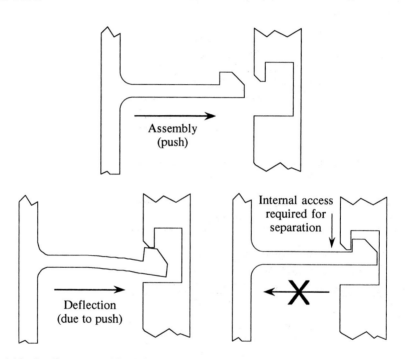

Figure 6.15. Cantilever snap with a 90° return angle must be manually deflected for separation.

Like annular snap assemblies, cantilever snap assemblies can be designed to be separable or inseparable. The assembly shown in Figure 6.14a is inseparable, while that in Figure 6.14b can be disassembled by simply "pulling" the cover off of the base. The pull-out forces are on the same order of magnitude as the push-in forces for an assembly of this type. Low push-in forces are desirable from an assembly point of view, however, a high separation force is often desirable in service, such as in the case of a toy or an appliance housing, where there is a potential for injury due to electrical shock. In such a case, 90° return angles can be used. When 90° return angles are used, provisions for separation can be designed into the product when desired (for purposes such as component repair) as shown in Figure 6.14c.

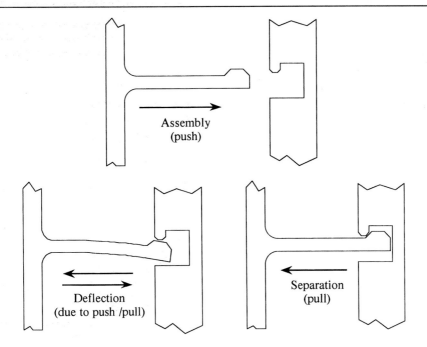

Figure 6.16. Cantilever snap beams with ramping return angles can be snapped in and out. The angles of inclination and the beam geometry control the relative assembly and disassembly forces.

Figure 6.17. The injection molded automobile wheel cover incorporates a number of separable cantilever snaps.

The joints shown in Figure 6.15 cannot be separated with a simple axial pull due to the 90° return angle, while those in Figure 6.16 are easily separable due to the incorporation of a ramping return angle. The molded thermoplastic wheel cover shown in Figure 6.17

is an example of a product that can be separated using axial force. The potential for cantilever beam damage due to improper use is relatively low for the wheel cover since the maximum beam deflection that occurs during assembly / disassembly is determined by the degree of undercut that is designed into the product. The potential for excessive deflection (and possible beam damage) is a very real possibility with the part design shown in Figure 6.14c. Whenever manually separable 90° return angle cantilever snap beams are used, it is good practice to design "stops" or deflection limiting features into the product.

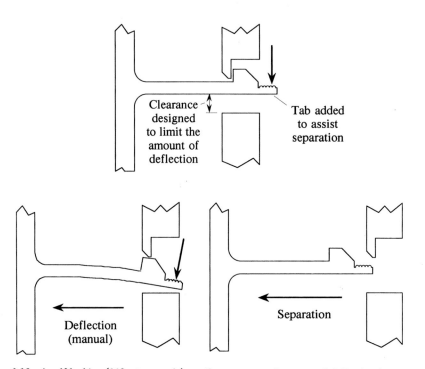

Figure 6.18. A self locking (90° return angle) cantilever snap requires manual deflection for separation. When beams require manual deflection, some type of molded in stop that limits the maximum deflection minimizes the potential of beam breakage due to over stressing.

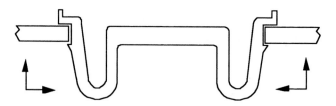

Figure 6.19. Externally activated U-shaped cantilever snaps are commonly used in the assembly of components such as battery access covers. Where repeated deflection is anticipated. The potential for failure is reduced because the maximum possible deflection is self limiting.

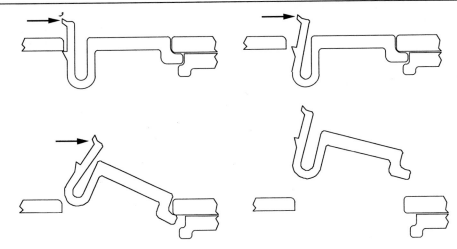

Figure 6.20. Deflection sequence for a U-shaped cantilever snap.

The cantilever beam assembly shown in Figure 6.18 limits the possible deflection and potential for damage. The U-shaped beams shown in Figures 6.14c, 6.19 and 6.20 can be designed to eliminate the damage due to excess deflection by controlling design variables such as undercut depth, wall thickness, length and the radius of curvature. Relatively large deflections can be achieved using U-shaped cantilever sections.

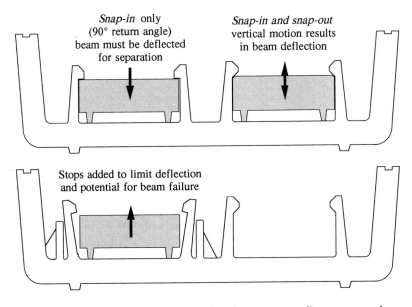

Figure 6.21. Electrical components such as circuit boards or power supplies are commonly mounted to a molded chassis using cantilever snaps. When 90° return angle snap beams are used (i.e. those requiring manual deflection for disassembly), stops can be added to limit deflection and potential beam damage.

Cantilever beam snaps are commonly molded into chassis assemblies for component /
subassembly mounting as shown in Figure 6.21. The snap beam design with the 90°
return angle will lock the component in place, however, preload control (to avoid the
potential for vibration, etc.) can be difficult to achieve. Control over preload requires
extremely tight control over tolerances, unless the component is oversized and compliant
in compression (has spring like characteristics). The cantilever snap beams with a
ramped return angle (<90°) on the right in Figure 6.21 can be used to provide a light
preload and constant pressure. When the shallow return angle is used, the component is
easily detached using an axial pull motion. This can be a benefit for component repair
operations, but may be a problem in situations where the product is subjected to impact
loading, since the captured component may be jarred loose (for example during
shipping). These push-in and pull-out forces are important considerations in all snap
joint applications. Variables such as beam length and angle of inclination have a very
large effect on the forces.

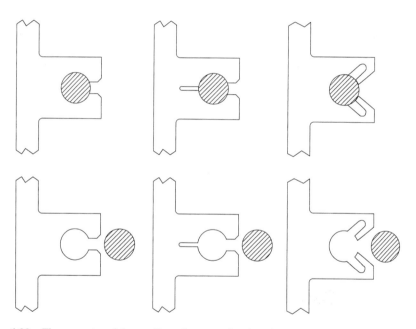

Figure 6.22. The geometry of the cantilever beam can be altered to control the relative insertion and
separation forces.

For example, both the push-in and pull-out forces for the shaft mount shown in Figure
6.22a would be very high due to the relatively short beam length. The stresses associated
with assembly could also be high, leading to the potential for failure during insertion.
The push-in and pull-out forces (along with stresses) could be reduced by extending the
effective length of the beam sections as shown in Figure 6.22b. Both push-in and
pull-out forces would be essentially the same with this design. Another option is the
design shown in Figure 6.22c, which is an assembly with low insertion resistance, yet a
high resistance to separation [6].

Preload control is also an important consideration when cantilever beam assemblies are designed. The importance of dimensional accuracy cannot be over emphasized when snap assemblies are used. Dimension demands can be relaxed when spring like or elastomeric components are incorporated into the design to facilitate preload control, as depicted in Figure 6.23.

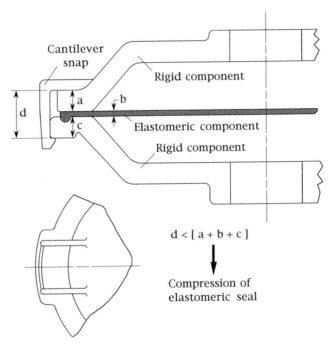

Figure 6.23.   Flexible foam or elastomeric components are commonly used in snap fit assemblies to minimize tolerance demands and to control preload and vibration.

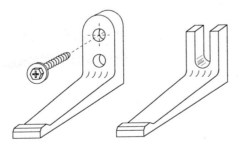

Figure 6.24.   Cantilever snap beams are sometimes molded as separate parts, and are attached to other plastic or metallic parts.

Cantilever snaps are sometimes molded as separate entities and attached to another component using mechanical fasteners or mechanical interlocking. Consider the component shown in Figure 6.21. If the chassis and components were subject to frequent repair or maintenance, the potential for cantilever snap beam failure as a result of repeated deflection would be relatively high. Failure of a single, integral beam could compromise the performance of the entire chassis. An alternative to the use of an integral beam is the use of a separate cantilever snap beam assembly. The beam shown in Figure 6.24 attaches to a chassis using self threading screws. The use of the beam may simplify component maintenance by offering the advantages of reversible snap assembling and separation, yet the beam is replaceable in the event it becomes damaged due to excessive deflection or abuse. A beam of this type can also be used in situations where the chassis materials is not well suited for integral snap beams (e.g. metal parts or parts produced from very brittle plastic materials).

6.3.3   Molding Cantilever Snaps

The use of snap joints does simplify and reduce the cost of assembly operations, however, they can add a very significant degree of complexity to the primary injection molding operation. Snap joints must have undercuts, and as a result, molds must be designed to facilitate part ejection and release of the undercut (either the hook or the hole/indentation where the hook snaps into). In addition, cantilever beams having thin walls and high length to thickness ratios can be difficult to fill during molding, and weld lines can sometimes occur. Cantilever beams with heavier walls can lead to the same types of sink mark and residual stress problems that are associated with the ribs or bosses. Of these manufacturing related problems, however, the difficulties associated with part ejection are the most significant.

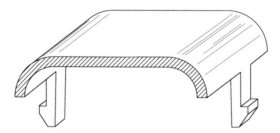

Figure 6.25. Cantilever snap beams can add to tooling costs and complexity. In this case, the snap beams are positioned in such a way (i.e. the hook facing outwards) that no special mold actions are required.

The in-plane cantilever beams extending down from the sidewalls of the part shown in Figure 6.25 are easily molded, and do not require any special mold actions (only simple, 2-plate, open and close shut-off actions are required). The addition of these beams to the part does not have any great impact on the ability to manufacture the part. The hook on the beam shown in Figure 6.25 faces outwards, and as a result the undercut associated with the hook is eliminated when the mold opens.

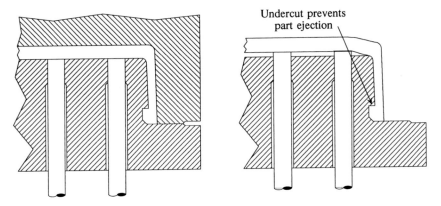

Figure 6.26. The snap beams with inward facing 90° return angles cannot be ejected using a conventional ejector system due to the undercut associated with the hook. Special mold actions are required.

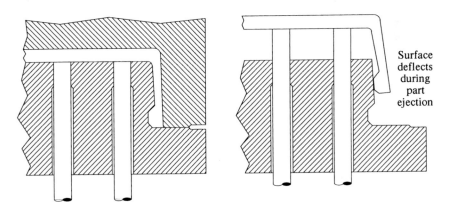

Figure 6.27. Certain snap fit geometries can be ejected by simply stripping the part from the core. This is most appropriate for parts produced with flexible, ductile polymers, where tolerance demands are relatively low.

However, a simple design change can lead to a significant injection molding problem. If the self locking (90°) beam hook faces inwards towards the core (i.e. it is rotated 180°), the part cannot be ejected or stripped from the mold core, as shown in 6.26. The 90° undercut catches in the core, and release is prevented. It may, however, be possible to eject inward facing snap hooks (annular snaps) that have ramped return angles less than 90° as shown in Figure 6.27. Beams with ramped return angles of inclination can pull-out of the core undercut at the time of ejection, but the part will be subject to tensile and bending stresses as it is stripped from the core. Permanent deformation is likely to occur since molded parts are relatively hot and soft at the time (or temperature) of ejection. As a result, tolerances for parts that are simply stripped from the core in this way may not be particularly good.

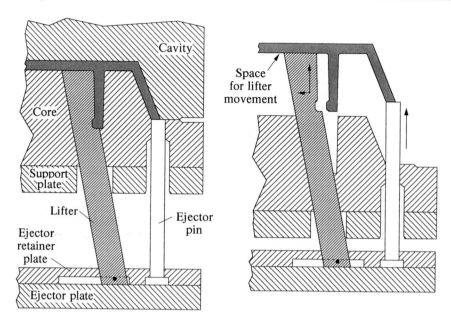

Figure 6.28. A lifter is used to assist in the ejection of a cantilever snap beam.

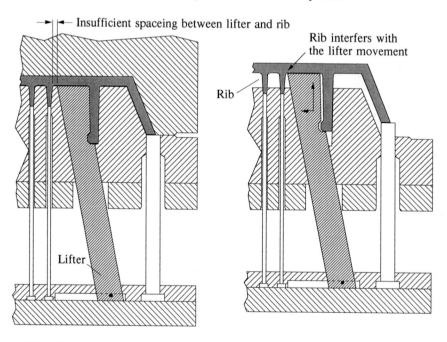

Figure 6.29. Ribs, steps, bosses or other design features cannot be placed in the immediate area of the snap beam as they can interfere with lifter movement.

Out of plane cantilever snaps that extend up from the nominal wall of a molding are impossible to eject without special mold actions. The cantilever snap beam shown in Figure 6.28 must be ejected using a lifter. The lifter is a movable core section that releases the undercut as it ejects the part. The need for the lifter has a significant impact on the cost of the tooling, however, the reduction in assembly costs associated with snap assembly will generally more than offset the additional cost associated with building the more complicated tool. In any case, it is important for the part designer to recognize that the use of the lifter does limit the design freedom to some degree. Design features such as ribs, bosses or steps cannot be placed immediately adjacent to the snap beams, since the lifter must slide across the surface of the part during ejection, as shown in Figure 6.29.

Ejector pins can also be modified to produce half round cantilever snap beams as shown in Figure 6.30. The ejector pin is ground down and keyed to produce the desired snap geometry, in much the same way that a Z-type sprue puller pin is produced. The snap beam geometries achievable with this approach are quite limited. It is also very likely that the molded part will "hang up" on the modified ejector pin since there is no lateral movement associated with ejection to release the undercut (especially if several beams are produced on the same part). The parts may need to be manually / robotically removed, or alternatively, a two stage ejection system can be used.

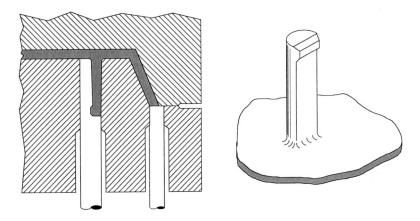

Figure 6.30. Modified ejector pins can also be used to produce rounded snap beams.

An alternative concept that can be used to simplify the manufacturing of cantilever snap beams is shown in Figures 6.31 and 6.32. The part shown in Figures 6.31 has two cantilever snap beams extending up from the nominal wall. The beam on the left requires the use of a lifter / movable core section for ejection, while the beam on the right, with a slot below the beam's undercut, can be molded using a simple cavity and core shut-off as shown in Figure 6.32. The concept is analogous to that of changing a hole in the side wall of a part to a slot, in order to simplify manufacturing. This snap beam manufacturing technique is especially suited for chassis components containing snap beams, since a slot on the underside of an appliance type product is usually not objectionable from a functional or esthetic viewpoint. The technique would not, however,

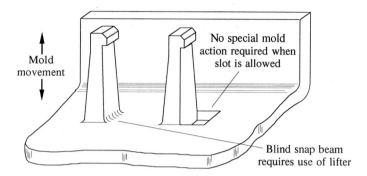

Figure 6.31. Part geometries can be modified to facilitate molding, specifically with consideration towards part ejection. Design features such as slots should be used in place of sidewall holes whenever possible as no special mold actions are required. No special actions are required for the cantilever snap beam with a slot below the hook.

be appropriate for the appliance "cover" since slots on the appearance surfaces are generally not permitted. It should also be noted that the geometry of snap beams produced in this way is somewhat limited as shown in Figure 6.32. The sides of the beam must be tapered to reduce the tendency for core / cavity skiving as the mold closes and to improve the melt flow shut-off capabilities. The upper horizontal surface of the beam (as shown in Figure 6.32) must be parallel to the line of draw while the lower horizontal surface can be tapered at the discretion of the designer. The dimensions of the slot in the part are determined by the maximum width of the cantilever beam in one direction, and by the sum of the interference, landed shelf width, and the taper associated with the shut-off angle in the other direction.

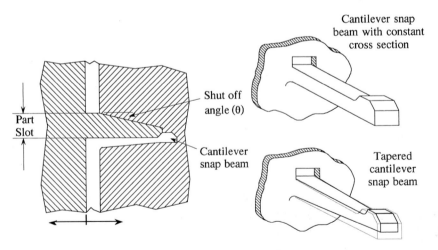

Figure 6.32. The cantilever snap beams shown can be molded in a simple two plate mold without any special mold actions. This method is appropriate when the resulting slot at the base of the snap beam is acceptable.

6.3.4   Design of Snap Joints

The design of a snap fitting joint assembly is no different that the design of any other plastic component or feature. The designer must consider both end-use performance and manufacturability. The structural requirements of a snap fitting joint are a particular concern since (i) the snap members are subject to large deflections during assembly / disassembly, and (ii) the snap members provide the mechanical continuity between components, and are therefore subject to stress during end-use. The mechanical and structural characteristics of a snap fitting assembly must be evaluated as part of an overall structural analysis for the product (see Chapter 4). The simplest of these structural analysis techniques treats the snap component as being separate from the rest of the part. For example, cantilever snaps may be idealized as constant or tapering cross section cantilever beams subject to end loading, while hoop stress equations are used to evaluate annular snap behavior. Classical beam formulas may be suitable for certain snap beams, particularly those beams that project off of the nominal wall, and have high length to thickness ratios (say greater than 5:1) [8]. Whenever possible, however, a finite element analysis will provide a more realistic approximation of the stresses and strains associated with snap beam deflection. These more complete analyses have the ability to take other factors such as adjacent wall deflections, radius (fillet) effects, and true geometries into account [8-10]. Several fundamental concepts associated with cantilever snap beam design are discussed here.

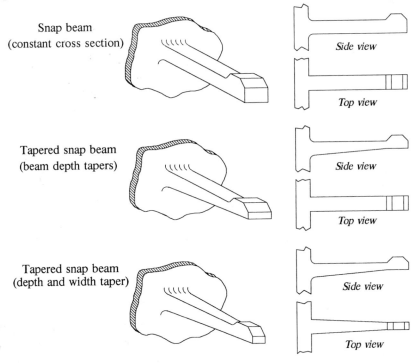

Figure 6.33. Cantilever snap beams can taper through both the width and thickness. Compared to constant cross section beams, tapered beams have a more uniform stress distribution, and greater permissible deflection.

The designer of a snap assembly is interested in establishing the relationship between beam geometry, loading condition, and the levels of stress or strain in the snap member. Design calculations are done to determine both the short term stresses during assembly/disassembly and longer term performance. In the latter case, creep or stress relaxation characteristics of the molding material must be considered. Short term material properties (at the appropriate strain rate) are generally used for the assembly/disassembly deflection and stress analyses since deflection during assembly is a short term event.

The deflections and stresses for cantilever beams such as those shown in Figure 6.33 can be determined using engineering formulas for constant cross section beams, or beams that taper in width and/or thickness. Constant cross section beams are rarely used in practice due to the non-uniform stress distribution along the length of the beam. Beams that taper in the thickness direction have more uniform stress distribution along the length, and permit a significant increase in maximum end deflection that is associated with a given maximum stress value. This minimizes the potential for damage and permits the use of larger hook undercuts. One of the more commonly used tapered snap beam design consists of a beam that tapers gradually from the support end to the free end by a factor of 50%, as shown in Figure 6.34.

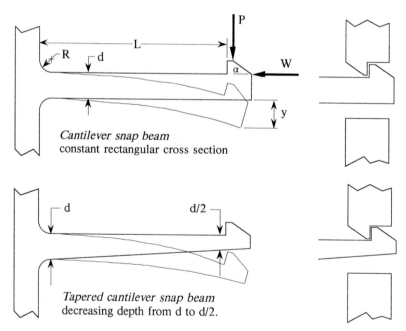

Cantilever snap beam
constant rectangular cross section

Tapered cantilever snap beam
decreasing depth from d to d/2.

Figure 6.34. Constant cross section and tapered rectangular cantilever snap beams.

The relationship between the end deflection of the constant cross section rectangular beam and maximum tensile strain (neglecting geometry effects due to the hook or base radius) is given by [11]:

$$y = 0.67 \cdot \varepsilon \cdot L^2 / d \qquad\qquad (6.9)$$

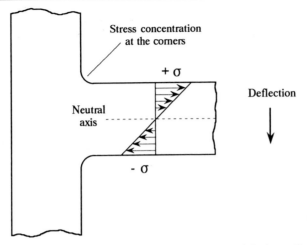

Figure 6.35. When a cantilever snap is subjected to a bending load, both tensile and compressive stresses develop. The stresses are highest at the outer surfaces of the junction with the nominal wall.

where ε is the maximum tensile strain, d is the depth of the beam, y is the end deflection, and L is the length of the cantilever section. For the tapered beam in Figure 6.34:

$$y = 1.1 \cdot \varepsilon \cdot L^2 / d \qquad (6.10)$$

A comparison of the two expressions shows that the permissible deflection for the tapered beam is about 60% greater than that of the constant cross section rectangular beam (for a particular maximum permissible strain value). There is however, a loss in ultimate tensile strength and a reduction in assembly / disassembly force due to the reduction in the stiffness of the tapered beam. The reduction in disassembly forces can be a problem when impact loads are possible.

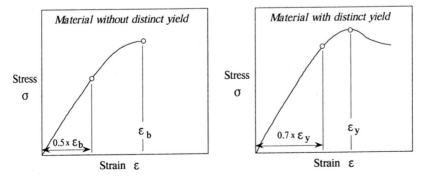

Figure 6.36. Maximum permissible strain values vary with material type. The conditions / strain rate associated with the stress-strain data should be similar to those associated with the end-use application.

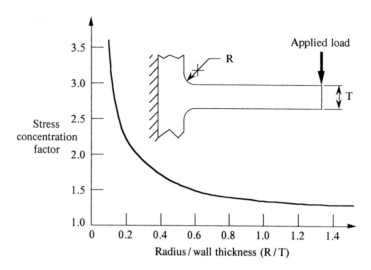

Figure 6.37. The stress values at the intersection of the cantilever snap beam and the nominal wall are higher than those calculated using standard engineering relations due to stress concentration effects.

Permissible strain values that can be used are dependent upon the properties of the material being used for the beam. Permissible strain is often given as a percentage of the yield stress as indicated in Figure 6.36 (at the appropriate temperature, relative humidity and strain rate). The calculation given above assures that the mating component is rigid, which provides a measure of safety, since some deflection is likely to occur in reaction to the beam deflection. Permissible strain values tend to be a higher percentage of the yield strain for ductile polymers. The permissible strain values are generally reduced to lower percentages of the yield stress when multiple deflections are anticipated in the end-use application. Material suppliers should be consulted for specific material recommendations. Care should also be taken to avoid molding related problems such as weld lines, unfavorable orientation, or shrinkage stresses in areas around the snap assembly.

It should also be noted that stresses and strains calculated using design equations should be corrected for stress concentration effects, since stress values are actually greater than the nominal value calculated. Stress concentration factors such as those shown in Figure 6.37 show that larger radius values tend to reduce the stress concentration and mold filling orientation related problems, however, excessive radii can lead to complications due to sinks, voids, shrinkage stress, and due to their effect on wall thickness (especially for short L/d beams). The radius value used in practice must be a compromise between that which provides for structural reliability and acceptable esthetics. Radius values less than 0.015 inch (0.38 mm) should generally be avoided [11].

The deflection force, P, for the constant cross section rectangular beam shown in Figure 6.34 can be determined using:

$$P = [b \cdot d^2 / b] \cdot [E_s \cdot \varepsilon / L] \qquad (6.11)$$

where b is the width of the beam, and E is the secant (strain dependent) modulus. The secant modulus is used in place of the initial modulus for the high strain applications since the maximum load values are likely to occur at strain values beyond the proportional limit of the material as shown in Figure 6.38.

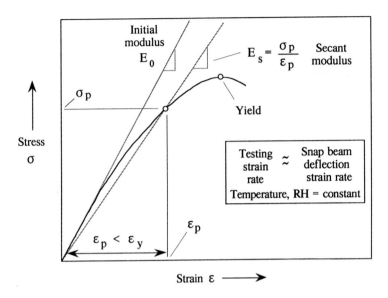

Figure 6.38. The large deflections associated with snap assemblies dictate the use of strain dependent secant modulus values in design calculations.

The mating force (push-on or separation force) for the snap fit assembly can be determined from the deflection and friction forces. The mating (assembly) force, W, is given by:

$$W = P \cdot [(\mu + \tan \alpha)/(1 - \mu \cdot \tan \alpha)] \qquad (6.12)$$

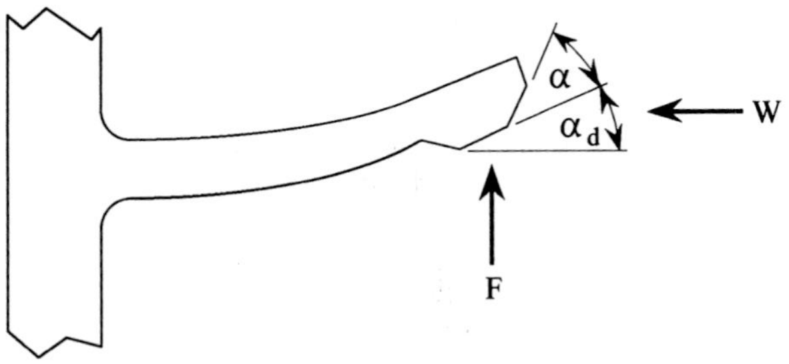

Figure 6.39. The angle of inclination, which affects assembly force, changes as the beam deflects during assembly.

where μ is the coefficient of friction between the mating materials, and α is the angle of inclination during either assembly (lead-in angle) or disassembly (return angle). It should be noted that the angle of inclination changes as the assembly process progresses as shown in Figure 6.39.

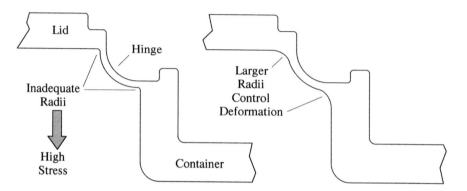

Figure 6.40. The classical living hinge is often used in conjunction with snap fits for clamshell type storage containers.

The use of snap joint assemblies for molded plastic parts will continue to increase as demands on cost competitive manufacturing and product quality increase. The versatility of the snap fit assembly technique is perhaps its greatest advantage. Snap assemblies, particularly annular snaps, are sometimes used in conjunction with hinges or straps. From both a *Design for Assembly* , and a *Design for Disassembly* point of view, the merging of these techniques provides the optimum fastening method.

6.4   Mechanical Fasteners

6.4.1   Introduction

A wide variety of mechanical fasteners are available for the assembly of plastic products. Many of these fasteners were originally developed to join metal or wood components and have simply been adopted for use with plastic materials, while others have been developed specifically to provide an effective means of assembling plastic parts. Mechanical fasteners include machine screws, self threading screws, metal inserts, push-in fasteners, speed clips and nuts, rivets, studs, staples, hinges and a variety of specialty hardware items. Certain types of mechanical fasteners can be used to produce fully operable or reversible joints that permit component repair and disassembly for component recycling, while other mechanical fasteners are designed for permanent assembly. Mechanical fasteners provide a fast and effective method for joining both thermoplastic and thermosetting plastic parts with parts produced in similar or dissimilar materials. The fasteners are available in a variety of sizes and materials, and in most cases, the joining practices are conventional.

Almost all mechanical fasteners are metal, and as a result have dimensions and properties that are nearly independent of temperature, time and relative humidity within the limited range of most plastic product applications. Fasteners produced from stainless steel or plastic materials can be used in very high humidity or corrosive applications. Threaded mechanical fasteners such as machine or self threading screws are ideal for use in applications where preload control is required, such as in applications where reversible fluid tight assemblies are achieved using a combination of gaskets and screws. Another advantage of mechanical assembly is that the ultimate joint strength is achieved instantaneously, unlike adhesive bonding. In fact, mechanical fasteners are sometimes used in conjunction with adhesives for joining larger plastic parts. The mechanical fasteners act as fixtures, keeping the parts in place while the adhesive cures, and also add a measure of safety during product service.

However, mechanical fasteners should be used with care since most of these fasteners are point fasteners, resulting in localized regions of potentially high stress. In addition, many of these fasteners involve the use of holes, adding the problems of stress concentration and weld line formation. As stated earlier, mechanical fasteners produced from aluminum, brass, or steel have relatively good dimensional stability, however, the plastic materials that they are used to join may not. This will result in a thermal expansion mismatch which must be carefully considered when designing the joint. Another disadvantage associated with the use of mechanical fasteners is the need for additional pieces / parts, which is contrary to the common goal of reducing the number of parts necessary to manufacture a product. It is also difficult to achieve a fluid or gas tight seal using mechanical fasteners, unless additional components such as compliant seals or elastomeric gaskets are used.

6.4.2   Screws

Screws are the most widely used category of mechanical fastening devices for the assembly of plastic products. Screws are generally used in applications where an operable or reversible assembly is required, namely parts that require disassembly for service or component replacement, and subsequent reassembly. Screws provide a simple, fast, and effective method of joining similar or dissimilar materials. These threaded fasteners provide infinite control over the assembly preload. There are in fact many screw types and configurations that can be used in the assembly of plastic products. Mechanical assembly methods based on the use of screws include:

- Machine screws (i.e. nuts and bolts)
- Machine screws with a threaded metal insert or molded threads
- Self threading screws

Each of these screw-based mechanical fastening techniques will be discussed separately.

It is important to note that the use of mechanical fasteners can have a great impact on the ability to recycle a plastic product. Products that are designed for disassembly (a prerequisite in many recycling operations) must have two factors in common: they must be simple and inexpensive to take apart, and their primary materials must be easily and economically recycled [17,18]. The fastening methods used are the main focus of design for disassembly. Reversible snap fit assemblies are the preferred method of assembly / disassembly for recycling, however, reversible screw based assemblies provide another option. The number of screws used in an assembly should be kept to a minimum, and screw sizes / types that are used should be standardized whenever possible. Screws can be removed quickly using pneumatic tools, or in cases where the mating thread is a plastic material, the screws can sometimes be pulled from the hole or boss in the mating part using brute force [18]. Self threading screws are the preferred screw type for disassembly since there is no threaded metal insert or nut to worry about (only one component, the screw itself, is associated with the joint). Metal inserts can be difficult to remove and can cause serious problems in subsequent granulation / repelletizing operations (especially since most threaded metal inserts are produced from nonferrous metals, such as brass).

6.4.2.1   Machine Screws and Nuts

Machine screws, nuts, and washers are commonly used to assemble plastic products. Their use is limited to applications where product appearance is not critical, since both the "nut" and the "bolt head" of the fastener are exposed and readily visible [15,19-21]. The bolt head and nut are generally recessed below the surface of the part (or countersunk) to improve product appearance. In some cases, hex shaped depressions are molded into one of the mating parts to restrain the nut from rotation, simplifying the assembly operation. Decorative fastening components, such as cap nuts, are sometimes used as an alternative to improve the assembly appearance. Machine screws and nuts are conventional fasteners and are readily available in a variety of sizes, shapes and qualities. A major disadvantage associated with their use is the requirements for access to both the upper and lower surfaces (or left and right sides) of the part during assembly. This, combined with the need for rotation, makes handling and automation of the machine screw assembly process extremely difficult.

Machine screw joints for flat, sheet like plastic parts or flanges can be produced using molded or drilled holes. If the two parts to be joined are produced from dissimilar materials, having different coefficients of expansion, then expansion joints, slots, or elastomeric grommets must be used to accommodate the differential expansion as shown in Figure 6.41.

When machine screws and nuts are used to join deeper draw, clamshell types of assemblies, hollow, cylindrical bosses must be incorporated into the part to provide local support around the screw, in order to prevent excessive surface deflection as the screw is tightened, as shown in Figure 6.42. The bosses themselves should have a clearance of approximately 0.010 inch (0.25 mm) on the internal diameter to assist in assembly, and account for temperature or tolerance variations [15]. The wall thickness of the boss should be sufficient to provide positive resistance to compression and structural stability.

The bolts are typically preloaded during assembly (i.e. they are tightened an additional amount after the mating parts make initial contact). This is done; to compensate for the thermal expansion mismatch, to compensate for warpage or dimensional variation, compress a gasket, or to minimize the potential for loosening due to stress relaxation or vibration. In most cases, the machine screws are manufactured from steel, and the potential for damage to the plastic part due to over-tightening can be very high, especially during subsequent assembly (part repair) where there may be no control over the magnitude of the tightening torque. The best solution to this problem is to use hollow, cylindrical metal sleeves around the bolts. These sleeves can be simply inserted, pressed

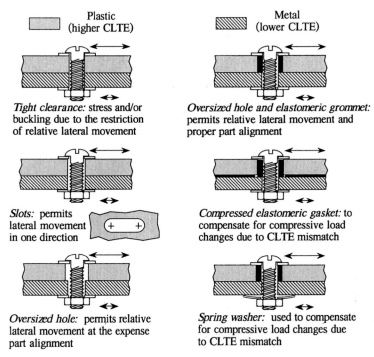

Figure 6.41. A variety of methods can be used to cope with the thermal expansion mismatch that occurs when plastic parts are fastened to parts produced from other materials (e.g. other plastics, metals, etc.).

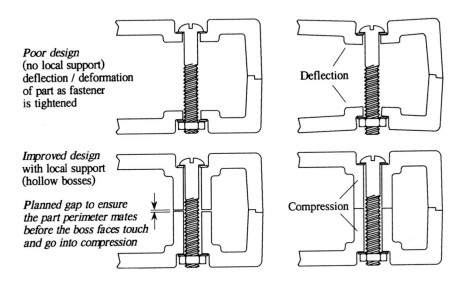

Figure 6.42. Hollow bosses are used with machine screws and nuts to limit deflection.

in, or molded into the bosses themselves, and limit compression of the plastic material [21]. It is also good practice to use load distribution washers under both the head of the bolt and the nut, to distribute the load over a somewhat greater area, thereby reducing stress concentration [16,19,21].

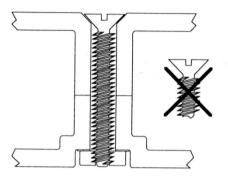

Figure 6.43. Conical head (flat head) screws should be avoided as high tensile stresses can develop.

The underside of the screw heads used in plastic part assembly should always be of the flat washer head variety. Screws with conical heads (commonly called flat head screws) should be avoided, as their use results in some degree of tensile stress [15], rather than compressive stress. When machine screws are used, the local compressive stress levels that developed during assembly can be extremely high and should be estimated theoretically and evaluated experimentally to ensure that the assembly is suitable for the application for which it was intended. Screws are generally used to assemble durable goods with relatively long service lives, and as a result, it is important to take stress relaxation effects into account for this constant, compressive strain application. Conventional flat load distribution washers can be used in combination with conical, wave spring or lock type washers to counteract the effects of stress relaxation or thermally induced dimensional variations.

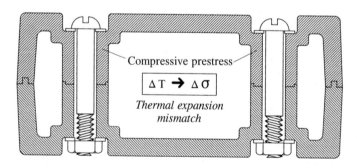

Figure 6.44. The coefficient of thermal expansion for steel fasteners is lower than that of most plastic materials. The CTE mismatch leads to change in compressive preload when the ambient temperature changes.

One of the major problems encountered when machine screws are used with plastic parts is that of thermal expansion mismatch. The linear coefficient of thermal expansion for many plastic materials is an order of magnitude greater than that of steel. Once a product is assembled, ambient temperature changes will lead to an increase or decrease in compressive stress level. As an extreme, at very cold temperatures, the plastic material may shrink so much that the prestress level (applied at the time of assembly) drops to zero, resulting in a loss of clamp pressure and the potential for vibration loosening. On the other hand, higher temperatures lead to a situation where the plastic material's thermal expansion is restrained.

As an example, assume the polycarbonate part shown in Figure 6.44 was assembled at room temperature using 1/4 - 28 TPI machine screws and nuts (1/4 inch diameter, 28 threads per inch). Each boss is 1.0 inch in axial length, resulting in a 2.0 inch overall length. Once the slack in the assembly is taken up and the mating faces touch, the bolts are tightened for 1/4 turn (a turn of the wrist) developing a compressive preload on the plastic part, and a tensile load on the threaded bolt. The compressive strain associated with the one quarter turn (assuming that the higher modulus bolt does not stretch significantly), is given by:

$$\varepsilon = \Delta L / L_o = [1/4 \text{ (turn)} \cdot 1/28 \text{ (inch/turn)}] / 2.0 \text{ (inch)}$$

$$\varepsilon = 0.0045 \text{ (inch/inch)}$$

If the compressive modulus, E, of the polycarbonate at room temperature is taken as 0.35 x 10^6 lbs/inch^2, then the compressive stress is:

$$\sigma = E \cdot \varepsilon = 350,000 \text{ (lbs/inch}^2) \cdot 0.0045 \text{ (inch/inch)}$$

$$\sigma = 1560 \text{ (lbs/inch}^2)$$

Over time, this compressive stress value will decrease due to stress relaxation effects. It is clear, however, that the mechanical advantage associated with screws, especially fine pitch screws, can lead to very high stress levels in the plastic parts, often resulting in part failure when service related stresses are superimposed on the assembly stresses.

Given average values of the linear coefficient of thermal expansion (CTE) for steel and polycarbonate (assuming here that the CTE values are independent of temperature), the effect of temperature on the assembly can be determined [22].

$$\alpha_L \text{ (steel)} = 6.7 \times 10^{-6} \text{ inch/inch/°F} \qquad \alpha_L \text{(PC)} = 38 \times 10^{-6} \text{ inch/inch/°F}$$

The CTE mismatch between the two materials is 31.3 x 10^{-6} inch/inch/°F. In other words, a 1.0 inch section of polycarbonate will grow or shrink (depending on whether temperature increases or decreases) at an additional 31.3 X 10^{-6} inch for every 1.0 °F change in temperature, compared to the steel bolt. The compressive stress level in the boss changes continuously with temperature due to the changes in both the compressive strain due to the CTE mismatch, and due to changes in the compressive modulus of the polycarbonate with temperature. The part temperature would need to reach -74°F before the CTE mismatch causes the bolt tensile / boss compressive stress to reach the "zero" value. On the other hand, an increase in the part temperature would result in an increase in the value of compressive strain due to the CTE mismatch. The absolute value of compressive stress at the higher temperatures can be higher or lower, depending on the modulus temperature behavior of the polymer. Stress relaxation effects for polymers are of course also more significant at elevated temperatures.

Machine screws and bolts, produced from thermoplastic materials such as nylon, acetal, polypropylene, polyetherimide, PTFE and polyimide, are also available in standard machine thread configurations. Plastic screws are also available with steel cores [24]. Plastic fasteners are ideally suited for applications where improved chemical resistance (especially acids and bases) or electrical insulation is required [19,23]. The use of plastic machine screws to assemble plastic parts also seems to be a logical approach to solving the CTE mismatch and over-tightening problems associated with conventional steel machine screws. The cost and limited tensile creep properties of most standard thermoplastic machine screws are factors that limit their widespread use. Aluminum machine screws, with a CTE about twice that of steel, offer a reduction in CTE mismatch compared to steel, have good mechanical properties, but unfortunately, have a relatively high cost [22].

6.4.2.2   Self Threading Screws

Introduction: Machine screws and nuts are sometimes used to assemble plastic products, however, their use is limited to applications where esthetic requirements are minimal, and access to both the top and bottom of the assembly is available. In applications where esthetic specifications require one smooth uninterrupted appearance surface, or in applications where accessibility is a problem, screws can be driven into "blind" metal inserts containing mating threads, or directly into the plastic material itself as shown in Figure 6.45. The latter technique is discussed here while insert assemblies are discussed latter in the chapter.

The primary advantage of incorporating the mating thread directly into the plastic material itself is that it eliminates the need for the threaded metal nut member (and associated washers), thereby minimizing the number of parts required to produce the assembly. The receiving threads can be molded directly into the plastic part when larger screws are used, say greater than 0.250 inch (6.35 mm) diameter, however, this adds significant complexity to the tooling requirements and part molding operation due to difficulties associated with ejection of the thread undercuts. As an alternative for both large and small screws, threads can be tapped or machined into a molded or drilled pilot hole. This secondary threading operation takes a great deal of time, and is not cost effective in most cases, especially when the limited durability of the plastic thread is considered (compared to the improved durability of a metal insert assembly). There are, however, a number of screw types that produce their own mating threads as they are driven into a drilled or molded pilot hole in the plastic part. These "self threading screws" reduce molding and assembly costs by eliminating the need for molded threads or secondary tapping operations.

The screws are available in a wide range of thread configurations, sizes, and head styles. Standard self threading screw sizes range from #2 up to about 5/16 inch (8.0 mm) diameter. Driving torques can become excessive for larger screws. The most commonly used screw sizes are #4, #6, #8, and #10. Self threading screws reduce the number of components required to produce an assembly by eliminating the need for the nut / washer

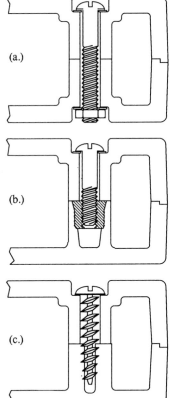

Machine screw and bolt
- Esthetic interuption on both top and bottom surfaces
- Many parts required for assembly
- Access to both top and bottom of part is required during assembly
- Need locking hardware to avoid vibration loosening
- Durable assembly

(a.)

Machine screw and insert
- One smooth surface obtained
- Fewer parts required for assembly
- Internally threaded insert must be inserted into boss during or after molding
- Requires special equipment / tooling for insert
- Good overall durability
- Suitable for repeated assembly

(b.)

Self threading screw and plastic boss
- One smooth surface obtained
- Minimum number of parts required for assembly
- Mating plastic threads formed during assembly
- Minimum fastener and equipment cost
- Limited durability (mating thread is plastic)
- Repeated assembly possible but limited

(c.)

Figure 6.45. Plastic clamshell assemblies are commonly assembled with mechanical fasteners. The options available include machine screws / bolts, machine screws / inserts, and self threading screws.

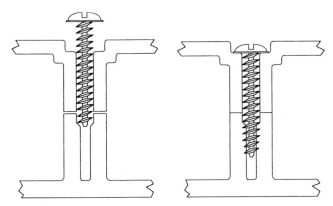

Figure 6.46. A self threading screw boss assembly typically includes the screw, a through clearance boss, and a blind pilot boss.

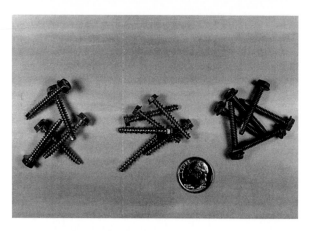

Figure 6.47. A wide variety of self threading screw types are available. The screws shown are size # 6, and have hex washer heads. (left) # 6 type BT thread cutting screw (center) # 6 HiLo® thread forming screw (right) # 6 type T thread cutting screw.

or the internally threaded insert. In many cases, the screws themselves are provided with integral washer heads.

Self threading screws can be used to produce a reversible assembly, and are ideal for use in applications where only limited reassembly is anticipated. Self threading screw assemblies are not as durable as internally threaded metal insert assemblies. However, when properly designed, self threading screws provide a fast, low cost, and effective means of joining plastic parts when reassembly is limited to a maximum of several times. Plastic parts joined with self threading screws are easily disassembled for recycling using high speed pneumatic drivers since there is no insert or nut member used.

Many of the self threading screws that are used with plastic materials are standard designs that have been used for many years with other materials (American National Standards Institute). Some of these screws work well with plastic materials while others are poorly suited. An additional group of fasteners, developed specifically for use with plastic materials, are also available and offer improved performance [25-28].

Self threading screws are also categorized as being either self tapping screws (also known as thread cutting cutting) or thread forming screws. Self tapping screws cut or tap mating threads as they are driven into the plastic boss, while thread forming screws have no cutting capabilities and simply displace material as they are driven. The screw type, size, and the design of the boss system used in a particular application are dependent upon a number of product requirements and performance criteria including:

- Screw pull out resistance
- Clamp load requirements and decay rate
- Repeated assembly requirements
- Torque retention and vibration resistance
- Hoop stresses for the boss assembly
- Assembly characteristics such as the strip to drive torque ratio

A number of terms related to the use of self threading screws are defined at this point to assist in the discussion [16,25,29,30].

Pilot Hole: A molded or drilled hole in the boss that accepts the screw. The diameter of the pilot hole is greater than the minor (root) diameter of the screw, but less than the screw's major (outside) diameter.

Drive Torque (Thread Forming Torque): The torque required to drive the screw into an untapped pilot hole. The maximum thread forming torque is the value measured when the full length of engagement is achieved (i.e. at the point where the mating parts engage).

Strip Torque: The torque necessary to cause the nut member (i.e. the plastic boss) threads to fail. In this mode of failure, the flanks of the plastic thread fail in shear as the screw is rotated.

Destruction Torque (Failure Torque): The level of torque required to cause failure of the screw / boss fastening system during assembly by any means. The term is more general than stripping torque, covering other modes of failure such as boss cracking, boss torsional failure, or screw torsional failure.

Seating Torque (Tightening Torque): The torque used to attain the required clamp loads. The magnitude of the tightening torque for the assembly must lie between the maximum drive torque and the destruction torque value. The seating torque value is the sum of the maximum drive torque and prestress torque.

Prestressing Torque: The difference between the tightening torque and the maximum drive torque. The prestress torque level used is a direct indication of the clamping load value for the assembly.

Destruction to Drive Torque: The ratio of the torque required to cause failure to the maximum drive torque. High destruction to drive torque ratios minimize the potential for damage due to overtorqueing during initial or especially during subsequent reassembly operations by increasing the magnitude of the safe operating torque range.

Prevailing Torque (or Resistance to Loosening): The torque required to remove the screw from the boss after the clamp load has been removed.

Screw Engagement Length: The total length (axial distance or number of turns of the screw) that the threaded portion of the screw penetrates into the pilot hole. This length value includes both the tapered starting threads and the non-tapered thread section engaged in the pilot hole. It should be noted that the tapered entry region of the screw provides little if any holding capabilities. A screw engagement length of approximately three diameters of fully developed threads, not counting the taper, is used in many applications [19].

Screw Thread Depth Utilization: The extent to which the fully developed flights of the screw cut into the boss wall. A pilot hole equal to the root diameter of the screw would result in 100% utilization while a pilot hole equal to the major diameter of the screw would result in a thread utilization of 0%. The thread depth utilization value, U, expressed as a percent can be determined using:

$$U = [(D_s - d_b) / D_s - d_s)] \cdot 100 \tag{6.13}$$

where D_s is the major screw diameter, d_s is the root diameter of the screw, and d_b is the inside diameter of the boss (i.e. the pilot hole diameter).

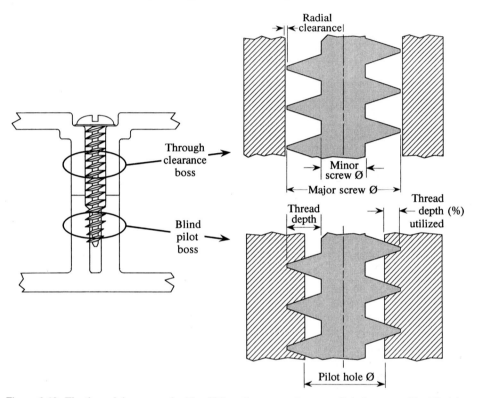

Figure 6.48. The through bosses used with self threading screws have a radial clearance. The blind (or through) receiving bosses have a pilot hole diameter that determines the percent thread depth utilization for the screw.

Screw Pull Out Force: The axial or tensile force required to pull the screw from the boss is known as the screw pull-out force. Other modes of tensile failure include tensile failure of the hollow cylindrical boss below the screw (typically at the intersection of the boss and the normal wall) or tensile failure of the screw.

Screw Performance During Assembly: The characteristic torque-turn behavior of a self threading screw is shown in Figure 6.49. The self threading screw is inserted into the open, clearance boss molded into one of the mating components (typically 0.010 inch, 0.25 mm clearance on the diameter) and contacts the top of the pilot hole. Lead-in sections, such as that shown in Figure 6.48, can be used when space permits, to assist in starting the screw and to minimize the potential for chipping. The lead-in section may not be necessary for screws with tapered or gimlet points, however, the lead-in section provides a measure of safety against chipping for brittle plastic materials. The screw then responds to the applied torque, which continues to climb as the screw is driven deeper into the boss due to the added frictional resistance associated with deeper engagement. Once the screw head sets, the torque climbs rapidly, as the two parts clamp together. Continued application of torque eventually results in shear loading levels on the plastic threads that exceed their yield value, and they elongate excessively, and eventually fail (i.e. thread stripping).

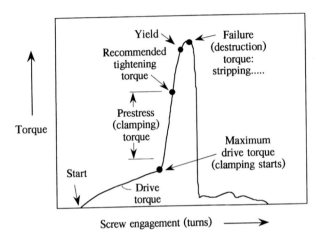

Figure 6.49 Typical torque vs. turns of engagement behavior for a self threading screw being driven into a plastic boss.

Under normal circumstances, the assembly is not driven to destruction, only to a tightening torque level, about half way (or less) between the maximum drive torque and the strip torque [16,30]. It is desirable to use screws and boss designs that maximize the separation between these two values, in order to minimize the danger of stripping the threads accidentally. Strip to drive ratios of at least 3 or 4:1 are desirable to ensure proper seating and safety when power tools are used. A strip to drive ratio as low as 2:1 may be acceptable only for skilled installation. Screws with anti-strip features such as serrations under the screw head can be used to increase the strip torque, and therefore the strip to drive ratio. It should be noted here that the use of oils, lubricants, or even mold release residues can reduce the stripping torque by as much as 50%, and their use should be avoided at all cost. It should also be noted here that there are torsional modes of failure other than thread stripping. The failure modes include shearing of the boss below the screw, boss cracking, or possibly shearing of the screw root. The preferred mode of failure is thread stripping, since this mode of failure does lend itself to repair using longer or larger diameter screws, or possibly a pilot hole repair using a gap filling adhesive [26,27,31,32].

Standard Thread Cutting Screws: Some of the common standard thread cutting screws are shown in Figure 6.50. These screws have either a slashed (ground) cutting slot (Figure 6.51a & c) or slotted flights. These screws cut threads into the plastic boss as they are driven into the pilot hole, and as a result generate "chips". When blind receiving (pilot) holes are used, the chips fall (or are pushed) to the bottom of the blind hole, which functions as a chip cavity (space for the chips must be provided when blind holes are used). The chips and debris can be a nuisance when through pilot holes are used [32].

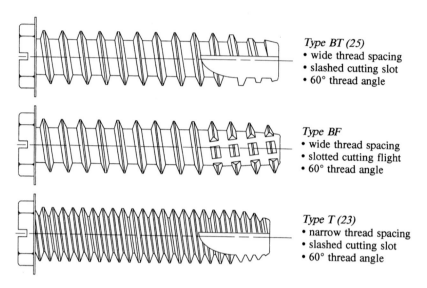

Type BT (25)
• wide thread spacing
• slashed cutting slot
• 60° thread angle

Type BF
• wide thread spacing
• slotted cutting flight
• 60° thread angle

Type T (23)
• narrow thread spacing
• slashed cutting slot
• 60° thread angle

Figure 6.50. Many of the ANSI standard thread cutting screws are commonly used with molded plastic parts. Thread cutting screws are most commonly used with rigid polymers.

Thread cutting screws are most commonly used with higher modulus thermoplastic or thermosetting polymers that do not have the ductility required for thread forming screws. The type BT (or 25) screw is the most common standard cutting screw due to its wide thread spacing and generous cutting slot. The BF screw also has wide thread spacing, however, the slotted cutting flights may tend to clog when working with softer materials [19]. The B series cutting screws have been used with materials having flexural modulus values as low as 2×10^5 lb/in^2 (1380 MPa) [27,32].

The type T (or 23) screw has been shown to be useful with very high modulus glass reinforced materials having flexural modulus values greater than 1×10^6 lb/in^2 (6900 MPa) [27]. Unfortunately, the threads that are cut into these very hard and rigid plastic materials tend to granulate during assembly / reassembly. In general, thread cutting screws have lower drive and strip torque values than thread forming screws, and the hoop stress level associated with their use is relatively low, making them suitable for use with glassy, amorphous materials subject to crazing [30]. Engagement lengths for thread cutting screws should be large enough to account for the fact that the tapered / cutting points of these screws provide little, if any holding power. Thread cutting screws should only be used in applications where the potential for disassembly / reassembly is very limited as the joint strength deteriorates rapidly if additional thread sets are cut during reassembly. To overcome this problem, oversized or longer thread cutting screws, or a thread forming screw having the same pitch diameter and thread spacing can be used in place of the original thread cutting screw during reassembly [16].

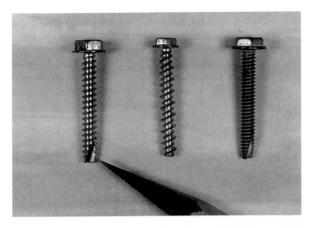

Figure 6.51. Several commonly used # 6 self threading screws. (left) The type BT thread cutting screw has a wide thread spacing and a slash cutting slot. (center) The HiLo® thread forming screw. (right) The type T thread cutting screw has a slash cutting slot and more closed spaced threads.

Standard Thread Forming Screws: Thread forming screws produce mating threads as they are driven into the pilot boss by displacing material. These screws do not contain cutting flights or slots, and do not generate chips. Thread forming screws are generally used with lower modulus plastic materials, since ductility or cold flow is a prerequisite for their use. The screws are generally used with plastic materials that have a flexural modulus less than 4×10^5 lb/in^2 (2760 MPa) [27,32], however, studies have shown that type B screws, with their wide spacing can also be used with rigid, glass reinforced materials if the boss is designed properly [33,34]. When thread forming screws are used with higher modulus polymers, thread depth utilization should be very low (i.e. relatively large pilot holes should be used). These standard thread forming screws with their 60° thread angle generate relatively high radial and hoop strains, resulting in high residual stress values. Compression of material between the flanks can also be high. The wider thread spacing associated with screws such as the Type AB or B is recommended over the type C for most applications [19,25,32]. The gimlet point style of the Type AB screws necessitates the use of additional engagement length compared to the Type B screw since the tapered point provides no significant strength contributions [19].

The stress level in the plastic boss member is due to several factors, including the seating torque applied to the assembly, the stress induced by the fastener during the driving operation, and service related stresses. The stresses induced by the seating torque can be controlled by altering the tightening procedure, while the fastener induced stresses can be adjusted by using the proper fastener type and pilot hole size. It is difficult, however, with rigid glassy polymers to keep the local stress levels within safe ranges [25]. The residual stresses combine with stresses induced by service loads, and can lead to reduced chemical performance and premature failure. As a result, these self threading screws are generally used for more ductile semi-crystalline polymers or toughened amorphous thermoplastics, where the residual stresses can relax to an acceptable level. When properly used, self threading screws offer a very high pull out resistance, and high resistance to back out. Clamp load and back out torque will decay with time at a rate that is dependent upon the stress relaxation characteristics of the plastic boss material. Thread

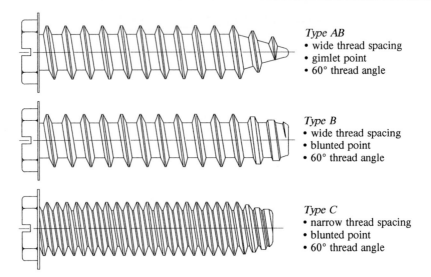

Type AB
• wide thread spacing
• gimlet point
• 60° thread angle

Type B
• wide thread spacing
• blunted point
• 60° thread angle

Type C
• narrow thread spacing
• blunted point
• 60° thread angle

Figure 6.52. Some of the ANSI standard thread forming screws are also used with molded plastic parts. The thread forming screws are typically used with softer, more ductile polymers.

forming screws are suitable for applications where limited serviceability is anticipated. Thread forming screws, rather than thread cutting screws, are more suitable for use with thermoplastic structural foams. However, due to the limited durability of many foamed materials, internally threaded inserts / machine screws are often used with these materials.

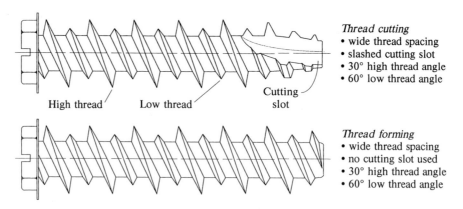

Thread cutting
• wide thread spacing
• slashed cutting slot
• 30° high thread angle
• 60° low thread angle

High thread   Low thread   Cutting slot

Thread forming
• wide thread spacing
• no cutting slot used
• 30° high thread angle
• 60° low thread angle

Figure 6.53. The specialty HiLo ® screw is available in a variety of configurations including the thread cutting and thread forming versions shown.

Self Threading Screws Designed for Plastic Materials: A number of self threading screws, both thread forming and thread cutting varieties, are specifically designed for use with plastic materials. Some of the more significant improvements, include a wider thread spacing and smaller thread (flank) angles. The smaller thread angle results in lower radial stress components, while the increased thread spacing reduces compressive strains between the flights [16,25,26,30,32]. Some of these specialty, yet widely used screws include:

HiLo®: The HiLo® screw [35] is a double lead screw that is available in both thread forming and thread cutting varieties (having a number of different point and head styles). The widely spaced high thread has a 30° thread angle, while the low thread has the more conventional 60° thread angle. Drive torques for the screw are relatively low while the strip to drive ratios are generally good [26,29,32]. The 30° high thread angle results in lower radial pressures and a reduced tendency towards boss cracking.

Plastite ®: The Plastite® screw [36] is a unique thread forming screw that has a trilobal (or slightly triangular) cross section rather than a circular cross section. A commonly used design has a 45° thread angle. The trilobal shape of the screw reduces the driving torque [25]. The most unique feature of this screw is its ability to provide high prevailing or back out torque, making the screw ideal for vibration applications. After installation, cold flow of the plastic material effectively locks the out of round screw into place, increasing the resistance to loosening.

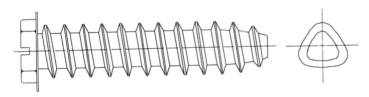

Figure 6.54. The Plastite ® thread forming screw. The screw has a non-circular, trilobal cross section (exaggerated cross section shown).

PT®: The PT ® [37] screw is a widely spaced single lead thread forming screw having a 30° thread angle. The 30° thread angle results in reduced radial and hoop stresses, permitting the use of thinner boss walls. This screw features a modified shank (root), which is said to improve flow of plastic during the thread forming operation [30,37].

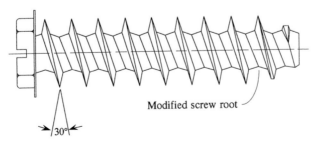

Modified screw root

30°

Figure 6.55. Configuration of the PT ® thread forming screw.

Polyfast ®: The Polyfast® self threading screw is unique in that it has an asymmetric screw profile. The widely spaced flights have a 35° leading edge and a 10° trailing edge. The screw has been shown to be suitable for use with more ductile thermoplastics [38].

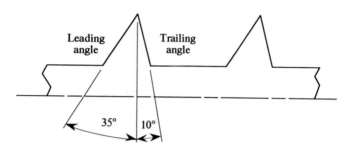

Figure 6.56. Thread profile configuration of the Polyfast® thread forming screw.

Screw Heads / Washers: Self threading screws are available with a wide variety of head styles, many with integral washers. Washers distribute the clamping load and joint stresses over a larger area. Spring washers may be employed either loose or preassembled with the screws. These washers are usually conical or have a waved configuration. Light duty spring washers are useful for cutting down on the rate of clamp load decay for plastic materials that tend to creep.

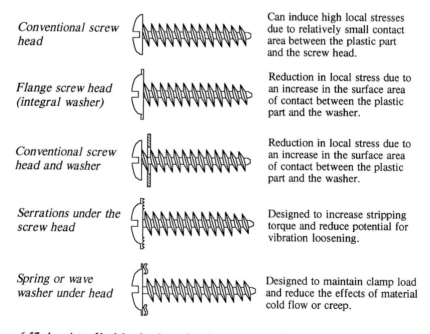

Figure 6.57. A variety of both head styles and washer types are used with self threading screws.

Self Threading Screw Boss Design: The performance and quality of a self threading screw / boss assembly is determined by both the screw characteristics and the receiving hole design. The wall thickness of most plastic moldings is insufficient to accommodate the physical dimensions and stresses associated with most screw fastener systems [16]. As a result, a local increase in wall thickness is required at the point of assembly. Local increases in part side wall thickness (integral bosses) are generally not recommended since they result in preferential flow and the likelihood of shrinkage stresses, sink marks or shrinkage voids as shown in Figure 6.58.

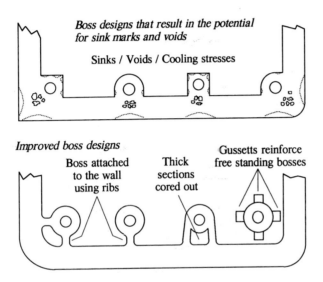

Figure 6.58. Whenever possible, bosses should be free standing, gussetted, or attached to sidewalls using ribs in order to minimize the potential for sink marks and shrinkage voids.

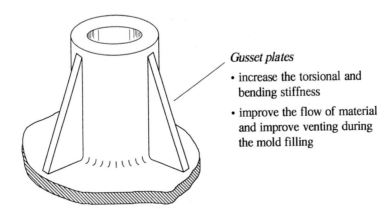

Figure 6.59. Gusset plates are often used to improve the torsional stiffness of free standing bosses.

Instead, the pilot holes and clearance holes should be located in bosses set away from the sidewalls. The bosses can be free standing, or can be connected to the sidewalls using ribs to increase the torsional and bending strength of the boss, and to boost manufacturability by improving material flow and venting efficiency [16]. Bosses, especially those located away from vertical walls, can be reinforced with gusset plates (triangular ribs) for the same reasons. Gusset plates are very helpful for thin wall bosses that may be difficult to fill well due to flow hesitation effects. Three or four gusset plates are generally used [26,33,34].

The depth of the pilot hole in the receiving boss should be greater than the screw engagement length (turns of penetration) as shown in Figure 6.60. The increase in the depth of the hole provides a chip cavity for thread cutting screws, but more importantly removes or cores out excess plastic material, resulting in a more uniform wall thickness. Locally thick sections lead to microvoid formation and shrinkage stress, both of which can contribute to premature failure since the boss is an area of high stress concentration (screws are point fasteners). In addition, sink marks in the region opposite the blind boss (generally the appearance surface of the molding) are esthetically unacceptable in many applications.

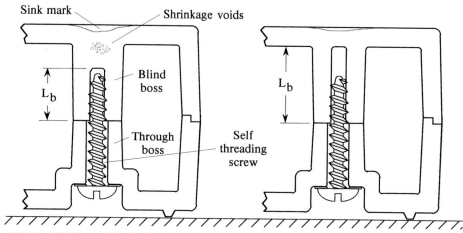

Hole in blind boss (pilot hole) is just long enough to accept screw, resulting in thick wall section at the base of the boss.

Core pin producing the blind hole is extended in order core out the thick section (also creates a chip cavity for thread cutting screws).

Figure 6.60. The core pins that are used to form the holes in blind bosses should be extended as much as possible to core out excess material.

The relative size of the sink mark is influenced by the material shrinkage, processing conditions, mold design and part design. Short core pins, large base radius values (fillets) and thick boss or part wall thicknesses all increase the tendency towards sink marks as shown in Figure 6.61. Unfortunately, the strength of the boss, or its ability to withstand assembly and service loads, increases as both wall thickness and base fillet increase (up to a point). The design of the boss is then a fine balance between that which

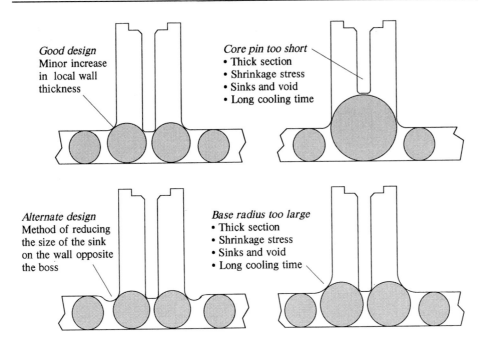

Figure 6.61. Excessively thick or thin sections at the base of the blind boss should be avoided. The radii values used for the fillet must be large enough to minimize stress concentration, yet must be small enough to limit shrinkage related problems such as shrinkage stress, sinks and voids.

results in acceptable esthetics (thin walls, small radius) and one which exhibits adequate strength (requiring thicker wall and larger radius).

Tool design and processing variables are also important factors in determining the relative size of the sink mark. For example, deep gates facilitate packing of the cavity to compensate for the shrinkage. Local cooling of the cavity surface directly opposite the boss (for example using a bubbler) is sometimes used to help with the sink problem, at the expense of possible void formation. The voids tend to reduce the strength of the boss assembly. While these factors help, it is best to simply avoid the thick wall section altogether by using the minimum wall thickness consistent with the structural requirements, and by using smaller diameter screws when possible, which require proportionally thinner walls. The use of reinforcing ribs or gusset plates also minimize boss wall thickness requirements by providing additional stiffness (i.e. they provide a very efficient means of increasing the polar moment of inertia). Material and screw manufacturers can recommend specific boss dimensional values, however, as a general guideline, boss outside diameters are often between 2.5 to 3.0 times the nominal screw diameter [27,32,33]. When ribs or gusset plates are used to reinforce the boss, wall thicknesses can be reduced. Ribs and gussets should also contain fillets to improve moldability and reduce stress concentration effects.

There are several molding problems associated with the manufacturing of blind, hollow bosses for self threading screws. These problems include:

(i) Limited ability to provide adequate cooling due to the small core pin diameter (no internal cooling and small surface area). The "hot" core pin can result in an increase in cycle time and a diameter towards the bottom of the hole, (i.e. the coke bottle effect). The larger diameter at the bottom section of the boss is due to the slower cooling rate, especially for semi-crystalline materials. The change in diameter is difficult to detect using pin gages inserted through the top of the hole, since the top of the boss cools at a faster rate. Cross sectioning of the boss is recommended for pilot hole inspection.

(ii) Ejection problems associated with shrinkage around the core pin. A slight draft angle dry lubricant core surface plating, and draw polishing are commonly used to improve ejection. Mold release agents are not recommended as they alter the driving and stripping torque characteristics, and can lead to inconsistent behavior during assembly.

(iii) Core pin deflection and fatigue. The long, small diameter (high aspect ratio) cantilever core pins use to produce the blind pilot holes may deflect during melt injection, and are subject to tensile stresses during ejection. Small diameter cantilever core pins may have a limited life.

All of these problems described above can be minimized by reducing the length of the core pin used to produce the blind pilot hole, to the minimum length required for acceptable thread engagement (and chip cavity for cutting screws). Short core pins can be used without any increase in the sink mark opposite the blind hole using the technique shown in Figure 6.62.

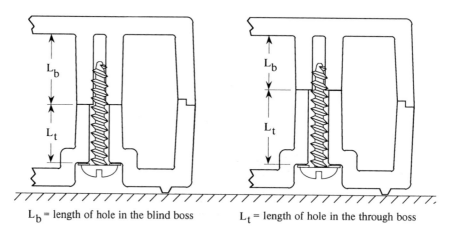

L_b = length of hole in the blind boss L_t = length of hole in the through boss

Figure 6.62. The blind boss core pin length is reduced to minimize the molding problems associated with long, cantilever core pins.

The through boss on the mating part is extended to compensate for the reduction in the cantilever core pin length. The overall core pin length for the through boss is increased, however, this is not a significant problem since:

(i) The core pin for the through hole is significantly larger in diameter (clearance hole vs pilot hole).

(ii) During molding, the through core pin can be supported at both ends (i.e. both the cavity and core side of the tool). Alternatively, the through hole could be produced using two self locating, shorter core pins, extending from each side of the mold as shown in Figure 6.3.

It is clear that both manufacturing and structural considerations must be taken into account when designing the screw boss fastening system. Unfortunately, the number of variables associated with self thread screw boss design make accurate theoretical analysis difficult. For example, driving and stripping torque values are highly dependent upon the coefficient of friction between the metal screw and the plastic nut material. This coefficient of friction value is highly dependent upon the surface temperature, normal stress, surface quality and the presence of lubricant. A theoretical analysis [39] provides a starting point for design, however, experiments are commonly conducted (or have been conducted by screw / material suppliers) to fine tune design parameters such as pilot hole diameter and length of engagement [19,29,30,33]. Test moldings such as the part shown in Figure 6.63 are used in conjunction with instrumented screw driving equipment (instrumented with an in-line or reaction torque transducer) to determine assembly characteristics of a particular screw / material / boss design.

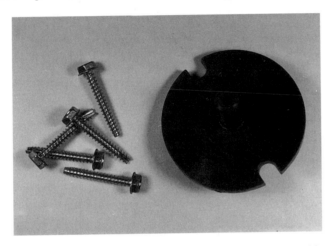

Figure 6.63. An example of a molded prototype test boss used to evaluate the assembly and performance characteristics of a particular screw / boss design / material combination.

It is important that the driving speeds used during these prototype test procedures are equivalent to those used in production, since both drive and strip torque are influenced by driving speed. The common objective of these experiments is to determine the set of variables that provides both a high strip torque and a high strip to drive ratio as shown in Figures 6.64 and 6.65. Drive and strip torque values for a given plastic material and screw are highly dependent upon variables such as screw type / size / surface finish, drive speed, pilot hole diameter and engagement length.

Other tests are conducted in order to determine the screw's pull out strength. The results of such a test are shown in Figure 6.66. Data of this type can be used to determine the tensile strength capabilities and mode of failure of the boss assembly due to tensile loading. Information of this type is useful in determining how variables such as screw type, engagement length, boss wall thickness, and base radius (fillet) affect the tensile strength of the boss assembly.

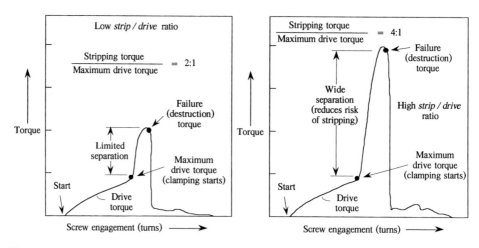

Figure 6.64. Torque-turn curve for a self threading screw showing poor strip / drive torque ratio (left) and high strip / drive torque ratio (right).

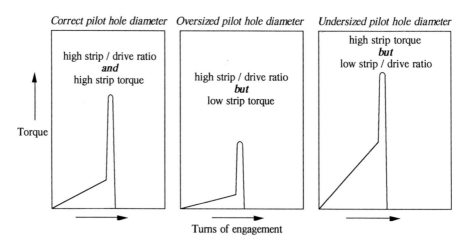

Figure 6.65. The boss pilot hole diameter has a significant influence on both maximum drive torque and strip / drive torque ratio. Low drive torque and high strip / drive torque ratios are most desirable as this limits the potential for failure during the initial or subsequent assembly procedures.

Other important experimental tests include: (i) hoop strain (circumferential expansion) evaluation using strain gauges, (ii) clamp load decay using strain gages or compressive load sensors, and (iii) torque retention. Unfortunately, all of these property values change

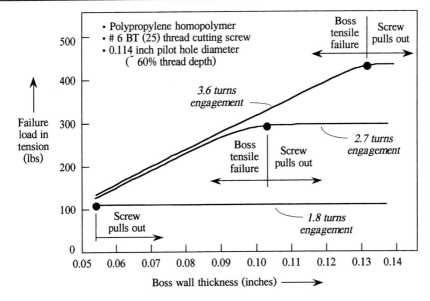

Figure 6.66. Tensile screw pull out results for a type BT screw and a polypropylene boss.

with time due to creep or stress relaxation effects. The clamp load and prevailing torque will generally decrease with time (exceptions include the prevailing torque retention due to creep for fasteners such as the trilobal Plastite® screw). Extrapolation procedures, similar to those used for generating creep data, can be used to estimate longer term behavior. Alternatively, the creep characteristics of the plastic material itself may give a good indication of clamp load loss; torque retention, however, is more difficult to predict since it is dependent upon such factors as screw surface finish and shape.

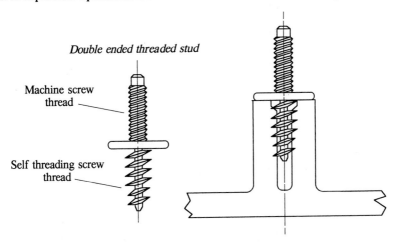

Figure 6.67. A double ended stud is a combination self threading screw and machine screw with a pancake washer between.

Double Ended Threaded Stud: A double ended stud is a combination self threading screw with a pancake type head in the middle. A typical stud design is shown in Figure 6.67. These specialty screws are driven into the plastic boss with a stud driver, leaving the machine screw thread end exposed. The second component (which contains a through hole) is then placed over the machine thread. A nut is then used to clamp the second component against the pancake head of the double ended stud, putting all of the clamp load on the machine screw [32].

Boss Caps: Boss caps are stamped metal fasteners that press over the top of hollow plastic bosses. The caps reduce the tendency for the bosses to crack by providing hoop and axial reinforcement. The caps are used with thread forming screws and include a single thread for additional strength [19,28,40].

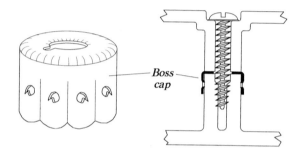

Figure 6.68. Sheet metal boss cap is pressed over the boss to reinforce the boss and provide additional assemble strength.

Drive Studs / Push-in Fasteners: Drive studs are push-in mechanical fasteners with contoured barbs or semi-buttress threads (with a nearly perpendicular trailing flank) pushed into molded or drilled holes to produce a finished assembly very rapidly. Most push-in fasteners utilize barbs or semi-buttress rings and are used for one time assembly applications such as pan handles [32]. The pull-out resistance of these fasteners is significantly greater than the insertion (push-in) force, however, clamp loadings achievable are very low since there is no mechanical advantage. Push-in fasteners are generally used with more ductile thermoplastics. The fasteners can be inserted immediately after molding when the part is warm if used with higher modulus plastic materials. The fasteners can also be inserted using heat or ultrasonic insertion. Some push-in fasteners have helical semi-buttress threads that produce mating threads in ductile plastic materials due to elastic deformation and creep. These screws can be turned out for service if necessary, and reinserted [19,28,36,41].

A unique push-in fastener is the press-in hinge shown in Figure 6.70. The hinge incorporates serrated edges on each leaf. The hinge leaf is pressed into molded slots in the part to produce a secure, non-removable assembly. The serrated hinges are most useful for ductile polymers and are ideally pressed into the plastic material immediately after injection molding when the material is warm and soft, resulting in improved flow and a shrink fit.

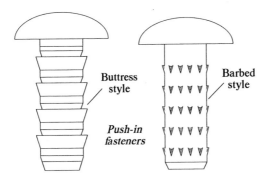

Figure 6.69. Unlike self threading screws that are rotated during insertion, push-in fasteners are simply pressed into pilot holes during assembly.

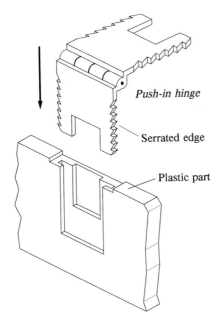

Figure 6.70. A metal hinge with serrations on each leaf. The hinge is pressed into a slot in the plastic part after molding to produce a permanent assembly.

Push-on / Turn-on Fasteners: Push-on, or turn-on fasteners are self locking or self threading fasteners that replace standard nut / lock washer assemblies. These fasteners are used with metal studs or posts or can be used with bosses molded into one part, capturing the mating component as shown in Figures 6.71 to 6.73. Push-on fasteners, such as Tinnerman ® clips [42], are self locking, spring steel fasteners that can be used in

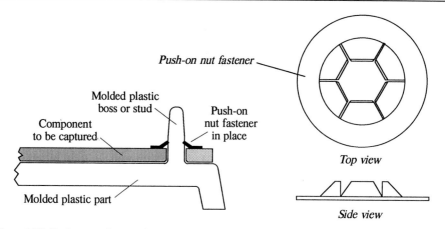

Figure 6.71. Push-on nut fastener is pressed over a stud to produce a permanent assembly.

light duty applications where clamp load requirements are minimal. The fasteners can be used to produce permanent assemblies, or can be used in applications requiring disassembly if the stud design is altered as shown in Figure 6.72.

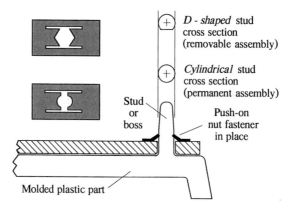

Figure 6.72. Push-on Tinnerman® clips are pushed over a molded stud or post to produce a permanent or removable assembly.

The speed clips or nuts are pushed on in most applications, however, self threading turn-on nuts are also available. These self threading turn-on nuts produce mating threads on the plastic stud as they are driven (much like self threading screws). These nuts are used in applications where reversible assemblies or additional control over preload are required. The molded studs used with push-on or turn-on fasteners should have a suitable radius at the base, 0.015 in (0.38 mm) minimum, to reduce the stress concentration and chance of fracture due to side impact or tensile loading. The radius value selected is a compromise between that which results in a balance between acceptable mechanical performance and esthetics [15,28].

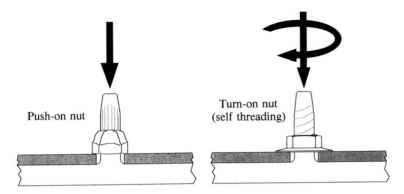

Figure 6.73. Push-on nut is pressed onto a molded stud, while self threading turn on fasteners are used when some degree of control over clamp pressure is required.

Rivets and Eyelets: Rivets or eyelets are sometimes used in the assembly of injection molded plastic products. A clearance between the rivet and the molded hole of 0.010 inch (0.25 mm) is recommended to account for tolerance variations and the coefficient of thermal expansion mismatch [16]. Tubular rivets are available with internal threads for secondary screw attachment, while rivets containing electrical contact or solder terminals are used in a variety of electronic applications. Load control devices should be used during rivet installation to ensure correct clinching pressure and consistent assembly thickness. Reinforcing washers or rivets having large head diameters are recommended in order to distribute assembly stresses over a larger area and should be placed several diameters from the edge of a part. Shoulder rivets can be used to limit the compressive stresses on the plastic material. Rivets produced from softer metals such as aluminum or even plastic materials such as LCPs are generally recommended [16,28,43].

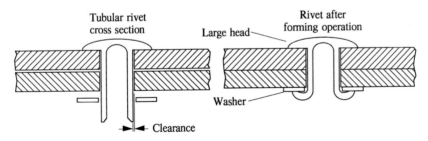

Figure 6.74. Rivets used to assembly plastic parts should distribute load over the largest possible area. Large rivet heads and washers are recommended.

6.4.2.3   Insert Assembly

Internally threaded metal inserts are commonly used with plastic parts to produce a high quality, durable means of mechanical assembly that is suitable for applications requiring serviceability (multiple assembly / disassembly operations). The inserts are designed for use with machine screws, where open or blind assemblies are required. The inserts can be molded in, or can be inserted into a hole in the part after molding. Each of the two techniques are discussed below.

Molded-in Inserts: Molded-in inserts are components that are placed into an injection mold prior to melt injection. The melt flows around and wets the insert during the injection phase of the process, and locks the insert in place as the melt cools, shrinks and solidifies. In the general context, inserts are used to provide points of attachment for threaded fasteners, reinforcement, electrical conductivity, or provide other special functions such as wear surfaces. Molded-in inserts can add a significant cost to the product, hence they are only used when there is a functional need and the costs associated with the inserting operation are justified [44,45].

Inserts Molded-in for Assembly: Inserts are sometimes molded into a product to provide a durable thread for assembly purposes. These threaded hardware items can have a variety of configurations and are produced from materials such as aluminum, brass steel, stainless steel or plastic materials. The inserts most commonly used for assembly are nut or stud type hardware items produced from brass due to its corrosion resistance and good machinability [46]. It is also best to work with softer metals for molded-in inserts to minimize the potential for tool damage and provide some ductility when the inserts must provide melt flow shut-off functions. Inserts are generally cold headed or machined, however, powder metal inserts may be cost effective when more complicated geometries are required [47]. Unlike fasteners that are inserted into holes or hollow bosses after molding, molded-in inserts offer additional design flexibility. They can provide a durable, high quality, method of assembly for parts subjected to frequent disassembly an a variety of geometries can be used. However, there are several significant concerns or problems that are associated with their use [16,19,44,48]. These problems include:

Cycle Time: The time required to place the inserts into the injection mold does add to the overall molding cycle time. Molding machine operating cost are significantly greater than that for post molding insertion equipment. Another problem is loading time variation (and cycle time variation), which can lead to non-reproducible product quality. In addition, if the inserts are loaded incorrectly (for example, if one insert is out of place or omitted), the entire part is either rejected or must be repaired after molding if possible. The use of robotics can improve the speed and repeatability of the insert loading process.

Rejected Parts: Parts that are of inferior quality for one reason or another (short shots, surface splay or improper dimensions, etc.) are more difficult to recover. Either the entire part must be scrapped, or the inserts must be removed before the part is granulated for recycling. These recovery operations can be expensive in terms of both materials and labor. When post molding insertion techniques are used, the molded parts can be inspected for quality prior to insertion of the metal fasteners.

Mold Damage: Inserts, even of softer brass or aluminum inserts, can cause a great deal of mold damage if their dimensions are not to specification or they are improperly loaded. Inserts that engage into the opposite side of the mold during mold closing should contain a radius or bevel as a lead-in to prevent skiving. The molding clamp systems should have sensitive low pressure safety controls to minimize damage to the mold should misalignment occur. Quality and dimensional inspection of the inserts is an important prerequisite to their use. Vertical clamp injection molding machines are preferred over horizontal clamps since gravity can be used to keep the inserts in place during the mold closing operation.

Weld Lines: Inserts and gates should be positioned in such a way that weld lines due to flow around the entire circumference of the insert is avoided. Wall thicknesses around inserts should be great enough so that flow is not restricted. Controlled preheating of the insert can improve the flow, wetting and weld line quality. Weld lines are a more significant problem when the inserts are used with filled or reinforced materials [44].

Molded-in Stress: Molded-in stress is perhaps the most significant problem associated with the use of molded-in inserts. The plastic material surrounding the insert is stressed since shrinkage of material around the rigid metal insert is restrained. The residual strain, which is essentially the mold shrinkage value for the plastic material around the insert, can result in delayed crazing or cracking around the insert [19,44,48]. Preheating the insert can reduce the problem of molded-in stress by allowing the insert to shrink along with the plastic material, however, the mismatch in coefficient of thermal expansion (most plastics having higher CTE than most metals) results in only a partial reduction in residual strain. The heating process for the metal insert should be well controlled and consistent to ensure repeatable part quality. When preheating is used, the tooling (that accepts the insert) should be sized for the hot insert. Processing conditions, such as holding pressure, which influence the plastic part shrinkage will also influence the shrinkage around the insert, and therefore the residual stress level.

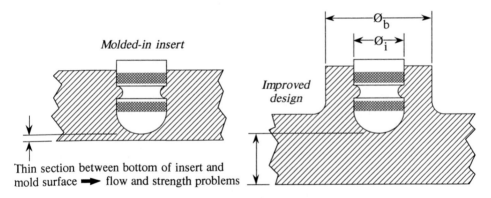

Figure 6.75. In most cases, metal inserts are inserted into molded pilot bosses after molding, however, inserts can also be molded-in during the primary molding operation.

In order to evaluate the potential for problems due to shrinkage around an insert, designers must consider two values, namely mold shrinkage and acceptable design strain. Plastic materials that have high mold shrinkage values can be used successfully if they are ductile and have high yield strains, while a high shrinkage, brittle material would not be as suitable. Inserts are successfully molded into a low shrinkage, ductile material such as ABS, while inserts are generally not suited for low shrinkage, general purpose polystyrene, due to its tendency toward crazing and relatively low recommended design strain (or even breaking strain) values. It is also important to take the stress relaxation characteristics of the plastic material into account, along with any temperature changes anticipated in the service environment, since stresses or strains due to the coefficient of thermal expansion mismatch will superimpose on the residual molding stresses and strains. Prototype molding and testing is generally recommended for applications utilizing molded-in inserts [44].

Inserts that are molded in for purposes of assembly are typically blind cylindrical devices with internal machine threads, although open internally threaded inserts (extending through the part) and threaded studs are used to a lesser extent. Inserts must have provisions for both axial and torsional anchorage. Inserts should have generous radii wherever possible to avoid stress concentration and improve material flow [44]. Grooves provide pull out strength while splines or knurls provide added torsional strength. The inserts should also be clean and free of surface contamination such as lubrication oils. Knurls should be rounded whenever possible and have depths of at least 0.010 inch (0.25 mm) [48]. The knurl should not extend up to the part surface to avoid flashing. In addition, shoulders (vertical or horizontal) should be provided to prevent flow of melt into the internal threads as shown in Figure 6.75. The insert should protrude at least 0.062 inch (1.6 mm) into the mold cavity to avoid flash. There also must be sufficient space beneath the blind insert to facilitate material flow, avoid weld line formation and provide additional strength. Open inserts (extending through the part) should have shoulders on each end or can be slightly longer, 0.001 - 0.002 inch (0.025 - 0.051 mm), than the cavity gap to provide positive shut off. Inserts in the direction of draw are most easily molded, and are supported by core pins (for internally threaded inserts) or by a recess in the cavity (for threaded studs). Some of these dimensional tolerances are therefore critical for threaded inserts.

Figure 6.76. Sharp edges on the metal insert result in stress concentrations and crazing due to the mold shrinkage of the polymer. Edges on inserts should be well rounded to provide a more uniform stress distribution.

Other Types of Molded-in Inserts: While the use of molded-in threaded inserts is a fairly common practice for thermoset molding, the practice is less widely used with thermoplastic materials since there are many secondary processes for insertion available that eliminate many of the disadvantages associated with molded-in insert processing. It should be noted here, however, that the use of an in-mold assembly extends well beyond the area of the threaded fastener inserts. Metal inserts are widely used in the electrical and

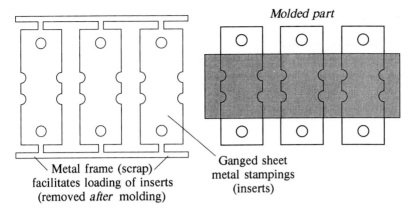

Figure 6.77. Metal frame (scrap) on stamped metal inserts can assist handling and alignment when loading the inserts into the mold.

electronics industries where the metal is a conductor, and the plastic material is used as an insulator. Parts such as impellers, gears, fans and bearings are commonly molded over metal hubs. In most of these applications, there is no other easy alternative. The design of the insert in these applications is such that secondary insertion is not possible. The molding practices associated with these inserts, with their more complicated geometries, is subject to the same restrictions as those given above for internally threaded inserts. Tool damage, weld line quality, residual stress level and stress concentrations are primary concerns. As the inserts become larger, the problem of insert support / deflection becomes even more significant. The part shown in Figure 6.76 consists of a thick metal plate molded into a polycarbonate frame. The sharp radii values at the corners of the metal

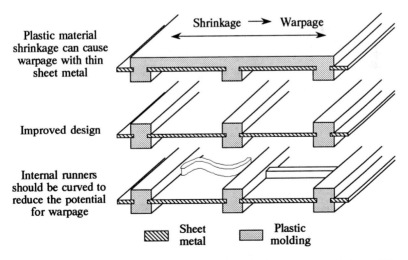

Figure 6.78. Warpage or buckling can be a problem when plastic parts are molded over light or gauge sheet metal inserts.

octagonal metal insert result in stress concentrations and crazing in the polycarbonate sometime after molding. The use of a disk or rounded octagon plate (to provide additional resistance to rotations) would improve product quality, at the expense of additional insert manufacturing / preparation costs. When multiple sheet metal stampings are inserted into the same part (or multi-cavity tool), it is useful to leave the metal frame / scrap on the part to assist in insert loading and location as shown in Figure 6.77.

In some cases, the plastic material is selectively molded over a thinner sheet metal insert to produce a metal stamping with smaller integral plastic features (i.e. outsert molding) as

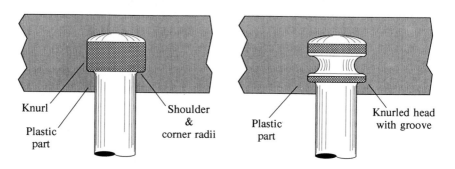

Figure 6.79. Rounded knurls on an insert provide resistance to both axial and torsional forces. Grooves provide improved pull out resistance.

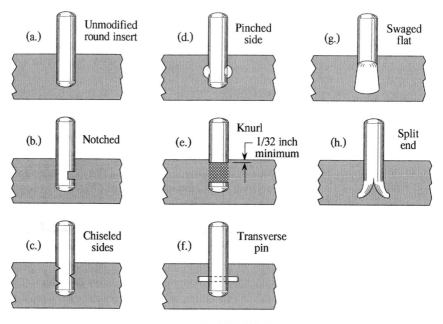

Figure 6.80. A variety of methods can be v͞   ͞rsional strength for round inserts.

shown in Figure 6.78. The prepunched metal parts, typically 0.040 - 0.080 inch (1.0 - 2.0 mm) thick, are held in the mold using locating pins. Three plate or hot runner molds are used to deliver the melt to the various locations around the part. When large areas are covered with plastic material, buckling, due to the plastic material shrinkage, can occur if the design is not properly balanced [46].

Round inserts or metal pins molded into a part can be anchored to resist both axial and torsional forces using a number of techniques, including those shown in Figures 6.79 and 6.80. Knurling is commonly used at depths of 0.010 inch (0.25 mm) for small diameters while course knurls having depths up to 0.030 inch (0.76 mm) are commonly used for larger diameter inserts. Inserts should also be located / designed so that the shrinkage of the plastic materials helps anchor the two components. The plastic material molded into the rim shown in Figure 6.81 would have a tendency to shrink away from the rim, resulting in a loss of contact between the two materials. The design of the insert must be modified in some way to promote anchorage as shown in Figure 6.81 [48].

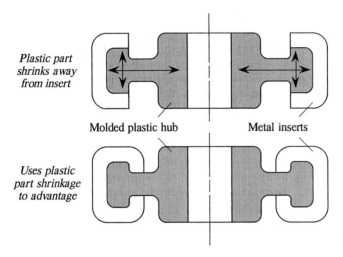

Figure 6.81. Inserts should be designed so that the plastic shrinks around the insert, rather than pulling away from the insert.

A number of processes are also available for molding over plastic (rather than metal) inserts. These in-mold assembly processes can be used to produce multi-color or multi-functional parts [49,50]. For example, elastomeric materials can be molded over more rigid thermoplastics, or multi-color automotive lenses can be produced using these in-mold assembly techniques. The plastic parts (inserts) can be loaded manually or robotically, or a multi-shot process such as that shown in Figure 6.82 or 6.83 can be used.

A commonly used method of multi-component molding uses a rotating mold and multiple injection units as shown in Figure 6.82. Once the part produced from the first material has solidified, the core and part rotate to a larger cavity, and the second material is then molded over the first part (i.e. molded insert). The process shown in Figure 6.83 utilizes

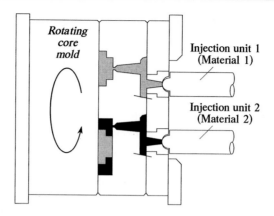

Figure 6.82. Two component (two shot) molding using the rotating mold process. This molding technique is essentially an automated, plastic over plastic, insert molding operation.

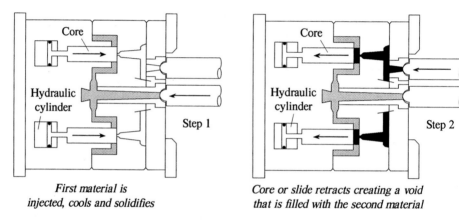

Figure 6.83. Two component molding using the retractable core process. After the tool is filled with one polymer (and cools), sections of the mold withdraw, creating open volumes that are filled with a second polymer.

movable cores or slides that expand the where of the mold cavity after the first material solidifies. Once the first material cools, the core retracts, and the void left by the core is filled with the second material. In some cases the bond between the two parts is purely mechanical, while in other cases, the process is analogous to welding or even reactive bonding. These processing operations are relatively complex and require special molding equipment and tooling, however, they reduce part handling, eliminate secondary assembly operations and can result in improved part quality and design flexibility.

Swaging: Swaging is another process that can be used to capture an insert. The insert to be captured is placed into a pocket within the molded thermoplastic part in much the same way that a threaded metal insert is placed within a hollow boss. The edges of the molded

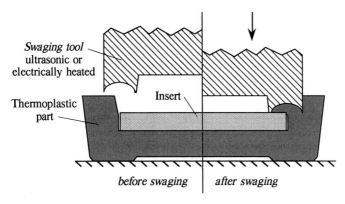

Figure 6.84. An ultrasonic or heated swaging tool can be used to capture an insert that has been placed within a molded thermoplastic part.

pocket are then reformed using either a heated swaging tool, or ultrasonic energy as shown in Figure 6.84 [51]. The formed material is allowed to cool and solidify, thereby capturing the insert. In most cases, the process produces a purely mechanical interlock. Softer, ductile thermoplastics such as ABS are most easily swaged. In some cases, it is possible to swage without the assistance of thermal energy (i.e. cold swaging). This cold forming process can only be used with materials that are capable of withstanding relatively large strains (e.g. ductile polymers). The molded parts are generally molded with thin wall sections to increase the permissible radius of curvature to capture an insert. The cold forming process is most suitable for either ductile semi-crystalline polymers or toughened amorphous polymers due to the large deformations associated with the process. Cold swaged joints are more prone to recovery, crazing or chemical attack than those produced using thermal or ultrasonic techniques.

Post-molding Insertion: Many of the disadvantages associated with molded-in inserts can be eliminated by inserting during a secondary operation after the part has been molded. The secondary inserting operation is limited to inserts having relatively simple geometries, usually special forms of nuts or internally threaded cylindrical metal inserts that are used for open or blind machine screw assembly. Inserts, used in conjunction with machine screws, result in a precise, durable, assembly method that is suitable for applications where repeated assembly is anticipated. The plastic part is molded with pilot holes at the locations where the inserts will be located (or alternatively holes can be drilled for prototype applications). A variety of methods can be used to install, and anchor the inserts within the hole. These secondary insertion processes include [19,24,51,52]:

- Cold press fitting (interference)
- Hot pressing
- Ultrasonic insertion
- Expansion inserts
- Self tapping inserts

Pressed-in Inserts (cold): The simplest means of inserting an internally threaded metal fastener into the molded hole is to simply push or press it in. The insert is pushed into the

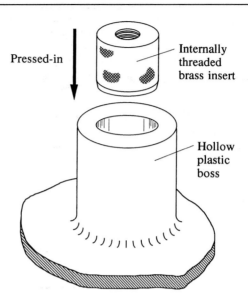

Figure 6.85. A variety of methods can be used to fix an insert within a molded boss. In the simplest case, the insert is simply pressed (press fit) into an undersize hole.

molded hole or hollow boss as shown in Figure 6.85. The insert can be flanged, pressed into a stepped hole, or pressed into the boss using a tool that contacts the top of the boss to ensure proper axial location.

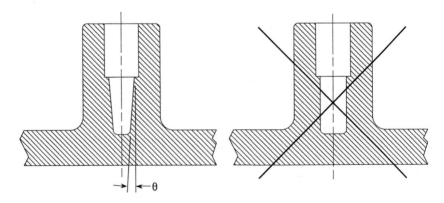

Figure 6.86. Pressed-in inserts require molded holes with zero draft, however, the core section below the insert can be drafted to facilitate part ejection.

Guidelines and design equations for press fits (given earlier in the chapter) can be used to determine an acceptable interference value. Initial prototype samples should be produced using core pins on the larger side (resulting in minimum hoop stress) and can be turned down if necessary (steel safe design). Like other press fits, cold pressing operation is most appropriate for higher elongation ductile polymers. The inserts themselves can be smooth, or diamond knurled / barbed to provide additional anchorage due to cold flow. Straight knurls are sometimes used for inserts requiring only rotational anchorage. Adhesives can also be used to assist in anchoring the insert, however, the adhesive should be selected carefully since the tensile stress at the interface is high (avoid aggressive solvents, etc.) [46]. The inserts are generally pressed into the part immediately after molding, while the part is relatively soft and continues to shrink. The wall of the insert and the hole should have a 0° draft angle to ensure uniform stress distribution and maximum anchorage.

When the inserts are used with extended bosses, the portion of the hole remaining below the insert can be tapered to assist in part ejection as shown in Figure 6.86. The use of cold pressed inserts is limited due to their relatively low strength and high stress level compared to other insert processes [16].

Hot Pressing: The pressing method described above can be modified to press "hot" inserts into the molded hole, resulting in improved performance. The thermal insertion process uses an undersized hole, and an insert with buttress type grooves, or knurls. The insert is pressed in using an electrically heated tool that causes the insert to heat by conduction. The plastic material in contact with the insert softens and flows into the undercuts on the insert as it is pushed into the hole. With hot pressed inserts, both the inserts and hole should be tapered to provide a more uniform pressure, and to prevent plowing of the molten material towards the bottom of the hole as the insert is driven in. The bosses used for thermal insertion should also have sufficient clearance below the insert (typically 0.030 inch, 0.8 mm) to allow for accumulation of flash. The inserts can be preheated to speed up the cycle, however, this can interfere with handling and loading. The equipment required for the process is simple, and the residual stress levels associated with thermal insertion are low. However, the process is slow since the entire insert must reach a temperature that is high enough to cause softening of the adjacent plastic material [16].

Self Threading Inserts: A self threading insert is a metal insert that has internal machine threads, and an external self threading thread configuration. Like self threading screws, the external thread configuration can have either a thread cutting or a thread forming geometry. Self threading inserts tap or form threads as they are driven into a molded or drilled pilot hole. Once in place, friction between the plastic material and the insert keep the insert from rotating, while the threads provide pull out resistance. The self threading insert provides a durable set of machine threads for use with a machine screw, for applications where repeated assembly operations are anticipated. The self threading inserts are available in a variety of sizes, having a variety of both internal and external thread configurations. The upper size limit on the external self threading screw is in the 0.375 inch (9.5 mm) range due to driving torque limitations during initial assembly, resulting in an upper machine screw size limit of about 0.25 inch (6.35 mm) diameter. Self threading inserts can be used with both thermosetting and thermoplastic materials. The specific plastic material type determines the external self threading screw thread configuration. Thread forming configurations are generally used with ductile thermoplastics, while thread cutting configurations are generally used with rigid, glassy or reinforced thermoplastics, or thermosets [24,52]. Most of the boss or hole design considerations for self threading inserts are similar to those of self threading screws.

Helically coiled wire inserts are sometimes used to provide a precise, durable machine thread. The inserts are not self threading, and must be inserted into a threaded hole (either molded or tapped). The inserts are available in a variety of sizes and are available with both free running or self locking internal threads [24].

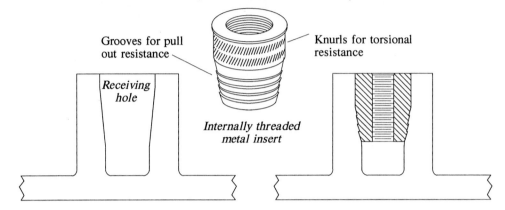

Figure 6.87. Ultrasonic welding equipment can be used to install specially designed metal inserts into a molded plastic boss.

Ultrasonic Insertion: Ultrasonic welding equipment (described latter in the chapter) can be used to generate the pressure and heat necessary for thermal insertion. The inserts used for the ultrasonic insertion process are generally brass with internal machine threads and a series of axial buttress type flutes for pull out resistance and knurls or vertical slots for torsional resistance as shown in Figures 6.87 and 6.88. The inserts and the slightly undersized receiving holes are generally tapered to facilitate loading, ensure more uniform heat generation due to the scarfing action, facilitate molding, and reduce installation time (generally less than 1.0 second). The interference fit of the hole must provide sufficient material to fill in the various insert undercuts [16,24,51].

Figure 6.88. Internally threaded brass inserts are available in a wide variety of sizes and shapes for ultrasonic insertion.

The insert is pushed into the boss using a cold tool (horn or sonotrade) which vibrates at low amplitude and ultrasonic frequency, while the plastic part is firmly fixtured. The vibration at the insert / boss wall interface results in friction, which softens the plastic material. As the insert is pressed in by the vibrating horn, molten polymer flows into the undercuts and cools / resolidifies when the vibration stops, locking the insert in place. Horns for the ultrasonic insertion process are subject to a great deal of abuse and should be produced from hardened steel or carbide faced titanium. Horns with replaceable tips are recommended for long production runs [51]. The process is significantly faster and more efficient than the conventional thermal insertion method because heat is generated only at the metal / thermoplastic interface where it is needed. The resulting assembly is strong, with a low residual stress value. Shrinkage of the melt film at the insert / polymer interface tends to relieve stress by pulling melt away from the insert during cooling [24].

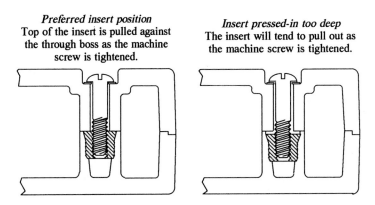

Preferred insert position
Top of the insert is pulled against the through boss as the machine screw is tightened.

Insert pressed-in too deep
The insert will tend to pull out as the machine screw is tightened.

Figure 6.89. An insert should be positioned so that it makes contact with the mating part as the screw is tightened.

Figure 6.90. While self threading screws can be used with structural foam parts, inserts are commonly used to provide a more durable assembly due to the limited shear strengths of the structural foam's core.

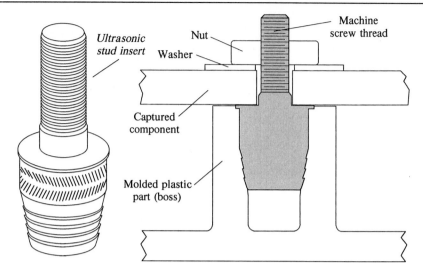

Figure 6.91. A variety of specialty hardware items can also be ultrasonically inserted, such as this ultrasonically inserted machine screw stud.

Insertion depth is an important process parameter. Situations where the insert is driven too far into the boss should be avoided as this reduces the strength of the assembly, as shown in Figure 6.89. Welding control based on position or a positive stop is used to obtain repeatable insert positioning. Ultrasonic insertion is the most commonly used method of post molding insertion. The technique is suitable for all thermoplastics and thermoplastic structural foams. The ultrasonic insertion process can be used to insert a variety of other mechanical fastening hardware such as the threaded stud shown in Figure 6.91.

Expansion Inserts: Internally threaded brass inserts that anchor themselves in a molded or drilled hole using an expansion principle are sometimes used with plastic materials. The inserts have longitudinal slots cut along their length. The insert actually consists of a series of cantilever beams as shown in Figure 6.92.

The inserts have a knurled or barbed external surface, and are pushed into straight sided molded or drilled holes. When expansion inserts are used with rigid thermosetting type materials, the receiving hole is generally oversized, allowing the insert to drop freely to the bottom of the hole. The hole depth is equal to the insert length (the radius at the base of the hole should not interfere with expansion) or the flange style insert can be used with a deeper hole as shown in Figure 6.93.

A special tool is used to push an integral spreader plate once it is in place, expanding the cantilever beams, locking the insert in place prior to machine screw installation. When expansion inserts are used with very ductile thermoplastics, the receiving hole is sometimes slightly undersized, and the expansion insert is pressed in. Expansion inserts are more commonly used with reinforced thermosetting polymers and should be used with care since the hoop stress level associated with their use can be very high [19,24,52].

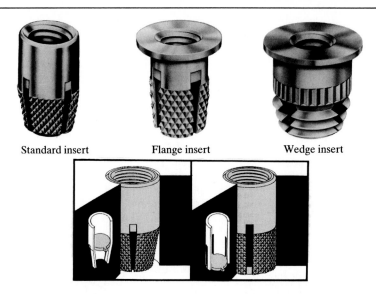

Standard insert   Flange insert   Wedge insert

Figure 6.92. Expansion inserts are available in various configurations. The inserts use a captivated spreader plate which is depressed and expands the knurled portion of the insert. (Courtesy of Heli-coil Division, Emhart Fastening Group, Danbury, CT).

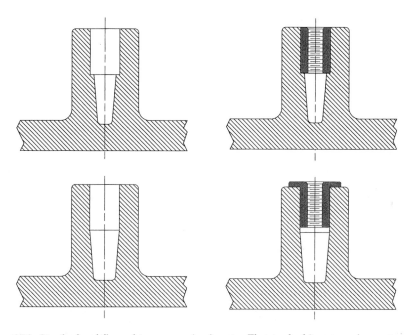

Figure 6.93. Standard and flanged type expansion inserts. The standard insert requires a stepped hole when used with deep bosses. Internal corner radii can interfere with expansion. The flange design prevents the insert from dropping to the bottom of the hole.

6.5   Welding of Thermoplastics

6.5.1   Introduction

A number of welding methods are currently available to join thermoplastic parts to one another. Most thermoplastics can be welded to themselves using one or more of the methods described in the the following sections. When a thermoplastic part must be joined to another thermoplastic part produced from a different thermoplastic material, welding may still be a possible assembly option. If the thermoplastic part must be joined to a non-thermoplastic part such as a metal part, or part produced from a thermosetting polymer, conventional welding is not an option, however, welding techniques that utilize tie layers or adhesives at the joint interface can sometimes be used.

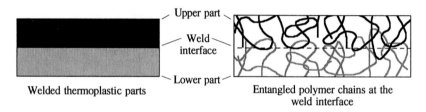

Welded thermoplastic parts

Upper part

Weld interface

Lower part

Entangled polymer chains at the weld interface

Figure 6.94. Molecular diffusion and entanglement must occur during welding. The molecular mobility can be the result of solvent swelling or thermal energy.

True welding processes require interdiffusion and entanglement of polymer chain segments across the weld interface. The welding process involves surface rearrangement, wetting, and intermolecular diffusion [53]. The molecular mobility for welding can be generated using solvents, for solvent welding, or heat for conventional thermoplastic welding processes. The different welding processes generate the heat energy in different ways. In processes such as hot tool welding, heat transfer is primarily by conduction, while in vibration processes, mechanical energy is converted into heat energy through surface friction and/or viscous dissipation. Selection of the appropriate welding method for a given application is determined by factors such as material type, structural requirements, esthetic requirements, fluid / gas seal requirements, part geometry / size, tolerances, equipment availability and process economics. The decision as to which welding method will be used to join a thermoplastic assembly should be made early in the part design process since the part design requirements for welding processes can be significant, and vary considerably between the different welding processes.

Thermoplastic welding techniques are generally considered to be irreversible. A few techniques, such as induction welding, can be used to produce a reversible assembly, although snap fits or mechanical fasteners are generally used when repeated assembly is anticipated. Several thermoplastic welding techniques that utilize heat to generate molecular mobility are listed below and are described in the following sections of this assemby chapeter. Solvent welding and adhesive bonding are considered in separate sections latter in the chapter.

- Ultrasonic welding
- Vibration welding
- Spin (rotational) welding
- Hot tool welding
- Induction welding
- Resistance welding
- Hot gas welding
- Extrusion welding

While techniques such as hot gas welding are generally used to weld plastic pipe, sheet or semi-finished goods rather than injection molded parts, the section is included here since many molded thermoplastic parts, especially thermoplastic automotive panels, are repaired using the hot gas welding technique. In addition, hot gas welding is sometimes used in the fabrication of prototype plastic parts.

6.5.2   Ultrasonic Welding

The most popular method used to weld molded thermoplastic parts is ultrasonic welding. The process is used extensively to weld molded thermoplastic parts used in the automotive, appliance, medical and toy industries. The process uses low amplitude, high frequency (ultrasonic) vibrational energy to generate surface and intermolecular friction, and the heat required to weld the mating thermoplastic parts. In this process, one of the two parts to be joined is fixed firmly within a stationary holding jig, while the mating part is subjected to sinusoidal ultrasonic vibration normal to the contact area as shown in Figure 6.95.

Ultrasonic welding occurs at frequencies in the 20 - 50 kHz range at amplitudes of vibration that typically range from 0.0005 to 0.0025 inch (15 - 60 µm) [54]. Sonic frequencies as low as 15 kHz (and higher amplitudes of vibration) are sometimes used for larger parts or softer materials [43]. The longitudinal vibrations are transmitted through the part to the joint interface where the parts are held together under pressure. Both external and internal friction generate heat selectively in the joint area, softening the material only in the local weld zone. Once the appropriate weld displacement has been achieved, the ultrasonic vibrations are stopped, and the weld is allowed to cool and solidify under pressure. The welding process generally occurs within 0.5 to 1.5 seconds [55,56]. Ultrasonic welding equipment is generally used to weld small to medium size parts, but very large parts can be welded using multiple welding stations [54].

Equipment for Ultrasonic Welding: The ultrasonic welding equipment shown in Figure 6.95 consists of a variety of components [51,54,55].

Power Supply / Generator: The power supply converts the 50 / 60 Hz AC electrical power into high frequency, 20 to 40 kHz electrical power.

Converter: High frequency electrical energy is converted to high frequency mechanical vibration of the same frequency. Piezoelectric transducers clamped between metal blocks are typically used for the converter.

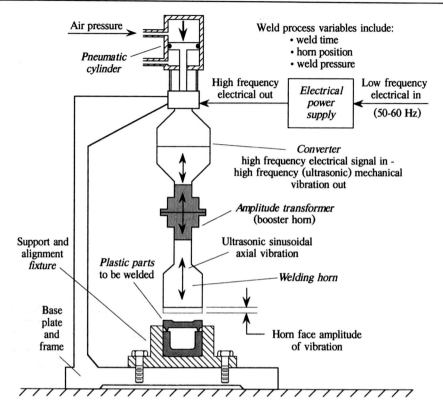

Figure 6.95. Schematic representation of typical ultrasonic welding equipment. The ultrasonic welding process is commonly used for the assembly of small to medium size thermoplastic parts.

Stand and Press: The rigid stand assembly houses the converter, horn assembly, pneumatic pressure cylinder, and part fixtures.

Booster: The booster is a half wavelength resonant section made of an aluminum or titanium alloy and couples the converter to the welding horn. The booster can serve as an amplitude increasing device, an amplitude decreasing device, or as a simple coupling bar.

Horn: The horn or sonotrode is a half wave resonator which impacts the ultrasonic vibrations to the workpiece. The horn is generally constructed using titanium, aluminum or steel alloys. Titanium and aluminum have the desired acoustic properties while carbide faced titanium and hardened steel offer improved durability. Carbide faced titanium is generally used for high amplitude and abrasive applications while heat treated steel is suitable for high durability, low amplitude applications such as insertion.

Fixture: The fixture holds and locates the parts to be welded. The fixed part is also subject to high frequency vibration from the mating component. The fixture may contain a urethane liner to damp the vibration and prevent part damage.

Controls: The ultrasonic welding process can be controlled based on either weld time, weld position (collapse distance) or weld energy. Additional controls for weld pressure regulation and cooling time are also provided.

Ultrasonic welders typically operate at frequencies of either 20 or 40 kHz. The 20 kHz units are more common, however, higher frequency welding does offer some advantages [57]. The wavelength of a 40 kHz unit is one half that of the 20 kHz system. As a result, smaller components can be used, which can be important when space is limited or automation is required. The higher frequency also reduces the amplitude of vibration required, and the potential for noise due to damped part vibrations (at sonic frequencies). This lower amplitude vibration also reduces the potential for part damage (due to the mechanical abuse). The higher frequency units do offer improved control, however, their power capabilities are limited. In addition, their lower amplitude of vibration and power capabilities mean that distances between the horn/·part interface and the joint must be kept to a minimum.

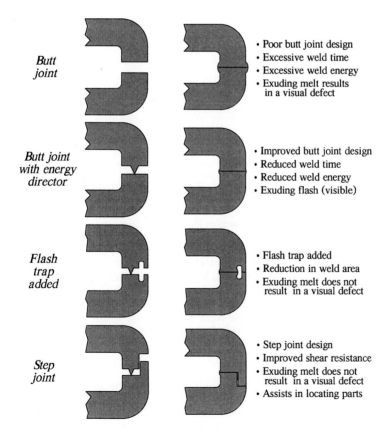

Butt joint	• Poor butt joint design • Excessive weld time • Excessive weld energy • Exuding melt results in a visual defect
Butt joint with energy director	• Improved butt joint design • Reduced weld time • Reduced weld energy • Exuding flash (visible)
Flash trap added	• Flash trap added • Reduction in weld area • Exuding melt does not result in a visual defect
Step joint	• Step joint design • Improved shear resistance • Exuding melt does not result in a visual defect • Assists in locating parts

Figure 6.96. There are a variety of joint styles and configurations used with the ultrasonic welding process. The step / butt joint is suitable for many polymers.

Joint Design Considerations: There are many types of joint configurations that are possible in ultrasonic welding, and these designs fall into one or two categories. The first, and most commonly used joint type, utilizes ultrasonic vibrations in a direction normal to the surfaces to be joined. Butt and step joints fall into this category. A second set of ultrasonic weld joints involve vibrations parallel to the mating surfaces, resulting in a state of shear. The various types of shear and scarf joints fall into this second category [58].   Rough guidelines for joint design are given below, however, material manufacturers should be consulted for material specific joint designs.

Butt Joints: A series of butt and step joints are shown in Figure 6.96. The first butt joint design with a flat contact surface at the weld interface requires excessive weld energy, and results in unsightly flash beads. As a result, this joint design is not used in general practice. Instead, one of the surfaces to be welded, preferably the surface closest to the horn, contains a wedge or triangular shaped protrusion, commonly called an energy director. The apex of the energy director contacts the mating part surface. During welding, the energy director softens to the point where it becomes molten, and flows across the weld zone under pressure before it cools. These energy director joints work best with amorphous materials, however, the larger energy director geometry shown in Figure 6.97 may be suitable for non-hermetic applications with some semi-crystalline materials [59].

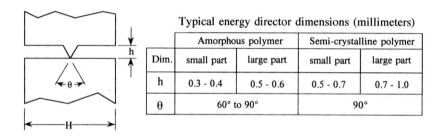

Typical energy director dimensions (millimeters)

Dim.	Amorphous polymer		Semi-crystalline polymer	
	small part	large part	small part	large part
h	0.3 - 0.4	0.5 - 0.6	0.5 - 0.7	0.7 - 1.0
θ	60° to 90°		90°	

Figure 6.97. Approximate energy director dimension for amorphous and semi-crystalline polymers.

Correct energy director design does not in and of itself ensure optimum weld strength or quality since welding process variables such as weld time, horn amplitude and pressure all have a significant influence on the joint characteristics. The energy flow is critical to the quality of an ultrasonic weld. Both insufficient and excessive energy reduce weld quality [60]. For example, excessive weld pressure can result in either insufficient energy director melting or excessive melt flow when coupled with long weld time. This situation can result in excessive collapse, severe flash, and unfavorable molecular orientation.

The weld joint shown in Figure 6.99 is a unique modification of the conventional butt energy director joint design [60]. This joint has a conventional energy director on one of the work pieces, while the opposite workpiece is modified with a rough or textured surface. The rough surface has been shown to increase the weld quality, weld strength, and the overall ease at which welding can be accomplished. A variety of other textured joint configurations are also possible.

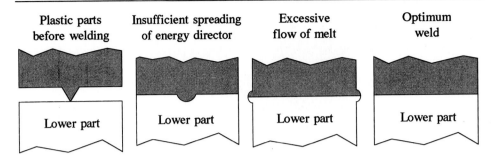

Figure 6.98. The welding process conditions used during assembly can have a very significant effect on the strengths and appearance of the welded joint.

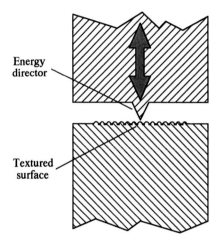

Figure 6.99. Surface textures opposite the energy director can improve weld quality for joints such as the butt joint.

The flash problem shown in Figure 6.100 can be reduced by incorporating flash containment traps into the joint design as shown in Figures 6.96 and 6.100. The traps are used in applications where flash is either esthetically or functionally unacceptable, resulting in a joint with improved appearance, at the expense of joint strength. Flash traps are typically designed with at least 10% excess volume capacity for safety [58].

Pinch joints provide an alternative to the standard butt joint [61] . The pinch joint is designed to trap or retain the melt within the weld zone in order to minimize the potential for flash formation. Pinch joints have also been shown to be useful for some semi-crystalline plastic materials, such as acetal or nylon, that pass quickly from the solid to molten state (i.e. with rather narrow melting temperature ranges). The part tolerance demands with pinch joints are relatively tight due to the more complex joint geometry. The larger joint geometry will also require additional amplitude and weld energy compared to the triangular energy director weld. Typical pinch weld geometries are shown in Figure 6.102 [61].

Figure 6.100. Cross section of a butt joint showing excessive welding flash.

Figure 6.101. Cross section of a butt joint that incorporates both interior and exterior flash traps.

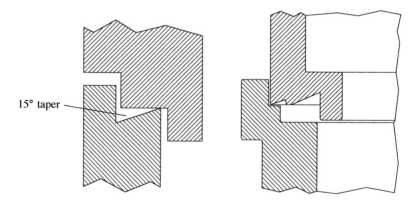

Figure 6.102. Typical geometry of an ultrasonic pinch weld joint.

Butt weld joints are usually located on the outer wall faces or periphery of a injection molded part, and sometimes along internal ribs or standoffs. In order to avoid welding difficulties at the corners of the part from excess material buildup, energy directors and the molding corners should have a generous corner radius. Alternatively, the energy director can be interrupted at the corners when a hermetic seal is not required, as shown in Figure 6.103 [59].

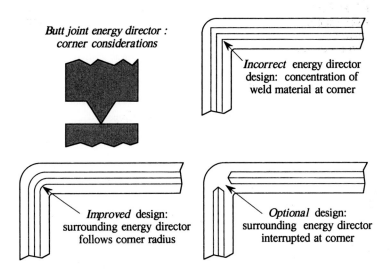

Butt joint energy director : corner considerations

Incorrect energy director design: concentration of weld material at corner

Improved design: surrounding energy director follows corner radius

Optional design: surrounding energy director interrupted at corner

Figure 6.103. The energy director can run around the entire perimeter of the part, or can be interrupted when fluid tight seals are not required.

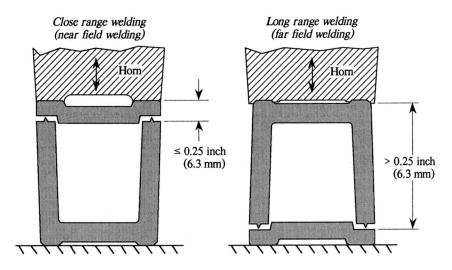

Close range welding (near field welding)

Long range welding (far field welding)

Horn

Horn

≤ 0.25 inch (6.3 mm)

> 0.25 inch (6.3 mm)

Figure 6.104. Schematic representation of near field and far field ultrasonic welding.

Near Field vs. Far Field Welding: It is important that the welding horn is in tight contact with the upper part, having sufficient area of contact, especially immediate above the joint location. The distance between the welding horn and the joint interface has a significant influence on weld quality as shown in Figure 6.104.

Joints that are within 0.25 inch (6 mm) of the horn / part interface are described as "near field" joints, while those greater than 0.25 inch (6 mm) from the horn / part interface are described as "far field" joints. It generally becomes more difficult to weld parts as the distance between the joint and horn increase. Near field welding is preferred for most materials, however, far field configurations can be used with glassy, amorphous materials when necessary.

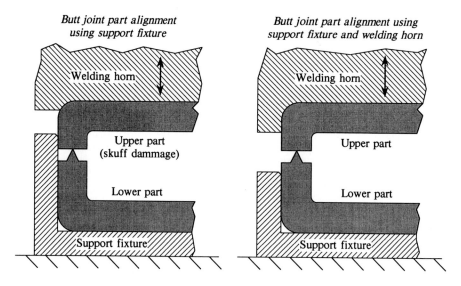

Figure 6.105. (left) Part alignment using the support fixture can result in a scuffing of the outer part surface. (right) Part alignment using only the welding horn can result in a welding mismatch.

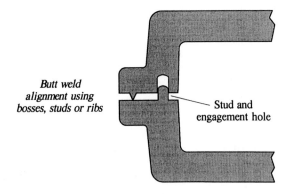

Figure 6.106. Part alignment can be improved using molded-in studs or other molded-in features.

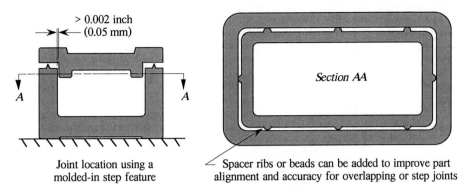

Figure 6.107. Part alignment using a molded in step feature and spacer ribs to improve location.

Part Alignment: Simple butt joints do not incorporate any provisions for aligning or centering the parts with respect to one another. The holding fixture can be used to align both parts when the part geometry is suitable. Alternatively, the holding fixture can be used to locate the bottom part while the welding horn itself is used to guide and locate the upper part [59] as shown in Figure 6.105. Part alignment is more appropriately accomplished using molded pins or studs as shown in Figure 6.106, or using step features on the parts themselves as shown in Figure 6.107.

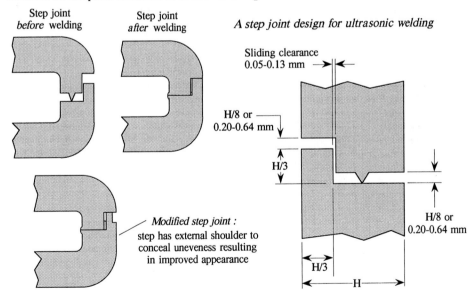

Figure 6.108. Typical step joint design for the ultrasonic welding process.

Step Joints: The simple butt joint is easily modified to produce the more esthetically pleasing and self aligning step joint as shown in Figures 6.108 and 6.109. The step joint resists tensile forces and offers improved resistance to shear loading in service. External flash is eliminated with the step joint design, resulting in improved product appearance. The modified step joint shown in Figure 6.108 has an external shoulder to disguise any unevenness, resulting in additional esthetic improvement. Spacer ribs of the type described previously and shown in Figure 6.107 are sometimes used with step joints to improve part alignment and minimize the sliding (shear) surface area of contact.

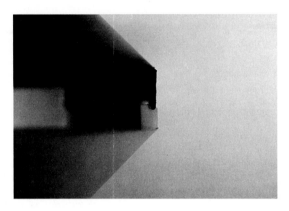

Figure 6.109. Cross section of an ultrasonically welded step joint. The step aligns the parts and disguises flash.

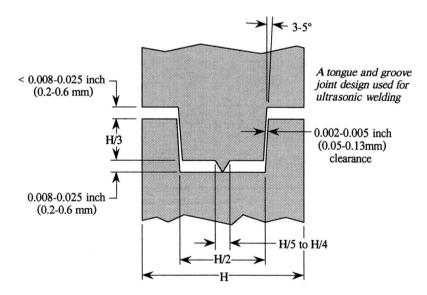

Figure 6.110. Typical tongue and groove joint design for the ultrasonic welding process.

Tongue and Groove Joints: Tongue and groove joint designs such as that joint shown in Figure 6.110 provide strength in both shear and tension. The joint is self centering and optically acceptable. During welding, melt from the energy director fills the lower cavity and is forced through the vertical gap as collapse continues, increasing the weld contact area, and improving the joint strength. Wall thicknesses in the joint region must be relatively large to accommodate the tongue and groove joint design. In addition, part tolerance requirements are relatively tight. Spacer ribs, similar to those shown in Figure 6.107, improve joint alignment.

Shear Joints: There are many possible shear joint configurations that are used with the ultrasonic welding process. The shear joints are commonly recommended when welding semi-crystalline polymers (or other polymers that are difficult to weld), and when hermetic seals are required. Typical shear joint configurations are shown in Figures 6.111 Shear joints are used on both circular and rectangular parts where high strength, high quality joints are required.

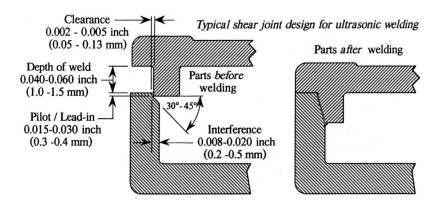

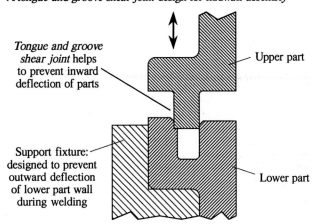

Figure 6.111. (top) Typical shear joint design for ultrasonic welding. (bottom) Typical shear joint design for a midwall assembly.

Shear joints are the preferred joint design for semi-crystalline polymers because they offer higher strength than energy director type butt or step joints. Shear joints have overlapping part wall segments that create an interference and local shear as the joints are welded and telescope into one another. A pilot section is included to assist in part alignment. The angle at the top of the interference on one side cuts down on the initial contact area, concentrating the energy for melting. Both surfaces melt uniformly as the parts are welded since the temperature of the molten material is maintained throughout the contact area [56]. Interference values in the 0.005 - 0.020 inch (0.13 - 0.51 mm) range have been used over depths of 0.040 - 0.080 inch (1.0 - 2.0 mm). The vertical part walls should be well supported with the holding fixture to prevent outward sidewall deflection during welding due to the interference. Ideally, the top part should be as shallow as possible, however, tongue and groove type joints, modified with a shear section on one side, can be used with deeper draw parts, to produce midwall joints that minimize sidewall deflections due to the interference as shown in Figure 6.111 [57].

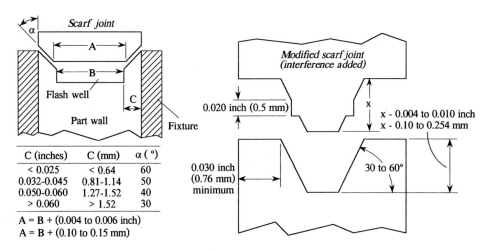

C (inches)	C (mm)	α (°)
< 0.025	< 0.64	60
0.032-0.045	0.81-1.14	50
0.050-0.060	1.27-1.52	40
> 0.060	> 1.52	30

A = B + (0.004 to 0.006 inch)
A = B + (0.10 to 0.15 mm)

Figure 6.112. Typical scarf joint design for the ultrasonic welding process.

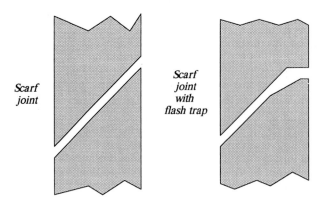

Figure 6.113. An example of an ultrasonic welding scarf joint incorporating a flash trap [58].

Scarf Joints: Scarf joint designs are also used to produce high strength hermetic seals for both amorphous and semi-crystalline polymers. The scarf joints are self locating and are most appropriate for small sized circular or oval parts. Weld energy requirements for scarf joints are very high. The scarf joints shown in Figures 6.112 and 6.113 show a few of the possible configurations [56,58].

The scarf joints have angles from 30 - 60°, and should be matched to within ± 1°. An interference of 0.004 - 0.010 inch (0.10 - 0.25mm) added as extra material thickness in the weld zone is used to produce the weld and flash. Traps are used when flash is either functionally or esthetically unacceptable [58].

Welding with an Inlaid Seal: Reliable seals can also be obtained using inlaid elastomeric sealing rings or compliant gaskets [59]. The joint detail shown in Figure 6.114 incorporates an elastomeric ring to improve the reliability of the seal achievable with the ultrasonically welded joint, or in situations where continuous perimeter welding is not possible.

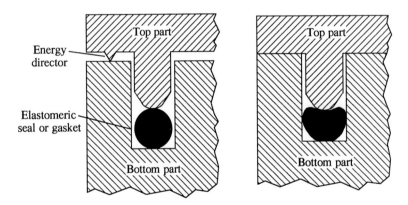

Figure 6.114. Hermatic seals are commonly required for ultrasonically welded parts. Soft gaskets or seals can be used to provide an extra measure of safety in critical applications [59].

Stud Welding: Ultrasonic welding equipment can also be used to produce stud or pin and socket point welds as shown in Figure 6.115. Pin and socket joints can be used to join similar plastic materials in applications where a hermetic seal is not required. The joints are essentially cylindrical shear joints having a circumferential interference. A self locating lead-in feature, located on either the stud or hole, is used to position and align the two components. Flash containment traps can also be incorporated into the joint as shown in Figure 6.115. The depth of welding should be about one half of the stud diameter for optimum strength [51,56,59].

Ultrasonic Staking: A variation of ultrasonic welding is ultrasonic staking. Staking is used to lock a thermoplastic component to a second component produced from a dissimilar material as shown in Figure 6.116. The thermoplastic stud protrudes through a hole in the component to be captured. Ultrasonic vibrations are imparted to the top of the molded plastic stud which melts and fills the volume of the horn cavity to form a head

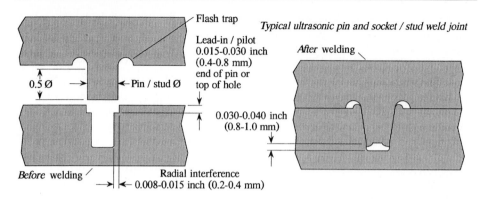

Figure 6.115. Ultrasonic welding equipment can be used to create pin and socket type shear joints [43].

thereby capturing the second component. The stud or boss should have a generous radius or fillet at the base to prevent cracking or melting. The top of the boss should be designed to minimize initial contact with the horn in order to concentrate the ultrasonic energy. The boss top can be flat or conical, conical being preferred for semi - crystalline

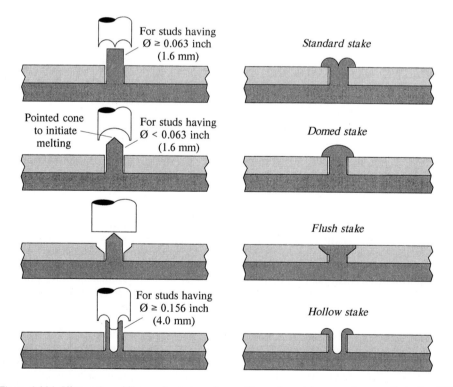

Figure 6.116. Ultrasonic welding equipment can be used to produce stakes or various configuration [51].

or filled polymers. The integrity of the ultrasonic stake is dependent upon the precise volumetric relationship between the stud and horn cavity. Proper stake design produces optimum strength and appearance, with minimum flash. A variety of stake designs including those shown in Figure 6.116 are used in practice [51,56].

Standard Stake: This general purpose stake is recommended for flat head studs having a diameter greater than 1/16 inch (1.6 mm) but less than 5/32 inch (4 mm) in diameter. The standard profile is recommended for both rigid and ductile, non-abrasive thermoplastics.
Dome Stake: The dome stake is recommended for studs having a diameter less than 1/16 inch (1.6 mm) in diameter. The stud should be capped with a cone shape to reduce the energy transmitted through the stud. The dome stake is suitable for abrasive plastics.
Flush Stake: Flush stakes are used in applications where a flat or flush surface is required, and the thickness of the captured part permits their use. Studs with a conical top are recommended.
Hollow Stake: Bosses or studs having diameters greater than 5/32 inch (4 mm) can be cored out to produce a blind hollow boss. The hollow boss minimizes the potential for sink marks opposite the boss or shrinkage voids at the base of the boss. The hollow bosses are relatively easy to form and cool due to their relative thin wall.

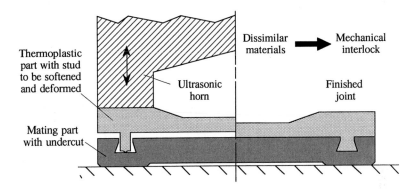

Figure 6.117. An example of a mechanical interlock formed using ultrasonic energy [62].

Ultrasonic welding equipment can also be used to create mechanical interlocks when through holes in the mating component are not permitted as shown in Figure 6.117. For this process, a molded thermoplastic stud (similar to that used for staking) and a blind undercut in the mating component are used to produce a purely mechanical joint based on interference (assuming the part with the undercut does not soften). Upon welding, the stud will soften and flow into the undercut section and cool, creating the permanent mechanical interlock [62].

Material Considerations for Ultrasonic Welding: The process of ultrasonic welding is suitable for most thermoplastic materials, however, there are a number of material related factors that should be taken into account when considering the use of the process. These material characteristics include morphology, melt flow characteristics, viscoelastic behavior, hygroscopicity, and the presence of additives.

Amorphous Polymers: Amorphous polymers, especially those that are in the glassy state at room temperature, are generally good candidates for the ultrasonic welding process [51,56,63]. Glassy, amorphous polymers with their random molecular arrangement are good vibratory energy transmitters. The weldability of the amorphous polymer is influenced by both its glass transition temperature, T_g, and its rigidity. Glassy amorphous thermoplastics are both rigid and have gradual thermal transitions, going from the glassy state, through T_g, through a broad softening range, and eventually reach the molten state. Upon cooling, the inverse gradual trend is observed, allowing the amorphous polymer to flow and diffuse, without premature solidification. The rigidity and gradual thermal transition result in design and processing flexibility, as well as lower energy requirements. The good transmission properties of glassy amorphous materials permit successful welding using both near and far field welding techniques [64,65]. The ultrasonic weldability of amorphous materials becomes more of a problem as the materials become more flexible. For example, it will generally take more energy and additional amplitude to weld high impact polystyrene than general purpose polystyrene [51]. In the extreme, it is essentially impossible to weld very flexible polymers such as thermoplastic elastomers due to excessive dampening of the vibrations [54]. While it is best to weld parts produced from the same grade of polymer, it is sometimes possible to cross weld amorphous polymers if their chemical structure, flow properties, and T_g values are similar. The T_g values of the two materials should not be more than 25-40°F (14-22°C) apart [54,55,61].

Table 6.1. General Guidelines on the Compatibility of Various Thermoplastics for Ultrasonic Assembly [a] [63]

Material	Notation	Complete compatibility	Partial [b]
ABS	A	A,B,D	T
ABS/polycarbonate alloy	B	A,B,K	D
Acetal	C	C	---
Acrylic	D	A,D	B,E, J,K,T
Acrylic Multipolymer	E	E	A,D,Q,T
Cellulosics	F	F	---
Fluoropolymers	G	G	---
Nylon	H	H	---
Polyphenylene oxide	I	I,Q	D,K,T
Polyamide-imide	J	J	---
Polycarbonate	K	B,K	D,I,R
Polyester	L	L	---
Polyethylene	M	M	---
Polymethylpentene	N	N	---
Polyphenylene sulfide	O	O	---
Polypropylene	P	P	---
Polystyrene	Q	I,Q	E,T
Polysulfone	R	R	K
PVC	S	S	---
SAN	T	T	A,D,E,I,Q

[a] Variations in resins may produce slightly different results.
[b] In some cases.

Polymer alloys or blends can be ultrasonically welded to one or more of the component resins in many cases. It is also possible to weld structural foam parts using the ultrasonic welding process, however, experimentation is generally required. The ability to weld the foam parts decreases with increasing density reduction. An additional problem can be the generation of foam in the weld zone due to the presence of unreacted chemical blowing agent [56].

Semi-crystalline Polymers: Semi-crystalline polymers are generally more difficult to weld using ultrasonic energy when compared with rigid or semi-rigid amorphous thermoplastics. However, semi-crystalline thermoplastics parts can usually be ultrasonically welded to parts produced in the identical material if proper processing conditions and joint designs are used [58]. Semi-crystalline polymers tend to dampen ultrasonic vibrations more than glassy amorphous polymers. In general, semi-crystalline materials are poor vibratory energy transmitters. As a result, when welding these materials, it is necessary to (i) increase the energy level emitted by the welding system (i.e. increase the amplitude of vibration) and (ii) shorten the distance between the horn / part contact area and the joint interface [63]. Near field ultrasonic welding techniques and joint designs are used almost exclusively when working with semi-crystalline polymers. Far field welds require excessive energy input due to attenuation of the signal over the longer distance, and can result in melting of the part at the horn / part interface, rather than at the joint [66]. The parts to be welded should be very well supported. Unsupported cantilever sections, especially those with insufficient corner radii can crack or even fracture during welding due to the relatively high amplitudes of vibration (i.e. due to mechanical abuse). Welding vibrations are further dampened by features such as holes, steps or bends which interrupt direct transmission of the ultrasonic energy. Semi-crystalline polymers require significant energy input, and as a result, horn amplitudes of vibration as high as 0.002 -0.005 inches (0.05 - 0.15 mm) must be used [63]. These high welding amplitudes necessitate the use of titanium horns. It is important that the welding horn contact the part at each of the welding points. Like amorphous materials, semi-crystalline polymers have welding energies that increase with increasing melt temperature, and decrease with increasing modulus or rigidity due to improved energy transmission. Materials such as PTFE, with its very high Tm, low coefficient of friction and poor flow properties are extremely difficult to weld.

Most sources indicate that the conventional energy director type of joint is not suitable for semi-crystalline polymers when high strength or hermetic assemblies are required. Ultrasonic energy applied to the energy director type of joint does melt the director material, beginning at the point of contact, ultimately spreading the melt over the adjacent joint surface. However, the relatively sharp melting and solidification range of the semi-crystalline material, combined with the need for additional energy input to overcome the heat of fusion, generally lead to poor weld strength. The molten polymer tends to solidify prematurely, before any significant degree of molecular diffusion takes place between the melt film and the adjacent part surfaces [58,66]. While energy director type of joints are generally not recommended with semi-crystalline materials, larger size energy directors, having an increased mass of molten material, are used in some cases [59]. Both shear and scarf joints have been shown to be suitable for semi-crystalline polymers when high strength, hermetic assemblies are required.

Welding Hygroscopic Polymers: Many plastic materials, specifically those containing polar groups are hygroscopic in nature and absorb moisture from the atmosphere after injection molding. The parts are dry as molded (due to predrying before molding) but will pick up moisture over time. The rate of moisture absorption is determined by the material type, initial moisture level, and by the ambient conditions. Highly hygroscopic polymers such as nylon 6,6 can reach surface moisture levels that interfere with welding shortly after molding. The presence of moisture can lead to foaming, voids, microvoids, increased energy to weld due to vibration dampening, or even hydrolytic degradation for many condensation polymers. As a result, it is desirable to eliminate moisture effects by [56,58,59,63]:

- Welding parts immediately after molding (while they are still dry)
- Drying parts before welding
- Storing parts in desiccators before welding

Self sealing polyethylene bags (preferably containing desiccant) are commonly used in place of desiccators for convenience. The simplest way to avoid the problem is to weld the parts immediately after molding while the parts are free from moisture, and are at a somewhat elevated temperature [58]. This solution works well for amorphous materials, however, it may be better to store semi - crystalline parts in sealed containers for at least 24 hours after molding / before welding to account for post mold shrinkage and morphological changes such as post mold crystallization [59].

The Effect of Additives on Ultrasonic Weldability: Almost all plastic material formulations contain one or more additives. In some cases, additives have little or no effect on material weldability, while in other cases ultrasonic weldability is affected significantly. While there is little quantitative information available on the influence of additives on weldability, there are qualitative guidelines.

Fillers and Reinforcements: Fillers and reinforcements such as calcium carbonate, talc, glass, carbon, or any inorganic / organic particulate that increases the rigidity of the composite material, can have both a positive and negative impact on the ultrasonic weldability of a polymer. Welding characteristics are generally enhanced at low filler concentrations, since the composite material exhibits improved rigidity, yet the part surface remains resin rich. It can be difficult to obtain hermetic seals at filler concentrations exceeding 35% [63]. Filler concentrations above 40% may prevent welding altogether, however, experimentation is required since some materials, such as a 40% talc filled polypropylene, can have good welding characteristics [56]. When abrasive fillers or reinforcements are used in concentrations greater than 10%, carbide face titanium horns, or alternatively hardened steel horns are generally used. It should be noted that certain fillers are hygroscopic in nature, resulting in the potential for moisture related welding problems. The use of higher frequency, lower amplitude welding equipment may improve the ability to weld heavily filled polymers [57].

Mold Release Agents: It is best to avoid the use of mold release agents when molding parts that will be joined using the ultrasonic welding process. Release agents adhere to the part surface and impede the generation of friction heat. The release agent residue also acts as a contaminate that must be removed / cleaned from the joint area before welding. If mold release agents must be used due to part ejection difficulties, only those agents described as paintable or printable are recommended [59,63].

Lubricants: Both internal and external lubricants impede welding by reducing molecular friction, however, external lubricants may also contaminate the part surface. The effect of an internal lubricant on the weldability of a polymer is said to be minimal if the internal lubricant concentration is low, and the additive is well dispersed. Experimentation is recommended in order to achieve optimum results[63].

Flame Retardants: The effect of flame retardant additives on the weldability of thermoplastics depends upon the type of additive, concentration and level of dispersion. Flame retardant grades can require higher weld amplitude and weld energy levels.

Plasticizers / Impact Modifiers: Any additive that improves the toughness of a polymer by increasing flexibility or softness, increases the materials absorption characteristics, thus increases the energy required for welding. Higher welding amplitudes and shorter welding distances (between the horn and the joint) improve the weldability of the more ductile materials [63]. In the extreme case, highly plasticized, elastomeric polymers may be impossible to weld using ultrasonic techniques. Non-permanent, migratory plasticizers may present additional contamination problems [56].

Pigments: In general, pigments have little or no significant influence on the weldability of materials, unless the pigments are used in very high concentrations, where dry pigments begin to act more like fillers, or when oil based liquid pigment systems can also cause difficulties if they exude [63].

Regrind: The use of regrind is not expected to be a problem unless contamination is present or significant molecular degradation has occurred [63].

6.5.3   Vibration Welding

Vibration welding is a frictional welding process in which the parts to be welded are rubbed together under pressure until sufficient frictional and shear heat are developed to cause the joint interface to reach the molten state. Once the melt film has developed and penetrates deep enough into the weld area, the relative motion is stopped, and the weld cools and solidifies under pressure [62]. The term vibration welding is generally synonymous with linear friction welding, however, angular vibration welding processes are also common [67]. These vibration welding processes can be used with nearly all thermoplastics, and are suitable for parts with welding seams that permit unrestricted motion in the direction of reciprocation. The process is generally used for medium to large size parts, having been used for parts as large as vehicle bumpers [68,69].

Materials: Most thermoplastics can be vibration welded. Even high performance materials such as PEI, PPS, PEEK and highly crystalline polymers that can be difficult to join using some of the other welding techniques can be vibration welded [43,70]. Material considerations for vibration welding are similar to those described for ultrasonic welding. Amorphous materials are generally easier to vibration weld than semi-crystalline polymers. Compatibility is generally limited to like amorphous materials, with most semi-crystalline materials being weldable only with themselves. The process is not suitable for very flexible materials such as thermoplastic elastomers [54,69,71]. Welding of hygroscopic materials using the vibration welding process requires additional consideration of polymer moisture content, however, the requirements for dryness may not be as severe as they would be for ultrasonic or hot plate welding [70]. The vibration welding process is also more tolerant to surface contaminations, such as mold release agent residue, compared to other welding processes. The nature of the process is such that these surface contaminants are swept away as the weld is created [62].

Angular Vibration Welding: Angular vibration welding can be used to join parts where the welding zone is approximately the same distance from the rotational axis. The ratio of length to width for parts to be welded with angular equipment should be less than 1.5 to avoid significant differences in relative welding surface speeds.

Linear Vibration Welding: The more common linear vibration welding equipment and process, can be used with any set of parts that permits linear vibration in one direction. The reciprocating motion of vibration welding equipment is achieved using an alternating electromagnetic or hydraulic linear motion generator. The motion generator acts on the vibrating platen or element, while the second platen remains fixed. The vibrating platen is supported by a set of flat springs that support the vibrating element against the welding pressure, permitting lateral displacement, and return the vibrating element (and part) to the aligned home position when the linear motion generator is de-energized [69]. The sinusoidal frequencies used in vibration welding range from 120 to 300 Hz. Linear displacements in the range from 0.030 to 0.200 inch (0.8 - 5.0 mm) are used with the process. The higher frequency vibration welding equipment can be used at the lower amplitudes, and is therefore more suitable for smaller parts, parts where motion is limited, and in applications where flash is a concern [43]. The higher frequency vibration welders may also improve weld quality for materials with a very low coefficient of friction [70]. Weld times range from 1 - 10 seconds (typically 2-4 sec) resulting in total cycle times from 6 to 15 seconds [54,62,64]. The vibration welding process does not permit the use of molded-in part alignment features. The final part alignment is achieved at the end of the vibration cycle when the vibrating element returns to the home position. It is important that the part clamping mechanism is a form fitting fixture, typically produced from aluminum, that is capable of uniformly supporting and aligning the part with no loss in reciprocation.

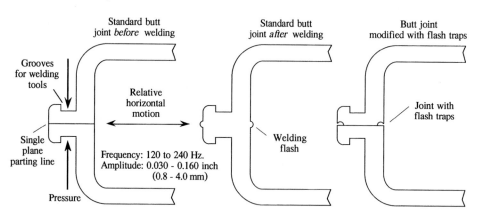

Figure 6.118. Typical joint design for vibration welding; the butt joint, and a butt joint modified with flash traps.

Joints: The vibration welding process is ideally suited for parts where the entire surface to be joined is flat or those having a small out of plane curvature [54]. Welding of multiplane part seams or joints is possible provided they do not interfere with linear travel. The basic joint design for vibration welding is the butt joint as shown in Figure 6.118 [62]. Vibration welding joints must permit relative motion and support the part walls during welding. The butt joint modified with a flange (typically having a width up to two times the part wall thickness) increases the rigidity of the wall, facilitates gripping, ensures a uniform pressure distribution, and provides additional surface area for improved weld strength [69]. The vibration welding process can generate a significant amount of flash, and butt joints can be modified with flash traps as shown in Figure 6.118.

Part features such as internal ribs or dividers can be welded along with the part perimeter if they reach the welding plane. Internal part ribs or walls that are to be welded and are perpendicular to the vibration direction should be reinforced with gusset plates, since the addition of flanges to the ribs is not practical in terms of part moldability (due to part ejection problems). Those internal walls that are parallel to the vibration direction should ride in grooves on the mating part to prevent snaking type deformation [43].

The mechanics of the vibration welding process, like spin welding, involve a number of sequential steps [54,62,71,72]. In the initial phase of the process, heat is generated by the rubbing action or frictional heating of the two part surfaces. Eventually, the surfaces soften and the mechanism of heating becomes viscous dissipation. The molten polymer begins to flow in the lateral direction (producing flash) increasing the weld penetration depth linearly with time in a steady state manner. When motion stops, the pressure and residual heat result in continued penetration and collapse, until resolidification occurs. The strengths achievable with vibration welding can often be as good as those of the base polymer, if proper weld penetration is achieved [54].

6.5.4 Spin (rotational) Welding

Spin welding is a friction welding process that can be used to join parts with rotationally symmetrical joining surfaces. The requisite heat for melting or softening is created by means of interfacial friction between the two parts to be joined. One part, generally the upper part, is rotated about an axis normal to the plane of the surfaces to be joined, while the lower part is held firmly within a stationary fixture or jig as shown in Figure 6.119. The weld is formed by simultaneously applying axial pressure on the rotating part. When the relative motion is stopped, the molten polymer in the weld zone cools and solidifies under pressure [54,62,73-75]. Spin welding is the most efficient process for joining small or large thermoplastic parts that have circular cross sections. Cylindrical parts up to 24 inches (0.6 m) having joint areas as large as 9 in^2 (58 cm^2) have been joined using the spin welding process [54,76]. The process can also be used to join parts having a circular cross section, to a larger non-circular thermoplastic assembly, provided suitable joint details are incorporated into the mating part. Spin welding equipment can range from a simple modified drill press or lathe for prototype work, to more automated and expensive production machines. The equipment generally consists of a motor, drive head, flywheel, and holding fixture [54]. Spin welding equipment operates on principles such as those listed below [73]:

A continuous drive method in which the speed of the rotating part is controlled directly with the drive system. Spin times can be controlled by a timer which activates withdrawal of the drive assembly or a dynamic brake.

The follow method in which the firmly fixed part is released after the melting phase is complete.

Gyrating mass welding (inertia welding) in which a flywheel or rotating mass is accelerated to the desired rotational velocity using a motor. The motor is disengaged at the start of the weld cycle, and the kinetic energy of the freely spinning inertia tool is converted into heat energy during welding.

The equipment costs associated with the more common, latter two methods is lower, however, the continuous drive method does offer advantages such as flexibility of rotation speed profiles. Pneumatic or A.C. motors are most commonly used to power the drive head and flywheel. Spring loaded pressure plates or pneumatic cylinders are used to generate the welding pressure.

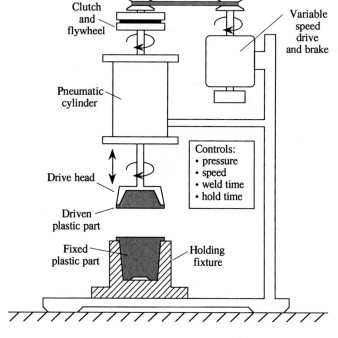

Figure 6.119. The spin welding process can be used for welding cylindrical thermoplastic parts. The basic concepts of the spin welding process are depicted schematically.

Spin welding joints are generally designed to be self locating and should provide adequate weld surface area without introducing significant linear speed differentials across the weld surface. Tongue and groove, scarf, or shear joints are most commonly used [54]. Flash traps can be incorporated into the joint design, or external flash can be removed after welding using a rotating fly knife, or by rotating the welded assembly against a stationary cutting blade or rotating wire brush. Alternatively, the flash can be removed using conventional or cryogenic tumbling deflashing operations [74]. Parts that are assembled using the spin welding process often incorporate features such as gusset plates perpendicular to their circumference in order to provide gripping points for the drive lugs, improving torque transmission as shown in Figure 6.121.

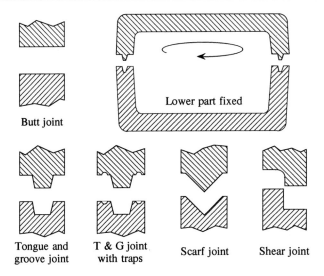

Figure 6.120. Typical basic joint configurations that are used for the spin welding process.

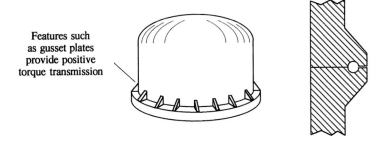

Figure 6.121. Gusset plates can be added to the molded part to facilitate spin welding by improving torque transmission capabilities.

The important process variables in spin welding are the relative tangential velocity, welding pressure, and welding time. Like vibration welding, the spin welding process can be idealized as a number of sequential steps or phases as shown in Figure 6.122 [73]. Once the rotating part has been brought to the appropriate rotational speed, the two joint surfaces are brought together under pressure. This starts the welding process.

In the first phase of welding, the surface roughness on each part is abraded until full surface contact is achieved. At this point, there is solid-solid friction, which causes the temperature of each part to increase. When the material temperature exceeds the point where softening occurs, the mechanism changes from external friction to internal viscous dissipation through shear. The initial temperature rise in this second phase of the melting process is rapid due to the extremely high shear rate in the thin layer. This rapid increase

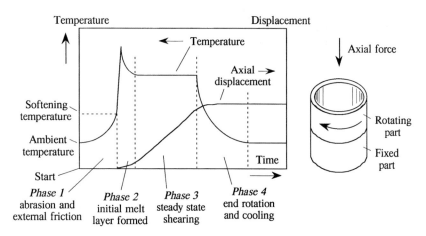

Figure 6.122. Typical temperature and axial displacement over the course of the spin welding cycle.

in temperature leads to an increase in the melt layer thickness. Eventually, a steady state phase is reached where the heat generation is balanced by the formation of the flash bead associated with the continuous lateral flow of melt from the axial pressure. In the last phase of welding, the rotary motion is stopped either abruptly or slowly before the weld solidifies.

The strength of the spin welded joint is determined by the material, joint design and by the process conditions used. Strong, hermetically sealed welds can be achieved with most thermoplastics. Spin welding is especially useful for welding materials that have poor transmission properties such as polyamides or polyolefins [43]. Weld times are short, generally less than 1.0 second with an additional second for cooling. Rotational speeds range from 1,000 rpm for larger parts to as much as 18,000 rpm for smaller diameters [75], resulting in surface speeds from 10 to 50 ft/s (3 to 15 m/s). Weld pressures at the interface range from 300 to 700 psi (20-50 bar). When angular alignment is important, a variant of the spin welding process can be used. The parts are rubbed in an oscillatory rotary motion instead of the conventional unidirectional motion [54].

6.5.5   Electromagnetic Welding

Electromagnetic welding, also known as induction welding, is a method of joining thermoplastic parts using inductive energy to achieve fusion temperatures. The versatile and efficient welding process can be used with most thermoplastic materials and could be described as a specific type of implant welding in which a magnetically active polymeric implant is heated by a high (radio) frequency electromagnetic field [43, 54, 62, 77-83].

The electromagnetic welding equipment consists of a radio frequency generator, water cooled coils, fixtures to contain and align parts, and most importantly, the magnetically active preform or electromagnetic welding material. The generator creates a high frequency oscillating current (typically between 2 and 8 MHz) which passes through work coils that are contained within both the fixed and moving part containment / alignment fixtures. The coils are positioned close to the joint area in fixtures that are built from materials that do not absorb or distort the radio frequency field [54]. Before welding, an electromagnetic welding material in the shape of a preform or gasket is laid into the groove on one of the parts to be welded as shown in Figure 6.123.

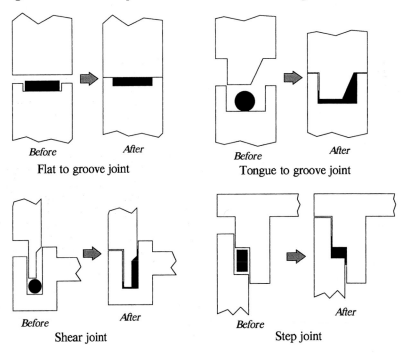

Figure 6.123. Typical joint configuration for electromagnetic or induction welding.

The welding material is generally a magnetically active filled polymer that is produced from the same base polymer as the parts or a compatible polymer [82,83]. This ferromagnetic-filled polymer contains finely dispersed micron sized particles of iron, iron oxide, stainless steel or other magnetic materials, that become targets for the electromagnetic energy. Loadings of the ferromagnetic powder are generally less than 15% by volume [77]. The inlaid gasket is heated inductively through heat loss from hysteresis and eddy currents. When parts produced from different polymers are to be welded, the ferromagnetic filled polymer matrix material may be a blend of the two polymers or potentially a third polymer compatible with both [77]. Metal filled adhesives or bonding agents can also be used in place of the ferromagnetic-filled polymer. These adhesives are generally used in applications where the parts themselves will not soften and weld together, such as when parts are produced from thermoset polymers [79].

During electromagnetic welding, current passes through the work coils producing an electromagnetic field at the joint area, which heats the electromagnetic sensitive material inductively. The parts to be joined are transparent to the magnetic field. Heat is transferred to the abutting plastic parts conductively while pressure is applied. The plastic parts soften and act as heat sinks after induction welding is complete, causing the joint to resolidify. The ferromagnetic filled polymer is generally supplied as extruded tape, strand or other profile, or can be molded as a gasket for complex geometries or to assist in handling. Electromagnetic welding materials based on hygroscopic thermoplastics may need to be dried to eliminate moisture related welding problems. It is also possible to use wire mesh or sacrificial metallic inserts as the electromagnetic welding material [43,54].

Joint designs for the induction welding process differ from those used with other welding processes as shown in Figure 6.123. The strongest welds are obtained when the applied forces on the parts result in shear forces at the welded joint. The joints most commonly used in practice are the tongue and groove and the step joint. The joints are designed so that the softened melt is contained within the joint area. This constraint combined with an overfill (typically 5%) results in complete wetting and fills any voids or surface irregularities [77].

The induction welding process offers a number of advantages to the plastic part designer. This unique welding process does overcome some of the limitations of other welding processes, however, at the added expense of the electromagnetic welding gasket material. Design flexibility is improved by permitting the welding of very complex 3D weld surfaces. The induction welding process is also useful for very low modulus materials such as thermoplastic elastomers, very thick parts, oriented materials or heat sensitive polymers. It can be used for welding very highly filled or reinforced materials, where surface resin content for conventional welding may be inadequate. Unlike other welding processes, the induction welding process is reversible, which permits the repair of misaligned joints or parts with defective components, and offers great potential for improving recyclability of welded plastic parts. The tolerance requirements for inductively welded parts are not extremely tight due to the gap filling ability of the inlaid material. The resultant weld joint is clean in appearance and is produced with minimum mechanical stress. Welding times are generally short, typically 3 - 10 seconds [62], however, large parts can require longer weld cycle times [78]. The process can be used economically for small parts and has been used for parts up to 20 feet (6 meters) in length [43,78]. The process does necessitate the use of the inlaid welding material with its added cost, and is not well suited for use with parts containing electromagnetic sensitive items, such as metal insets [62].

6.5.6   Resistance Welding

Another type of implant welding based on the use of electrical energy is resistance welding. In this process, an electrically conductive wire or braid is placed directly into the joint interface. The wire is connected to an electrical circuit and is directly heated by electrical resistive losses. The heat from the wire is transferred to the abutting plastic material by conduction, thereby softening or melting the plastic mass in the local area. Pressure is used to ensure mating part contact as power is switched off and the weld area cools. The welding process is simple and fast, and is especially suited for very large parts due to the minimal equipment requirements. The process does necessitate the use of the sacrificial heating wire, which remains in place after welding, adding to the process cost. The presence of the wire may also have a negative effect on the strength of the finished weld [54].

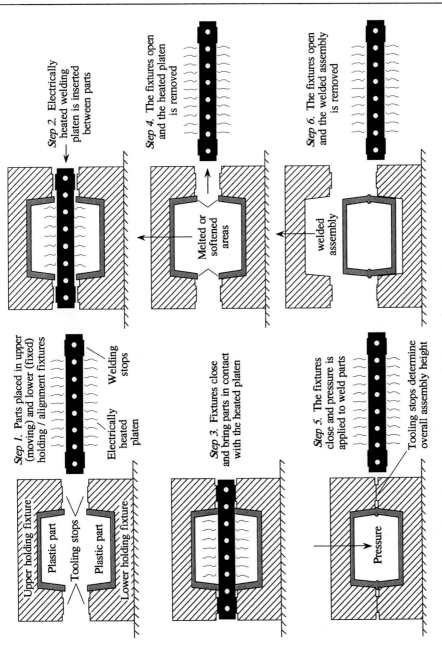

Figure 6.124. Basic concepts, components, and steps invelved with the hot plate (or hot tool) welding process.

6.5.7   Hot Tool Welding

Hot tool welding, commonly called hot plate welding (for flat parts), is a thermoplastic welding process that uses electrically heated metal tooling to soften the plastic part surfaces to be joined. After heating, the platen or tool is removed, and the parts are brought together under pressure before the surfaces cool and solidify. Hot tool welding can be used for both large and small parts produced from almost any thermoplastic material. The process is especially suited for welding softer semi-crystalline thermoplastics such as polyethylene or polypropylene, which can be difficult to weld using other techniques. The process is ideally suited for welding dissimilar materials as different tool surface temperatures can be used for the two different thermoplastics [54]. The process is also suited for parts having complex multiplane welding surfaces, or deep thin walled parts that may not tolerate the motions associated with processes such as vibration welding [54,70,84,85].

Hot tool welding equipment consists of a press, electrically heated metal tooling, and part fixtures. Tool temperatures are generally very high to cut down on heating times. The heating tools are often coated with sinter deposited PTFE or replaceable PTFE film. The platen temperatures cannot exceed approximately 270°C when the PTFE coatings are used [54,85,86]. More durable PTFE impregnated electroless nickel plating or other low coefficient of friction surface coatings can be used as an alternative. Other methods that can be used to overcome the sticking problem include (i) non-contact heating (radiation & convection) which may result in non-uniform weld quality [54], and (ii) very high platen temperatures, up to 400°C, where the melt residue degrades, leaving the surface relatively clean for the next heating cycle [86]. The latter method is not suitable for many thermoplastics and requires additional ventilation and safety requirements.

The basic hot tool welding process steps [54,84] are depicted schematically in Figure 6.124. The heated platen or tool is inserted between the two parts to be welded. The heated tool must follow the joint contour precisely, and as a result, relatively high initial pressures are used to account or compensate for part warpage or mismatch [54,84,86]. The initial melting produces a smooth mating edge by leveling surface imperfections, flash or sinks. Parts produced from hygroscopic materials may need to be dried before welding. Once lateral flow begins, pressure is decreased as the melt film grows until the positive stops on the platen contact the tooling stops on the part holding fixture. The parts are then held against the platen until sufficient heat conduction and penetration have occurred. It is important to note that the heat histories of the various weld layers will be different, and there is the potential for thermal degradation at the melt/platen interface or degradation in the presence of oxygen when the fixtures open. After heating, the holding fixtures open and the heating tool is removed quickly. The parts are then brought together under pressure, squeezing the melt resulting in lateral flow and flash, until the tooling stops and the fixtures come in contact with each other. After cooling, the fixtures are separated and the welded (assembled) part is removed.

Butt joint designs are generally used for hot tool welding. Typical butt joint configurations are shown in Figure 6.125 [62]. The weld strengths achievable with hot tool welding are very high if proper processing conditions are used. Unfortunately, the cycle times for the hot tool welding process can be relatively long, ranging from 15 seconds for small parts to several minutes for very large parts [54,85]. The economics of the process can be improved by welding a series of parts in the same cycle if platen space is available and tooling costs are not excessive.

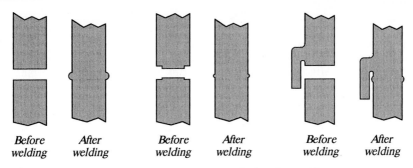

Before welding *After welding* *Before welding* *After welding* *Before welding* *After welding*

Figure 6.125. Typical butt joint configurations used with the hot plate welding process.

6.5.8 Hot Gas Welding

Hot gas welding is a welding method that has been used extensively in the joining of very large parts produced from thermoplastic profiles and sheeting. The process is not used extensively with injection molded parts since their size is generally limited to the point where many other more automated welding process options are available. Hot gas welding is, however, used with smaller injection molded parts in areas requiring field assembly, in thermoplastic part repair, and for prototype part fabrication [54,87-89]. The equipment used for hot gas welding is relatively inexpensive, simple and is generally portable, however, more specialized automated, larger scale equipment is also available.

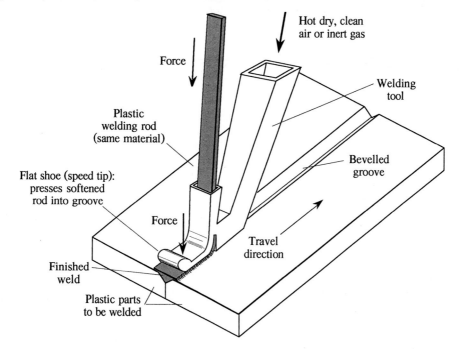

Figure 6.126. The hot gas welding head heats both the surfaces and the rod, and applies joint pressure.

The hot gas welding equipment uses hot air, or possibly hot nitrogen for materials subject to oxidative degradation, to simultaneously soften the welded workpieces and the welding (or filler) rod as shown in Figure 6.126. The hot gas must bring both the weld joint area on the part and the welding rod, both of which should be produced in exactly the same thermoplastic / grade, to a temperature where fusion can take place. The processing is generally done manually, holding the welding tool in one hand and the welding rod in the other hand. The welding rod is softened and pushed into the joint area to create the welding pressure. Welding tools modified with shoes or rollers increase both the speed and quality of welding by providing improved control over the welding pressure.

The quality of the weld obtained is dependent upon a number of material, equipment, and processing related variables. It is important that the welding rod is produced using the same polymer grade as that for the parts to be welded, however, it is common practice to use an off the shelf welding rod which is simply from the same thermoplastic family, often resulting in less than optimum joint performance. The welding rods themselves are most commonly produced with round cross sections, however triangular or U-shaped profiles can improve heating and flow. Two component rods, such as those containing a high strength or glass reinforced core, are also available [87].

The welding process begins with the chamfering of the part edges as shown in Figure 6.127. The edges should be kept clean and dry to ensure proper welding. The moisture content of both the part and welding rod are a concern when hygroscopic polymers are to be welded. The parts are then clamped or placed in a fixture to ensure proper positioning. The hot gas temperature and flow rate are adjusted for the materials and part thickness being welded. Air temperatures for some common thermoplastics are shown in Table 6.2 [87].

Table 6.2. Typical Air Temperatures for Welding Thermoplastics

Material	Temperature	
	°C	°F
Rigid PVC	220-300	430-570
HDPE	250-280	480-540
LDPE	270-300	520-570
Polystyrene	250	480
Acrylic	350	660
Polycarbonate	350	660
ABS	350	660
Polypropylene	300	570

The air used to weld should be free from moisture and contaminants such as oil. A method, such as the pendulum method, where an operator heats the work pieces and rod in an alternating fashion, is used to create the weld. The hot gas welding process is widely used in the plumbing and automotive repair fields, particularly with the advent of thermoplastic bumper and body panels. A study on bumper repair [89] has shown that the welded joint strengths are best when double V-joint designs are used. Even when the

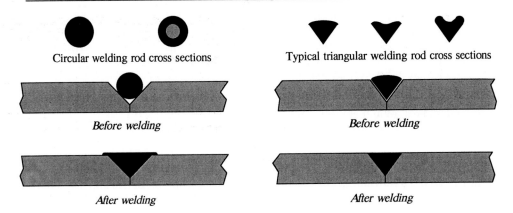

Figure 6.127. Typical joint and welding rod configurations for hot gas welding.

the double V-joint design was used, completely satisfactory results could not be achieved due to the inability to apply sufficient pressure as the weld solidifies and shrinks, and due to gas pockets at the weld interface. The use of a heated roller following the welding shoe was shown to improve weld quality, as was the use of a holding fixture which permits air flow through the weld gap.

6.5.9 Extrusion Welding

Extrusion welding is a welding method which has evolved from hot gas welding. The extrusion welding process uses hot air or gas to soften the V-joint area on the thermoplastic parts to be welded via convective heating. The weld groove is then filled, under pressure, with identical weld filler material that has been plasticized by means of extrusion. Once the weld filler material has been deposited into the V-groove, pressure is maintained using either a welding shoe or roller system. The process is used primarily for automated welding of larger sheet type structures [54,87,90].

6.6   Adhesive Bonding

6.6.1   Introduction

Adhesive bonding is widely used as a method of assembly for both thermoplastic and thermosetting plastic parts. Adhesives can be used to join plastic parts produced from the same base polymer, and are commonly used to join parts produced from dissimilar materials. Designers often use adhesives to join thermosetting plastic parts to one another or plastic parts to metals since some other assembly options such as welding cannot be used. Adhesives are versatile and offer a number of advantages over other fastening techniques, however, there are also a number of limitations associated with their use. A designer must consider many factors when working with the adhesives in an effort to obtain a strong and reliable assembly. The advantages of adhesives include:

- Esthetics and design flexibility
- Uniform stress distribution
- Can join dissimilar materials
- Can provide weather / water / gas tight seal
- Flexible adhesives, compliant in shear, can compensate for thermal expansion mismatches between components
- Flexible adhesives can dampen vibration
- Can be used with thin, flexible substrates
- Provide electrical and thermal insulation

In many cases, adhesives provide multiple functions. For example, a semi-rigid polyurethane adhesive system could be used to attach a transparent polycarbonate lens to a filled nylon 6,6 reflector in an automotive lighting application. In this application, the adhesives provides the means of assembly, has good esthetics (no holes, etc.), functions as a gasket producing a moisture seal, offers vibration resistance, and has the ability to distribute or absorb stresses associated with the thermal expansion mismatch. There are, however, a number of disadvantages or uncertainties associated with the use of adhesives. These factors should also be considered carefully before choosing this assembly method. Each limitation is discussed separately.

Joint Performance Uncertainty: The strength of an adhesive assembly is not easily predicted at the design stage of product development. Adhesives are polymers, and as a result, their mechanical properties are influenced by time, temperature, relative humidity and other environmental factors. Like any plastic material, the bulk or cohesive strength of the adhesive can be determined or obtained from the material manufacturer. However, the adhesive joint performance is not easily predicted, since the weak link in most cases is the interface between the adhesive and of the substrates. The adhesive or interfacial strength is influenced by both the adhesive properties, and the surface characteristics of the parts to be bonded. Prototype testing is necessary in order to establish the interfacial strength, however, the long term effects of moisture or other environmental agents on the adhesive strength are not easily determined. Other production related factors can also influence the reliability of the assembly. The uncertainties associated with the long and even short term bond strengths have caused many designers to opt for a "belt and suspenders" type of approach. Adhesives are commonly used in combination with more reliable mechanical fasteners. For example, a limited number of machine screws might be used in combination with an adhesive. The mechanical fasteners provide a measure of reliability and safety, as well as a built-in fixturing mechanism to clamp the adhesive as it cures. The adhesive reduces the number of mechanical fasteners that would be required and may act as a moisture seal, vibration dampener or perform other secondary functions.

Permanent Assembly: Like welding, adhesives are generally used in applications where permanent, non-serviceable assemblies are required. In certain applications, low melting point thermoplastic hot melt adhesives can be used where limited access or repeated assembly is required, provided the entire assembly can be heated to the appropriate temperature.

Integration of a Chemical Process: Many assembly operations are purely mechanical in nature. However, many adhesive based assembly operations call for the use of chemicals and cleaners, and, hence, involve chemical reactions. For example, part surface cleaning operations can involve the use of potentially hazardous solvents or chemicals. The adhesives themselves may also contain potentially hazardous chemicals or solvents, and as a result, materials handling, ventilation and disposal practices must be well regulated. In addition, the quality of the adhesive joint and the ability to work with the adhesives will be influenced by variables such as adhesive storage conditions, degree of mixing and the ambient conditions. For example, the strength of two part epoxy adhesive assembly will be influenced by the age of the components, stoichiometric ratio used, mixing procedure and cure conditions. Automated or cartridge dispensing devices ensure that the correct stoichiometric ratios are delivered. Equipment of this type can also incorporate motionless mixing elements that mix the two components as the adhesive is delivered, as shown in Figure 6.128.

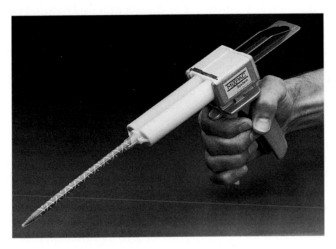

Figure 6.128. An automated adhesive dispensing / mixing system for two component thermosetting adhesives. (Courtesy of ConPro Tec. Inc., Salem, NH)

The addition of the mixing element eliminates the possibility of air entrapment or improper mixing and therefore improves the repeatability of the bonding process and the quality of the adhesive joint. The disposable mixing nozzle is replaced at the end of a production run or after an extended delay during which time the adhesive in the nozzle may cure. In general, the potential for reaction related problems can be minimized by automating as many process steps as possible, or by using non-reactive adhesive systems such as thermoplastic hot melt adhesives.

Clean Surfaces Required: Since adhesive bonding is assembly by surface attachment, the quality of the surfaces to be bonded must be consistent from part to part. The surfaces must be kept clean and free from oil, mold releases, dust or other surface contaminants. Surfaces of parts to be bonded generally undergo some degree of preparation prior to the adhesive bonding process. Storing the molded parts in plastic bags minimizes the potential for contamination.

No Joint Inspection: Once the adhesive has been applied, and the parts have been assembled, it is not easy to inspect the quality of the assembly. It may be impossible to determine whether the correct quantity of adhesive was applied to the correct location. Improper adhesive application or part surface preparation will influence the strength of the assembly, yet these problems are not easily detected. In contrast, in mechanical assembly, the presence or absence of a mechanical fastener is easily detected, as is the torque level that is used during assembly. It is therefore extremely important that stringent quality engineering practices be followed during all phases of the adhesive bonding process. Joint strength should be good if variables such as surface preparation and adhesive mixing procedures are carefully monitored. Preparation of destructive test samples (quality control samples) produced in parallel with the production process is also recommended.

Time to Achieve Maximum Strength: Unlike many mechanical fastening or thermal welding operations, it can take a great deal of time for adhesively bonded joints to achieve their ultimate assembly strength. Many adhesive mechanisms involve the evaporation of a solvent, water, or involve a chemical reaction. All of these events take time. These times can range from a few seconds to a few days. The parts being bonded must be fixtured during a portion of this time to ensure proper wetting, establish the proper bond line thickness, and compensate for part warpage. Adhesives generally develop enough strength so that the fixturing device can be removed before the adhesive has achieved full strength. Cure or evaporation times can also be reduced using elevated temperatures, however, this can result in a reduction in joint strength due to a number of factors. Elevated temperature and faster cure rates may result in voids, thermal stress due to expansion differences, a residual stress, and possible additive migration to the boundary layer. In some cases, however, elevated temperatures are necessary to achieve the final cure and ultimate strength. In such a case, programmable, or ramped heat cure cycles are often used.

6.6.2   Adhesive Theory

An adhesive can be described as a material that is capable of holding parts together by surface attachment. The key word here is surface. Designers are most often concerned with the bulk properties of a material (e.g. tensile strength, modulus etc.), however, surface characteristics of the materials to be joined must also be considered for adhesive bonding applications. It should also be noted here that there is no universal adhesive that is suitable for use with all plastic materials. There are in fact a multitude of adhesives to choose from. Adhesive material selection is probably one of the designer's most difficult tasks. The designer relies on a combination of adhesive theory, previous experience, the adhesive manufacturer's recommendations, and prototype testing when selecting an adhesive for a particular application.

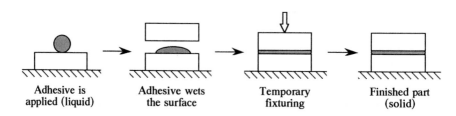

| Adhesive is applied (liquid) | Adhesive wets the surface | Temporary fixturing | Finished part (solid) |

Figure 6.129. A number of steps are involved with the adhesive bonding process.

The adhesive bonding process is a multi-step process that begins with the application of a "liquid" adhesive to one or both of the substrates (i.e. parts to be bonded). At this point the adhesive must be fluid enough that surface attraction, gravity, or external pressure will cause the adhesive to spread over the joint surface. Once the adhesive is distributed over the surface, it must develop into a strong solid that attracts the surfaces to be joined effectively. The adhesive must:

- Wet the surfaces to be bonded (spreading and capillary action)
- Attract surfaces effectively (adhesive strength)
- Develop into a strong solid (cohesive strength)

The first phase of the adhesive bonding process is wetting. Nature dictates that liquids will wet a solid surface only if the surface energy of the solid substrate is greater than that of the liquid. [91-93] To ensure proper wetting, the critical surface tension of the plastic substrate must be greater than the surface tension of the adhesive.

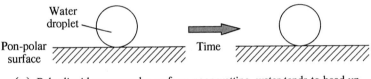

(a.) Polar liquid on non-polar surface: poor wetting, water tends to bead up.

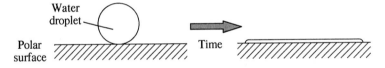

(b.) Polar liquid on polar surface: good wetting, water spreads over surface.

Figure 6.130. Surface energy / surface tension will influence the ability of an adhesive to wet a surface.

High energy surfaces, those having high critical surface tension, such as metal or metal oxide, are easily wet by a variety of organic and inorganic fluids of lower surface energy. A droplet of water will tend to wet or spread over the surface of a metal oxide, however, the polar water droplet tends to bead up on a non-polar, low energy surface such as wax or polyethylene. The contact angle between the liquid and the substrate can provide a visual indication of wetting. Many of the problems associated with the adhesive bonding of plastics are related to wetting. The critical surface tension of clean polymeric surfaces and surface tensions of common liquids are given in Tables 6.3.a and 6.3.b [91,92,94].

A review of Table 6.3 shows that the surface energy criteria for wetting would not be met by a standard epoxy adhesive applied to a polyethylene surface. Wetting is a significant problem with very low surface energy materials such as polyethylene or polytetrafluoroethylene. In order to bond materials of this type effectively, the surface layers of the substrate must be modified chemically to increase surface energy, and an adhesive formulation, such as a fluorinated epoxy, with a relatively low surface energy may be required.

Table 6.3.a. Critical Surface Tension of Common Plastics and Metals

Material	Critical surface tension (dynes/cm)
Copper	1,000*
Aluminum	500*
Acetal	47
Epoxy	47
Polyamides	< 46
Polycarbonate	46
Cellulose	45
Polyethylene terephthalate	43
Polysulfone	41
Polyimide	40
Polymethyl methacrylate	39
Polyvinyl chloride	39
polyphenylenesulfide	38
ABS	35
Polystyrene	33
Polyethylene	31
Silicone	24
Polytetrafluoroethylene	18

*approximate values

Table 6.3.b.   Surface Tension of Common Adhesives and Liquids

Material	Surface tension (dynes/cm)
Epoxy resin	47
Fluorinated epoxy resin	33
Glycerol	63
Petroleum lubricating oil	29
Silicone oil	21
Water	73

The wetting process is also influenced by the viscosity of the adhesive as it is being applied. Assuming the surface energy criteria is met, lower viscosities tend to improve wetting, yet detract from the gap filling abilities of an adhesive. Consider the use of polyethylene as a hot melt adhesive for two polycarbonate moldings. The surface energy values given in Table 6.3 indicate that the polyethylene melt should wet the polycarbonate surfaces. A very low molecular weight polyethylene or wax will have a very low viscosity and spread easily over the surface, while a higher molecular weight, viscous thermoplastic polyethylene will not spread as well, since melt viscosity is a strong function of molecular weight as shown in Figure 6.131.

It must also be noted that the cohesive or bulk strength of a polymer (adhesive) is also a function of molecular weight. High strength is achieved only at high molecular weights,

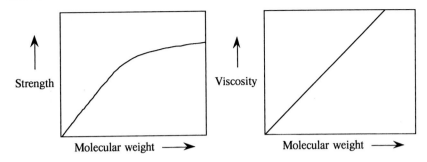

Figure 6.131. The molecular weight of the adhesive will effect both its viscosity and its mechanical properties.

which indicates very high melt viscosity. While the wax may be more fluid, it also has a significantly lower tensile and shear strength than the higher molecular weight polyethylene. The strength of the adhesive is important since failure of an adhesive assembly can occur at the interface, or cohesively within either the adhesive or one of the substrates as shown in Figure 6.132.

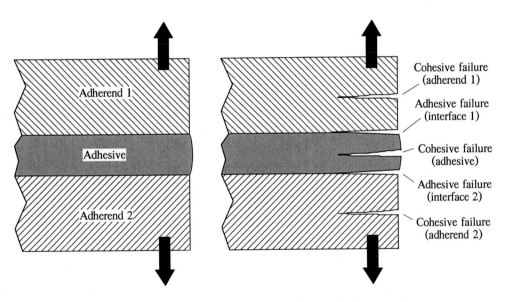

Figure 6.132. There are many possible failure zones for an adhesively bonded assembly.

Adhesives must then be fluid enough to wet the surface at the time of application, however, they must also develop into a strong solid that attracts the surfaces to be joined effectively. In order to become a strong solid, the polymeric adhesive must ultimately achieve a high molecular weight. Therefore a challenge that an adhesive manufacturer faces is the development of an adhesive that is both (i) fluid as it is applied, and (ii) develops into a strong solid within a reasonable period of time, without excessive volumetric shrinkage. This liquid - solid transition can be accomplished in many ways.

High MW polymer / solvent High MW polymer / emulsion	→ Solvent / water evaporation →	Strong solid
Reactive monomer Low molecular weight	→ In-situ polymerization →	Strong solid
Reactive prepolymer Medium molecular weight	→ Chemical Cure Reaction →	Strong solid
"Hot" polymer melt High molecular weight	→ Phase change / cooling →	Strong solid

Polymer / Solvent: Solvent based systems use one or more volatile solvents to dissolve the polymeric adhesive, producing a relatively low viscosity solution. After the adhesive is applied to the surfaces to be joined, the solvent evaporates, leaving only the high molecular weight polymer behind. Solvent based elastomeric or rubber based adhesives fall into this category. Doped or bodied thermoplastic cements also consist of quantities of parent resin dissolved in a mixture of solvents. The solvents selected influence working time and bond quality, while the polymer concentration influences the viscosity and gap filling ability of the system. These bodied thermoplastic cements are more appropriately described as solvent welding materials with gap filling ability, rather than true adhesives. The safety and environmental hazards associated with solvent based adhesives have led to a significant reduction in their use. Aqueous emulsion systems can be categorized accordingly, and are rapidly gaining popularity.

Reactive Monomers: Low molecular weight monomers having solvent like consistency are also used in adhesive applications. These fluid adhesives are generally used in applications where a thin bond line is appropriate, and polymerized in-situ. The polymerization is initiated by light, heat, and a lack of oxygen (anaerobic adhesives). Acrylics and cyanoacrylates are common monomeric adhesive systems.

Reactive Prepolymers: Low to medium molecular weight prepolymers are commonly used as adhesive materials due to their versatility, ease of handling, low shrinkage, and gap filling ability. These adhesives are available as either one or two component systems. The systems are solvent free (100% solids) and are chemically reactive. Upon cure, the prepolymers produce a chemically cross-linked thermosetting polymeric adhesive. One component systems are generally heat or atmospheric moisture / oxygen cured, while two component systems react with one another at ambient or elevated temperature. Structural epoxy adhesives, tough / versatile polyurethane adhesives, and tough / flexible silicone adhesives fall into this category.

Hot Polymer Melts: Many thermoplastic materials can also be used as adhesives in their bulk form. The polymers are heated to the point where they become fluid enough to wet the surfaces to be bonded, and resolidify upon cooling. The change is purely physical, and as a result, hot melt processes are relatively easy to automate. The adhesives are fairly viscous, solvent free, and have good gap filling abilities. Hot melt thermoplastic adhesives are used in a wide variety of light to medium duty applications, however higher performance systems are also available.

While most adhesives can be categorized as following one of these four mechanisms, some are described as hybrid systems, such as a polyurethane thermoplastic hot melt that is blended with a one component reactive thermosetting polyurethane prepolymer. The hot melt provides short term strength while the thermosetting component provides improved performance.

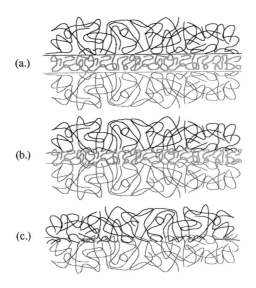

Figure 6.133. In theory, adhesive bonding is bonding by surface attachment. However, when polymeric adhesives are used to bond plastic parts, molecular diffusion can occur (i.e. welding). A number of situations are possible: (a) no diffusion of adhesive, (b) adhesive / substrate interdiffuison, and (c) diffusion due purely to solvent welding (no adhesive).

It should be noted here that the use of polymer adhesives in the bonding of polymer substrates can differ significantly from the process of bonding metal parts. True adhesive forces or strengths at the interface are the result of bonding due to Van der Waals forces (physically adsorbed bonds) or primary chemical bonding (chemisorbed bonds) [91] as depicted in Figure 6.133a. However, when polymer adhesives are used with polymeric substrates, there is a potential for diffusion of chains across the interface as shown in Figure 6.133b. This situation is likely to be realized when the adhesive systems contain solvents that may soften the surface of the substrate. This situation can occur when solvent based adhesives (dopes) or solvent like monomeric adhesives are used, or even to some extent when hot melt adhesives are used (due to thermal effects). In fact, the adhesive bonding process for many polymeric parts, especially those produced in amorphous thermoplastics is a cross between solvent bonding (welding) and adhesive bonding. It is important to consider the presence or absence of chain diffusion. The extreme case of solvent bonding (or welding) is depicted in Figure 6.133c.

Part Surfaces: Since adhesive bonding is a surface attachment process, the characteristics of the surface wall have a direct influence on the adhesive joint quality. It has been noted that part surfaces are never truly clean, flat or smooth. [91] For example, a common problem with molded plastic parts is that of part warpage. It can be very difficult to produce parts that are perfectly flat, especially when the parts are produced from semi-crystalline polymers. As a result of this warpage, there is always some degree of gap between the two surfaces to be bonded. In such a case, the part manufacturer has several options. The parts could be "straightened" prior to assembly using an annealing / fixturing operation, or a gap filling adhesive can be used. Gap filling adhesives are more viscous and allow greater part flatness variation. The gap filling requirements can be reduced if the parts are straightened during the bonding operation using fixturing or clamping equipment. In this case, however, the parts must be fixtured while the adhesive solidifies. In addition, the adhesive itself will be subject to stresses over the long term as the part attempts to return to the warped shape.

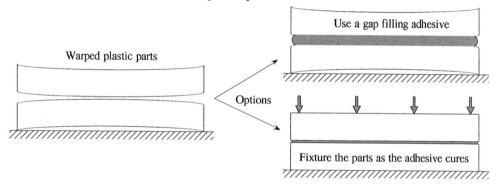

Figure 6.134. Warped parts can be bonded using a gap filling adhesive or can be fixtured to minimize the gap filling requirements.

Part surfaces are also inherently rough. Molded part surfaces have a certain roughness value as molded, or can be abraded after molding to increase the surface roughness. Rougher surfaces tend to improve adhesion by providing an increase in both surface area and the potential for mechanical coupling. It is important, however, that the adhesive in fact does wet the rough surface, which can sometimes be a problem due to trapped air voids or when viscous adhesives are used. Abrasive treatments include sanding, machining, scouring, and abrasive blasting. The relative direction of loading and abrasion should be taken into account when surfaces are abraded in order to maximize any improvement in shear or tensile strength.

The cleanliness and chemistry of a surface are also critical parameters. The potential for adhesive failure can be minimized if the part surfaces are prepared properly. Surface treatment is more important in true adhesive bonding applications compared to those operations involving solvents and partial welding. Surface treatments are designed to perform one or more of the following functions [92,95]:

- Remove contaminates
- Remove a weak boundary layer
- Chemically modify the surface

Simple solvent wiping, vapor degreasing, detergent cleaning or ultrasonic cleaning operations are designed to remove contaminates and in some cases weak bonding layers. Internal or external mold releases, lubricants, plasticizers, degradation products, dust, oil or grease should be removed from the surface prior to bonding. The use of lubricants or release agents should be avoided whenever possible, since it can be difficult to ensure complete and consistent removal during production (in some cases, release agents are tagged with dyes to aid in detection). Part handling should also be minimized during molding and assembly. Gloves, sealed storage containers and automation reduce the potential for surface contamination.

It has already been shown that the surface energy of many plastic materials is relatively low. The problem is especially severe for polyolefins such as polyethylene or polypropylene, and fluoropolymers such as polytetrafluoroethylene. These materials have low surface energies, and excellent solvent resistance, and as a result, solvent based adhesive systems / solvent welding are not viable options. In order to improve wetting, the critical surface tension of plastic parts produced from these materials can be increased by chemical modification or oxidation of the part surfaces. This can be accomplished by a number of techniques including chemical etching, flame treatment, corona discharge, hot air or gas plasma [92]. ASTM D-2093 describes surface treatments that can be used with the more common plastic materials. Almost all chemical surface preparation techniques involve the use of hazardous chemicals. As an example, a sulfuric acid-dichromate solution is sometimes used to modify the surface of polyethylene. Even simple operations such as solvent wiping can be hazardous to the workforce and environment, unless suitable precautions and equipment are used.

Cold plasma processes can be used as an alternative to these chemical systems, to remove surface contaminants, weak boundary layers, and enhance wettability by altering the polarity / chemistry of surface layers. Processes of this type have been shown to offer an alternative to chemical pretreatment. [96]. Gas plasma processing equipment is available in a variety of sizes, and can be used to treat a series of parts in the same batch operation. The plastic parts to be treated are placed in the gas plasma batch reactor. Parts containing significant levels of mold release or other surface contamination may be precleaned in order to reduce the gas plasma process cycle time. The chamber is sealed and an internal high vacuum is created. Gas enters the chamber and is excited with radio frequency energy. The process creates a plasma containing ions, electrons and various neutral species at different energy levels. The electrons gain energy from the RF field, then transfer the energy by colliding with neutral gas molecules. The free radicals and ions formed interact with solid surfaces (parts) placed in the plasma, resulting in surface modification. The plasma process causes changes only to a depth of several molecular layers leaving the bulk of the material unaffected by the process. Gasses commonly used with the plasma process include oxygen, ammonia, air and the halogens. The process is versatile and has been shown to improve adhesive bond quality for a number of thermoplastics [92,96].

Regardless of the method that is used to clean and prepare the surface, it is important to keep the surface clean after the surface pretreatment operations. Handling should be minimized, and the plastic parts must be kept in a grease / oil / dust free environment. In

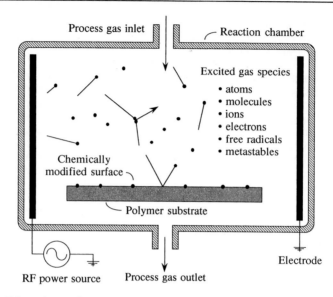

Figure 6.135. Schematic gas plasma reactor where molded plastic part surfaces are modified prior to adhesive bonding.

addition, the time delay between the surface treatment operation and the adhesive bonding operation is an important process variable. Continuous operations provide the most consistent results, and in general, it is best to bond the parts immediately after pretreatment to limit the potential for contamination. In addition, time delays are also likely to result in surface chemistry changes for activated surfaces [92].

6.6.3   Adhesive Selection

The selection of an adhesive for a particular application is dependent upon a large number of factors including:

- End use environment
- Stress levels
- Substrate(s) surface chemistry
- Substrate(s) rigidity vs temperature behavior
- Substrate(s) coefficient of thermal expansion
- Gap filling requirements
- Method of application

End-use Environment: Adhesives are plastic materials and as such have properties that are highly dependent upon temperature, relative humidity and other environmental factors. It is important that the adhesive selected will perform properly within the end-use environmental extremes anticipated. This can be a significant problem since adhesives that work well at high temperatures may become brittle at low temperatures, or conversely, adhesives that are tough at low temperatures, tend to be weaker or softer at high temperatures. It is also important to note that long term environmental effects or aging can have an influence on surface chemistry and, hence, adhesive bond strength. The process where a weak boundary layer preferentially displaces the adhesive at the interface is known as desorbtion. Moisture present in both the polymer and environment can cause desorbtion over the long term [92].

Stress Level: The anticipated loading levels will influence both the joint design and the adhesive selection. Factors such as the rate of loading, frequency of loading and duration of loading must be quantified prior to adhesive selection. In addition, the potential for misuse must also be given careful consideration.

Substrate Surface Chemistry: The adhesive selected must wet and attract both surfaces to be joined effectively. The adhesive options available to the designer are limited when bonding materials have very low surface energy values. It is also easier to select an adhesive for applications where components produced from the same polymer are to be bonded (e.g. ABS to ABS) rather than applications involving dissimilar materials (e.g. ABS to aluminum) where the adhesive must have an affinity for both substrates.

Substrate Rigidity: The rigidity of a substrate, relative to that of the adhesive (at a given temperature) is an important consideration. Adhesive joints are generally designed so that service loads place the adhesive in a state of shear. However, in certain cases, this may not be fully achievable and the adhesive is subject to other less desirable bending, cleavage or peel stresses. This problem can arise when bonding very thin, flexible or thermoplastic parts [92].

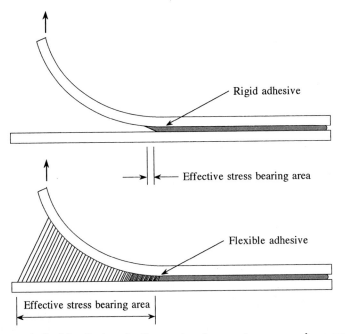

Figure 6.136. Tough, flexible adhesives distribute peel or cleavage stresses over a larger area.

Rigid adhesives tend to be weak in peel since the stress tends to concentrate in the thin layer at the tip of the crack. Tougher, more flexible adhesives distribute the stresses over a larger area, resulting in greater strength in peel or cleavage. It is also important to consider the modulus-temperature behavior of both the adhesive and the substrate materials. The use of an adhesive below the glass transition temperature can result in low peel and impact strength, however, the strength and creep resistance necessary for structural applications limits the use of materials with low T_g values.

Substrate Coefficient of Thermal Expansion (CTE): Adhesives should also be selected so that the relative difference in CTE between the substrate and the adhesive are as small as possible, in order to minimize thermally induced strains. In cases where the two substrates have significantly different coefficients of thermal expansion, the adhesive would ideally have a CTE value midway between that of the two substrates, and should be compliant enough in shear to account for the CTE difference. Adjustments in the CTE value of an adhesive can also be accomplished using fillers or additives. The effects on CTE mismatches are compounded when the product is subject to thermal cycling [92].

Gap Filling Requirements: The surface roughness and flatness of the substrates determines the gap filling requirements of the adhesive. Plastic parts can generally be molded to fairly tight tolerances, however, they do have a tendency to warp due to orientation or shrinkage effects. The parts are commonly flexible enough so that fixtures can be used to straighten warped parts during the bonding process. Hot melts and reactive prepolymer adhesives generally have good gap filling abilities, while monomeric adhesives have a lower viscosity and poor gap filling ability. The gap filling ability of a doped solvent system (solvent bonding) is determined by the polymer concentration in the solution.

Design of Adhesive Joints: A wide variety of adhesive joint designs are used for the adhesive bonding of molded plastic parts [91,92,97,98]. The design of an adhesive joint will have a significant impact on the strength of the overall assembly. Ideally, joints should be designed so that the adhesive is subject to shear stress when the part is loaded in service. Joint designs that result in bending, cleavage or peel stresses at the adhesive interface should be avoided. Shear areas should be maximized to reduce the shear stress level. Joints should also be designed so that they are easily manufactured, self locating and esthetically pleasing.

The butt joint shown in Figure 6.137 is the simplest joint type, however, its configuration is not self locating and can result in undesirable peel or cleavage loading due to bending stresses. Traps can be incorporated into the joint design to catch excess adhesive. The scarf joint offers some improvement over the butt joint, however, the V-joint, lap joints, and tongue and groove joints offer improved positioning and performance. The V-joint ensures positive positioning as well as shear and tensile strength. The joint also provides a channel for locating the bead of adhesive during assembly. Lap joints and tongue and groove joints provide high strength and part alignment. Tongue and groove type joints may require local increases in wall thickness at the joint area and relatively tight tolerance control. The tongue and groove joints are widely used for injection molded parts, and have the added benefit of providing a channel in which the adhesive bead can be delivered. One additional consideration for injection molded parts is that of gate location. Gates should be located away from the surfaces to be bonded, since residual stresses in the gate area could lead to cracking or crazing due to the action of surface preparation chemicals, or the adhesive system itself.

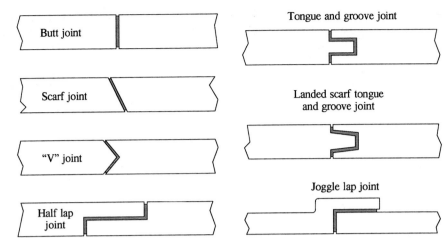

Figure 6.137.   A number of possible joint designs commonly used for injection molded plastic parts.

6.7   Solvent Bonding

Solvent bonding is an assembly process that can be used with certain types of thermoplastic parts, and is most commonly used for parts produced from amorphous thermoplastics. The solvent bonding process, which is sometimes called solvent welding or solvent cementing, is a process in which the joining surfaces of the parts to be assembled are treated with a solvent that tends to swell and soften the surface. The parts are then fixtured or clamped together while the solvent evaporates. The process is truly a welding process where molecular mobility and interdiffusion are facilitated using a fugitive solvent rather than thermal energy. [16,99,100]

The process is most commonly used with amorphous thermoplastic parts since most semi-crystalline thermoplastics have good solvent resistance. Ideally the thermoplastic parts to be joined should be produced from the same material, however, the process can be used to join dissimilar materials only if the dissimilar materials are soluble in a common solvent, or can be dissolved using a mixture of two miscible solvents specific to the different polymers. It is important to note here that the coefficients of thermal expansion for dissimilar materials should also be well matched, since there is no intermediate layer, such as a flexible adhesive, between the two materials to account for the expansion mismatch.

The solvent bonding process begins with the application of the solvent to one or both of the surfaces to be joined. Parts having a single joining surface are simply pressed against a sponge or felt pad that has been impregnated with solvent. The quantity of solvent used should be kept to a minimum to avoid drips and the potential for crazing. More complex multiplane joining surfaces require contoured solvent applicators. After solvent application, the parts are either immediately clamped together, or allowed to sit for a short time to ensure sufficient swelling without excessive loss of the volatile solvent. The parts are then clamped together under pressure for a period of time ranging from seconds to minutes depending upon the joint design and solvent selection. In order to obtain joints of consistent quality, pneumatic clamping equipment equipped with a timer are recommended. The parts are then removed from the clamping equipment, and must be allowed to sit for a period of hours before full strength is achieved, which can approach the strength of the base resin. Heat can be used to speed the overall rate of evaporation and cycle time.

Solvent selection is based upon a number of factors including working time, volatility or vapor pressure, solubility parameter, safety, and the potential for stress cracking or crazing. In many cases, mixtures of solvents are used to obtain a balance of properties. The joints that are used in bonding should be flat and held to very tight tolerances. Self locating features such as studs assist in part location. Tongue and groove joints can be used if the joints are relatively shallow, so that solvent entrapment is avoided. Entrapped solvent can cause crazing over the long term and lead to part failure. Parts that are to be solvent bonded should be molded with a minimum of internal stress, and in many cases are annealed or stress relieved prior to assembly. Gates should be located away from the areas to be bonded. One should also exercise caution when working with "closed" parts where solvents can become trapped inside the part.

Solvent bonding is a simple, relatively inexpensive method that can be used to produce strong, hermetic assemblies for amorphous thermoplastic components. The low viscosity of the solvent dictates that the parts to be bonded should be free from warpage and molded to relatively tight tolerances. Parts with larger gaps can be filled with solvents doped with the parent resin (see discussion of adhesives). Unfortunately, this bonding process does involve the use of solvents and as such poses health and environmental risks, and is subject to a great deal of regulation. The use of this process should therefore be limited to only those applications where other assembly methods are not suitable.

6.8   References

1.   Bassler, R, *Kunststoffe* , **76** (9) 777 (1986).
2.   Boothroyd, G. and Dewhust, P., *Product Design for Assembly,* Boothroyd Dewhurst, Incorporated Wakefield, RI (1989).
3.   Stokes, V., *SPE Annual Technical Conference* , **35** 442 (1989).
4.   Nussbaum, B., *Business Week* , 102, September 17 (1990).
5.   Kaeufer, H., *Kunststoffe* , **79** (4) 339 (1989).
6.   Miller, E., *Plastics Product Design Handbook*, Marcel Dekker, Inc., NY (1981).
7.   Anonymous, *Plastics Design Forum* , **2** (2) 34 (1977).
8.   Lee, C., and Dubin, A., *SPE Annual Technical Conference* , **34** 1564 (1988).
9.   Lee, C., Dubin, A., and Jone, E., *Plastics Design Forum* , **12** (5) 65 (1987).
10.   Trantina, G., and Minnichelli, M., *SPE Annual Technical Conference*, **33**, 438 (1987).
11.   Technical Bulletin, *Snap Fit Joints in Plastics*, Miles Corporation, Pittsburgh,PA (1990).
12.   Wuebken, G., *Plastics Design Forum* , **9** (3) 37 (1984).
13.   McIntyre, R., *Plastics Design Forum* , **9** (4) 35 (1984).
14.   Schonewald, H., *Kunststoffe* , **79** (8) 46 (1989).
15.   Technical Bulletin, *Mechanical Fastening* , Miles Corporation, Pittsburgh, PA.

16. Technical Bulletin, *General Electric Data Base Design Guide*, General Electric Co., Pittsfield, MA.
17. LaVerne, L., *Plastics Design Forum*, **16** (4) 25 (1991).
18. LaVerne, L., *Plastics Design Forum*, **15** (4) 17 (1990).
19. Lincoln, B., Gomes, K., and Braden, J.,*Mechanical Fasteners for Plastics*, Marcel Dekker, NY (1984).
20. Shigley, J., and Mischke, C., *Fastening, Joining and Connecting* , McGraw Hill, NY (1986).
21. Bauhof, M., *Maintaining Bolt Preload in Plastic Assemblies* , DuPont, Wilmington, DE.
22. Moore, G. and Kline, D., *Properties and Processing of Polymers for Engineers*, Prentice-Hall, Englewood, NJ (1984).
23. Technical Bulletin, *Fastening Systems*, Catamount Manufacturing, Inc., Orange, MA.
24. *Technical Bulletin* , Emhart Fastening System Group, Heli-coil Division, Danbury, CT.
25. Braden, J., *Plastics Design Forum*, **9** (5) 64 (1984).
26. Englehart, W., and Richter, C., *Modern Plastics*, **54** (7) 72 (1977).
27. Keller, C., *Plastics Design Forum*, **8** (6) 56 (1983).
28. Anonymous, *Plastics Design Forum*, **1** (6) 76 (1976).
29. Malloy, R., Orroth, S., and Arnold, E., *Plastics Engineering*, **41** (4) 43 (1985).
30. Burton, J., *Plastics Design Forum*, **15** (6) 45 (1990).
31. Technical Bulletin, *Dupont Design Guide*, Assembly Techniques, DuPont, Wilmington, DE.
32. Wagner, D.,*Modern Plastics Encyclopedia*, **54** (10) 425 (1977).
33. Massey, F.L., *Modern Plastics*, **54** (9) 90 (1977).
34. Massey, F.L., SPE Annual Technical Conference, *Reinforced Plastics*, **32** 2-F 1 (1977).
35. Technical Bulletin, *ITW Shakeproof*, Illinois Products, Elgin, IL.
36. Technical Bulletin, *Plastite* ®, Continental / Midland, Park Forest, IL.
37. Technical Bulletin, *PT* ® *Fasteners*, ATF, Inc., Lincolnwood, IL.
38. Technical Bulletin, *Polyfast* ® *Fastener Data*, N L Industries, Statesville, NC.
39. Reib, M., *Kunststoffe*, **67** (3) 17 (1977).
40. TRW, Palnut Division, Mountainside, NJ.
41. Camcar Textron, Rockford, IL.
42. *Tinnerman* ®, Eaton Corporation, Engineered Fastener Div.
43. Klein, A., *Plastics Design Forum*, **13** (5) 39 (1988).
44. Crate, J.H., *Plastics Design Forum*, **6** (6) 61 (1981).
45. Galli, E., *Plastics Design Forum*, **11** (3) 29 (1986).
46. Beck, R., *Plastics Product Design*, Van Nostrand Reinhold Co., NY (1980).
47. Tews, H., *SPE Annual Technical Conference*, **35**, 1689 (1989).
48. Strasser, F., *Plastics Engineering*, **36** (10) 17 (1980).
49. Wilder, R., *Modern Plastics*, **67** (9) 65 (1990).
50. *Technical Bulletin*, Vestoran®, Bunawerke Huls GmbH, K&K Technologies, Akron, OH (1988).
51. Ultrasonic Plastics Assembly, Bronson sonic Power Company, Danbury, CT.(1979).
52. Tobias, T., *Plastics Design Forum*, **7** (1) 80 (1982).
53. Wool, R., Yuan, B., and McGarel, *Polymer Engineering & Science*, **29** (19) 1340 (1989).
54. Stokes, V., *Polymer Engineering & Science*, **29** (19) 1310 (1989).
55. Plender, A., *World Plastics & Rubber Technology*, 17 (1991).
56. Anonymous, *Plastics Design Forum*, **5** (6) 81 (1980).
57. Wolcott, J., *SPE Annual Technical Conference*, **36**, 1829 (1990).
58. Jaarsma, F., *SPE Annual Technical Conference*, **28**, 316 (1982).
59. Herrmann, T., *Kunststoffe*, **77** (7) 15 (1987).
60. Sager, T., United States Patent, No.4,618,516, October 1, 1986.
61. Baudendistel, S.and Herrmann, Th., *Kunststoffe*, **79** (10) __ (1989).
62. *Engineering Data Base Design Guide*, General Electric Company, Pittsfield, MA.
63. Gallagan, S., *Plastics Engineering*, **41** (7) 35 (1985).

64. Benatar, A., and Eswaran, R., *SPE Annual Technical Conference*, **35**, 514 (1989).
65. Benatar A., Eswaran, R., and Najar, S., *Polymer Engineering & Science*, **29** (23) 1689 (1989).
66. Benatar, A., & Cheng, Z., *Polymer Engineering & Science*, **29** (23) 1699 (1989).
67. Pontente, H., *Kunststoffe*, **70** (4) 6 (1980).
68. Land, W., *Kunststoffe*, **76** (9) 3 (1986).
69. Mock, J., *Plastics Engineering*, **39** (6) 27 (1983).
70. Mengason, J., *Plastics Engineering*, **36** (8) 20 (1980).
71. Pontente, H. and Kaiser, H., *Polymer Engineering & Science*, **29** (23) 1661 (1989).
72. Schalarb, A., and Ehrenstein, G., *Polymer Engineering & Science*, **29** (23) 1677 (1989).
73. Tappe, P. and Potente, H., *Polymer Engineering & Science*, **29** (23) 1655 (1989).
74. La Bounty, T., *SPE Annual Technical Conference*, **31**, 855 (1985).
75. Thews, H., *Kunststoffe*, **71** (10) 81 (1981).
76. Kenney, W., *Dupont Design Guide*, "Joint Design a Critical Factor in Strong Bonds", DuPont, Wilmington, DE.
77. Anonymous, *British Plastics & Rubber*, January, 28 (1986).
78. Chookazian, M., *Modern Plastics Encyclopedia*, **68** (11) 345 (1992).
79. Leatherman, A., *Modern Plastics Encyclopedia*, **68** (11) 347 (1992).
80. Chookazian, S., SPE Annual Technical Conference, **36**, 1834 (1990).
81. Leatherman, A., SPE Annual Technical Conference, **29**, 214 (1983).
82. Emabond Systems, Inc., Ashland Chemical Company, Norwood, NJ.
83. Hellerbond Division, Alfred F. Leatherman Co., Columbus, OH.
84. Ryan, C., *Modern Plastics Encyclopedia*, **68** (11) 347 (1992).
85. Watson, M., and Murch, M., *SPE Annual Technical Conference*, **35** 446 (1989).
86. Land, W., *Kunststoffe*, **76** (9) 3 (1986).
87. Miller, R., and Winkleman, D., *Plastics Engineering*, **36** (4) 38 (1980).
88. Atkinson, J., and Turner, B., *Polymer Engineering & Science*, **29** (19) 1368 (1989).
89. *Technical Bulletin # 53*, Leister Hot Air Tools, Switzerland.
90. Michel, P., *Polymer Engineering & Science*, **29** (19) 1376 (1989).
91. Cagle, C.V., *Handbook of Adhesive Bonding*, McGraw Hill, NY (1973).
92. Petrie, E., *Adhesives Age*, 6, May 15 (1989).
93. Petrie, E. M., *Handbook of Plastics and Elastomers*, McGraw Hill, NY (1975).
94. Rauhut, H., *Plastics Design & Processing*, 22, April (1971).
95. Snagren, R.C., *Handbook of Surface Preparations*, Palmerton Publishing Co., Inc., NY (1973).
96. Kaplan, S. and Rose, P., *SPE Annual Technical Conference*, **34**, 1542 (1988).
97. Mohan, R., *Plastics Engineering*, **46** (2) 47 (1989).
98. Durn, L., Moniatis, G. and Rasche, M., *Kunststoffe*, **79** (7) 3 (1989).
99. Klein, A., *Plastics Design Forum*, **14** (3) 59 (1989).
100. Licata, M. & Haag, E., *Plastics Engineering*, **42** (6) 53 (1986).

SI UNITS

Pressure, Stress (pascal)	N/m^2
Energy, Work (Joule)	N-m
Power (Watt)	J/s
Angular Velocity	Rad/sec
Density	kg/m^3
Heat Capacity	J/K
Specific Energy	J/kg
Thermal Conductivity	W/m K
Dynamic Viscosity	Pa-s
Volume	m^3

LENGTH

1 Centimeter (cm)	= 0.3937 in
1 Inch (in)	= 2.54 cm
1 Inch (in)	= 25.4 mm
1 Foot (ft)	= 0.3048 m
1 Milliinch (mil)	= 0.001 in
1 Micron (μm)	= 1.0 E -06 m
1 Yard (yd)	= 0.9144 m

VOLUME

1 Cubic Cm (cc)	= 1.0 E -06 m^3
1 Liter (L)	= 1.0 E -03 m^3
1 Milliliter (mL)	= 1.0 E -06 m^3
1 Cubic Inch (in^3)	= 1.639 E -05 m^3
1 Cubic Foot (ft^3)	= 2.832 E -02 m^3
1 Gallon US (gal US)	= 3.785 E -03 m^3

MASS

1 Gram (gr)	= 1.0 E -03 kg
1 Ounce (oz)	= 2.83 E -02 kg
1 Pound (lbm)	= 4.536 E -01 kg
1 Ton US (tn)	= 907 kg

DENSITY

1 Gram/cc (gr/cc)	= 1.0 E -03 kg/m^3
1 Pound/cu in (lb/in^3)	= 2.77 E -02 kg/in^3
1 Gram/cc (gr/cc)	= 3.61 E -02 lb/in^3

STRESS

1 Newton/m^2 (N/m^2)	= 1.0 Pa
1 Atmosphere (atm)	= 1.013 E +05 Pa
1 Pound/$Inch^2$ (psi)	= 6.8947 E +03 Pa
1 Mega pascal (MPa)	= 145 psi
1 Atmosphere (atm)	= 14.6885 psi
1 Pound/$Inch^2$ (psi)	= 0.0681 atm

VISCOSITY

1 Poise (gr/cm-s)	= 0.1 Pa-sec
1 Pound sec/In^2 (psi-sec)	= 6.8947 E +03 Pa-s
1 Pound sec/In^2	= 6.8947 E+04 poise

ENERGY/WORK

1 Erg (dyn-cm)	= 1.0 E -07 J
1 Newton meter (N-m)	= 1.0 J
1 Watt sec (W-sec)	= 1.0 J
1 kgf meter (kgf-m)	= 9.81 J
1 Foot Pound (ft-lbf)	= 1.356 J
1 Calorie (Cal)	= 4.184 J
1 Brit Therm Unit (Btu)	= 1.0551 E +03 J
1 Inch Pound (in-lbf)	= 0.113 J

SPECIFIC ENERGY

1 Calorie/gram	= 4190 J/kg
1 Btu/pound	= 2326 J/kg
1 kWh/kg	= 3.60 E +06 J/kg

THERMAL CONDUCTIVITY

1 Cal/cm-s ^{o}C	= 4.18 E +02 J/ms K
1 Btu/ft-h ^{o}F	= 1.7307 J/ms K
1 W/m K	= 1.0 J/ms K

TEMPERATURE

Kelvin (K)	$T_K = (5/9)(T_F + 459.67)$
Celsius (C)	$T_C = (5/9)(T_F - 32)$
Kelvin (K)	$T_K = T_C + 273.15$
Fahrenheit (F)	$T_F = (9/5)T_C + 32$

Index